Donald McMullan

April 17, 1965.

FUNCTIONAL NEUROANATOMY

FUNCTIONAL NEUROANATOMY

Including an Atlas of the Brain Stem

By

N. B. EVERETT, Ph.D.

Professor and Chairman, Department of Biological Structure
University of Washington School of Medicine
Seattle, Washington

With the Assistance of

Charles W. Bodemer, Ph.D.

Associate Professor, Biological Structure; Assistant Dean, School of Medicine; Head, Biomedical History, University of Washington School of Medicine, Seattle, Washington

William O. Rieke, M.D.

Associate Professor and Administrative Officer, Department of Biological Structure, University of Washington School of Medicine, Seattle, Washington

Fifth Edition, Thoroughly Revised, 304 Illustrations, 35 in Color

LEA & FEBIGER

Philadelphia   1965

Library of Congress Catalog Card Number: 65–12967

Printed in the United States of America

Preface

THE four previous editions of "Functional Neuroanatomy" were prepared by Dr. A. R. Buchanan, Professor of Anatomy at the University of Colorado School of Medicine. Dr. Buchanan having recently retired from teaching has turned over the book to me. It is indeed a pleasure to revise this book in its fifth edition.

In this edition I have continued the policy of presenting the material necessary for understanding the structure and function of the nervous system in the least number of pages. Additionally, as in previous editions the longitudinal approach has been used in the presentation. For example, ascending and descending tracts are traced from origin to termination at the time they are first mentioned in the text. This approach, in my experience, has made the subject of neuroanatomy more stimulating and comprehensible to the student. A particular advantage of treatment in this way is to provide for an effective correlation with the study of neurophysiology which students often study concurrently with neuroanatomy. The practice of many schools, as has been the case here for many years, is for the anatomist and physiologist, with some support from the clinical neurologist, to join forces in offering a conjoint course in neuroanatomy and neurophysiology for medical and graduate students. Within this framework the longitudinal approach is particularly valuable to students and faculty in making the appropriate structural and functional correlations. The importance of regional considerations of the central nervous system is recognized, however, and in this edition a number of photographs of the various levels of the brain stem and spinal cord are interspersed throughout the text along with diagrams of the corresponding levels to provide more adequately for regional study. These photographs of sections, primarily of Weil stained preparations, are well labeled and may be used in conjunction with the accompanying diagrams of sections. This combination allows for considerable flexibility in using the text in accord with varying needs for detailed study of the nuclei and fiber tracts of the brain stem and spinal cord. In addition to these photographs a number of new and improved drawings and diagrams have been added. These include several new half-tone and pen and ink drawings, line diagrams and 21 new color illustrations.

Major changes have been made in much of the text material. The chapter on development has been completely rewritten and a new chapter has been added on the genesis and histology of the neural elements which includes a consideration of nerve degeneration and regeneration. Treatment of tactile, pain, thermal, visceral, afferent and proprioceptive pathways has been combined into one chapter. The chapters on the motor systems have been rewritten and rearranged, bringing together the considerations of the extrapyramidal system and basal ganglia. The chapter on the cerebellum has been thoroughly revised, as well as the chapter on the diencephalon which includes a more complete treatise of the thalamus and hypothalamus. Another major change concerns a revision and expansion of the chapter on the rhinencephalon.

I gratefully acknowledge the contributions of three departmental associates to this edition. Chapter 2, "Development of the Nervous System," and Chapter 3, "Genesis and Histology of Neural Elements: Degeneration and Regeneration of Nerves" are the contributions of Dr. Bodemer. The rewriting and reorganization of the material incorporated in Chapter 5, "Somatic Tactile, Proprioceptive, Pain and Thermal Pathways: Visceral Afferent Pathways" are the contributions of Dr. Rieke. In addition, both Drs. Bodemer and Rieke have given general assistance throughout all phases of this revision. Dr. John W. Sundsten contributed significantly to Chapter 20, "The Diencephalon," particularly the section on the hypothalamus. He also made important suggestions for Chapter 23, "The Rhinencephalon."

I am grateful for the contributions made by the medical artists to this revision, particularly those of Miss Jessie Phillips, Director of Health Sciences Illustration and of Marjorie L. Domenowske who made many of the new drawings. The careful and efficient preparation of the manuscript and the valuable contribution to proof reading made by my secretary, Mrs. Doris E. Ringer, are deeply appreciated. Acknowledgment is made to Mr. George W. Reis for the newly added photographs of the brain stem and spinal cord sections.

Finally, I acknowledge the full cooperation of the publishers throughout the course of this revision.

N. B. EVERETT

Seattle, Washington

Contents

FUNCTIONAL NEUROANATOMY

Chapter 1

Divisions of the Nervous System; Origin and Distribution of Peripheral Nerves; Functional Components of Cranial and Spinal Nerves

THE nervous system is responsible for maintaining contact between the individual and his external and internal environments and for the proper adjustments to those environments. Contact with the external environment is maintained through receptors at the surface of the body and with the internal environment through receptors in muscles, joints and ligaments and in the visceral organs of the thorax and abdomen. Adjustments to the environment are facilitated by reflex arcs consisting of afferent neurons, centers within the spinal cord or brain, and efferent neurons. The efferent neu-

rons carry motor impulses from the central nervous system to effector mechanisms including smooth and striated muscle (cardiac and skeletal) and glandular structures.

The adult nervous system may be divided into *central* and *peripheral divisions*. The central nervous system includes the spinal cord and brain. The main subdivisions of the brain are *cerebrum, cerebellum,* and *brain stem*. The brain stem consists of the *diencephalon, mesencephalon, pons,* and *medulla oblongata* (Fig. 1).

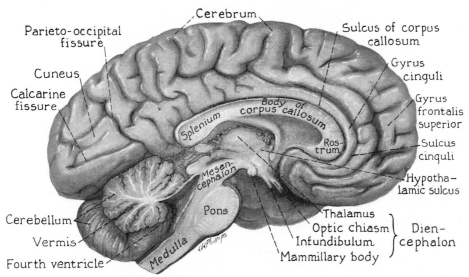

FIG. 1. Drawing of the medial surface of the adult brain illustrating the major divisions and the structures visible in a sagittal section.

The **peripheral nervous system** includes the spinal and cranial nerves and the numerous ganglia and plexuses concerned with visceral innervation. Each **spinal nerve** is attached to the spinal cord by two roots—a ventral or anterior and a dorsal or posterior; these unite to form the spinal nerve which then divides into ventral and dorsal rami (Fig. 2). The anterior or ventral rami of the spinal general visceral efferent fibers which end in relation to ganglionic cells of the autonomic system and are concerned with the innervation of visceral organs. The somatic efferent fibers arise from cells in the ventral gray columns of the cord and the general visceral efferent fibers arise from the lateral gray columns.

The *dorsal roots* contain general somatic afferent (sensory) and general

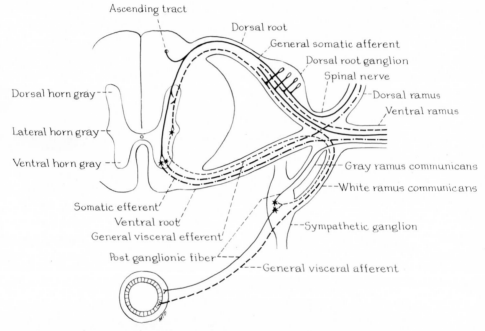

FIG. 2.   Cross-section diagram of the thoracic spinal cord with an attached spinal nerve. The component fibers of the nerve are shown.

nerves form the cervical, brachial, lumbar, sacral, and coccygeal plexuses and, in the thoracic region, the intercostal and subcostal nerves. The posterior or dorsal rami are distributed to the skin on the dorsal aspects of head, neck, and trunk and to the erector spinae group of muscles.

The *ventral roots* of all spinal nerves contain somatic efferent (motor) fibers which innervate skeletal muscles (Fig. 2). Those of the thoracic, upper lumbar, and middle sacral nerves also contain visceral afferent fibers which have their origin in dorsal root ganglia cells. The single processes of these cells divide into peripheral and central divisions. The peripheral divisions of the processes of general somatic afferent neurons are distributed to somatic receptors by way of the spinal nerves and those of general visceral afferent neurons to visceral receptors by way of the spinal nerves and the various plexuses of the visceral nervous system. The central divisions of the processes of both somatic and visceral afferent neurons enter the spinal cord through the dorsal roots (Fig. 2).

The **cranial nerves** are less regular in their arrangement than the spinal nerves. Some have motor and sensory roots; some are entirely sensory in function and at least one—the hypoglossal—is purely motor. Sensory ganglia, structurally and functionally analogous to the dorsal root ganglia of the spinal nerves, are associated with the sensory roots of cranial nerves. Sensory fibers terminate in and motor fibers originate from gray areas in the brain stem which are functional analogues of the gray columns in the spinal cord.

The *cranial* (or *cerebral*) and *spinal nerves* contain seven functional types of fibers: general somatic afferent, special somatic afferent, general visceral afferent, special visceral afferent, somatic efferent, general visceral efferent, and special visceral efferent. There are no special somatic efferent fibers and, as will be noted below, no given nerve contains all seven types of fibers.

General somatic afferent fibers are present in all the spinal nerves (except Cl which usually has no sensory root) and in a number of cranial nerves. Their cell bodies are in sensory ganglia and they conduct impulses to the central nervous system from receptors in skin, muscle, and connective tissues.

Special somatic afferent fibers are found only in the optic and vestibulocochlear nerves. Those in the optic nerve conduct visual impulses from the retina to the brain and arise from cell bodies within the retina (Chapter 8). The vestibulocochlear nerve is composed of the axons of neurons whose cell bodies are in the spiral and vestibular ganglia (Chapter 8). The dendrites of these neurons are distributed to special receptors in the internal ear.

General visceral afferent fibers are present in the spinal nerves and in some of the cranial nerves. They are distributed to receptors in the visceral structures of the neck, thorax, abdomen, and pelvis, and to blood vessels and glandular structures everywhere. Their cells of origin are in the sensory ganglia of spinal nerves (Fig. 2, dorsal root ganglia) and in the ganglia of certain cranial nerves. General visceral afferent neurons function as afferent limbs of visceral reflex arcs and in conduction of impulses (including particularly pain impulses) to the conscious level.

Special visceral afferent fibers are concerned only with the special senses of smell and taste; we therefore find them in the olfactory, glossopharyngeal, vagus and facial nerves (nervus intermedius). The cell bodies of the olfactory nerves are in the olfactory mucous membrane, those of the facial in the geniculate ganglion, those of the glossopharyngeal are in the petrosal ganglion (inferior ganglion) and those of the vagus in the nodose ganglion. The *petrosal ganglion* of the glossopharyngeal nerve is located in a groove on the posterior aspect of the petrosa of the temporal bone, at the upper limit of the jugular foramen. The *nodose ganglion* (also called *inferior*) of the vagus is manifested by an ovoid enlargement on the nerve immediately inferior to its emergence from the jugular foramen. The geniculate ganglion is in the facial canal within the petrosa of the temporal bone (Chapter 7) and is so designated because of its association with the external genu of the facial nerve.

Somatic efferent fibers arise from motor nerve cells in the spinal cord and brain stem. They are distributed to striated muscles of mesodermal somite origin and are found in all spinal nerves and in the oculomotor, trochlear, abducens and hypoglossal nerves. Their occurrence in these four cranial nerves is due to the presence in the embryo of head and occipital somites.

General visceral efferent fibers are present in the oculomotor, facial, glosso-pharyngeal and vagus nerves, in all the thoracic nerves, the upper two or three lumbar nerves, and in the middle three sacral nerves. They arise from cell bodies in certain nuclei of the brain stem and in the lateral gray column of the spinal cord; they are distributed to the peripheral ganglia of the autonomic system (Fig. 2). The axons of the ganglion cells, upon which they synapse, are then distributed to smooth muscle, cardiac muscle and glands throughout the body.

The term *"special visceral efferent"* is unfortunate in that these fibers are distributed to striated or voluntary muscles, but only to those which originate from the mesoderm of the branchial or *visceral* arches. A more appropriate characterization would be *"branchial motor fibers."* The muscles supplied by these fibers include those of the larynx, pharynx, and soft palate, the muscles of mastication, and the muscles of expression. Special visceral efferent fibers are, therefore, found in the vagus, spinal accessory, glossopharyngeal, trigeminal, and facial nerves. The spinal accessory also supplies the trapezius and sternocleidomastoid muscles which are believed to be at least partly branchial in origin.

Chapter 2

The Development of the Nervous System

THE human nervous system begins to develop during the third week of embryogenesis as an induced hyperplasia in the superficial ectoderm in the midline cephalic to Hensen's node (Fig. 3). This structure, the *neural plate,* gives rise to all divisions of the adult nervous system. Soon after its formation the neural plate is converted into a trough, the *neural groove*; the neural groove is bounded by prominent *neural folds,* which are most clearly defined in the extreme cranial end of the neural plate. During the first month of development, the neural folds grow from their dorsal borders, and continued overgrowth results in the approximation of the free edges of the folds. An apparent selective affinity of the constituent epithelial cells produces a fusion of the two neural folds with the consequent formation of a *neural tube.* The *neural crest* is a differentiation of cells at the lateral edge of each neural fold in a zone intermediate between the neural plate and skin ectoderm, which separates from the latter at the time the neural folds fuse. Closure of the neural groove does not occur simultaneously along the length of the embryo, but begins in the future thoracic region, progressing thence cranially and caudally. The ends of the neural tube remain open for some time at the *anterior* and *posterior neuropores.* The anterior neuropore finally closes at the 20-somite stage; the caudal end of the tube is completely closed with obliteration of the posterior neuropore at the 25-somite stage of development. With completion of the neural tube, the neural epithelium is completely dissociated from the superficial ectoderm, and the tube lies bounded dorsally by the epidermis, ventrally by the notochord and laterally by the mesodermal somites (Fig. 3). The neural crest cells form ear-like clusters at the dorsolateral borders of the neural tube, occupying the angle formed by the neural tube, superficial ectoderm and mesoderm (Figs. 3 and 4).

From the outset the cranial portion of the neural tube expands at a greater rate than the more caudal portions of the tube, and, consequently, the prospective brain is clearly visible even before closure of the neuropores. Soon after the neural tube has closed, the brain is divisible into three prominent hollow swellings. These initial cavities are designated as the *primary brain vesicles* (Fig. 5). The most cephalic vesicle is the *prosencephalon,* the middle vesicle is the *mesencephalon,* and the large caudal chamber is designated as the *rhombencephalon.* The latter vesicle continues insensibly into the *myelon,* or future spinal cord. The three primary brain vesicles soon divide further into five *secondary brain vesicles* (Fig. 5). Thus, the prosencephalon is subdivided into the *telencephalon* and *diencephalon,* and the rhombencephalon constricts to form the *metencephalon* and *myelencephalon.* The mesencephalon does not undergo further division.

Establishment of the five secondary brain vesicles completes the initial stages of development preparatory to differentiation of the various regions of the brain, and the derivatives of these several vesicles soon begin to form. The telencephalon gives rise to the *cerebral*

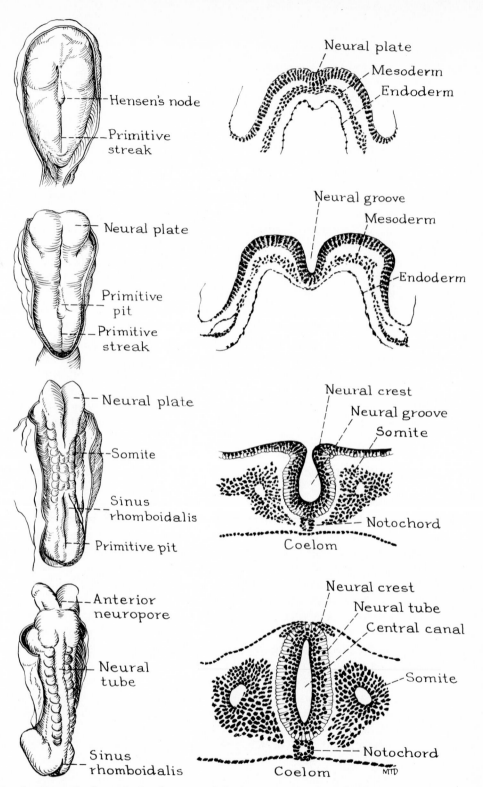

FIG. 3. Stages in the early development of the human nervous system from the presomite stage to closure of the neural tube except at the anterior and posterior neuropores (after Streeter). The embryo is illustrated at left in external view and at right the same stage is shown in transverse section.

(14)

hemispheres, rhinencephalon and *corpus striatum,* and encloses the *lateral ventricles* and the foremost part of the third ventricle. The diencephalon gives origin to the various components of the *epithalamus, thalamus* and *hypothalamus* in the adult brain, and encloses the major part of the third ventricle. The mesencephalon, containing the cerebral aqueduct, differentiates into the *corpora quadrigemina* and the *crura cerebri.* The *cerebellum* and *pons* arise from the metencephalon. The myelencephalon is represented in the adult by the *medulla oblongata.* The *fourth ventricle* extends through both metencephalon and myelencephalon. The boundaries between the secondary brain vesicles, never distinct,

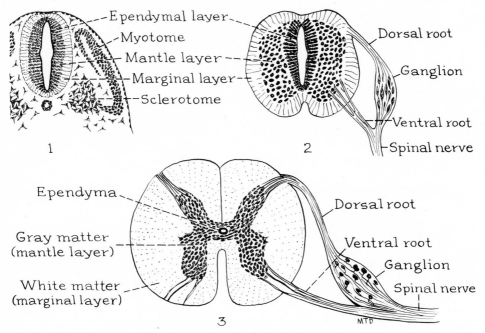

FIG. 4. Semidiagrammatic transverse sections of developing embryos illustrating the early development of the neural tube and formation of a spinal nerve.

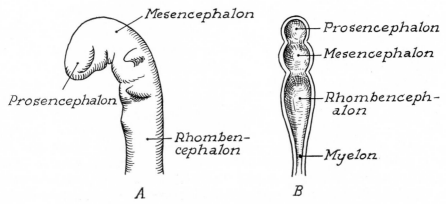

FIG. 5. *A,* Lateral view (after Pölitzer) and *B,* longitudinal section (after Arey) of early human brain. The three primitive brain vesicles are indicated.

are further obscured in the adult brain by growth shiftings, elaboration of various structures from the ventricular walls, and the development of large fiber tracts, such as the *middle cerebellar peduncle* (*brachium pontis*) and *pyramids.* The original longitudinal continuity of the brain vesicles is indicated in the adult, however, by the brain *ventricles,* and the intraventricular pressure caused by accumulation of fluid secreted by the ependyma and the developing choroid plexuses. Between the fifth and sixth weeks of development an imbalance between the rate of neural expansion and available space manifests itself in the development of *flexures* of the brain (Fig. 6). During the fifth week, primarily

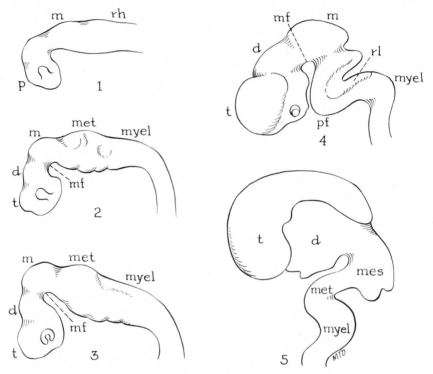

Fɪɢ. 6.   Flexures and secondary brain vesicles in the human embryo.

secondary vesicles of the embyronic brain provide a useful and commonly used frame of reference for analysis of the adult brain.

    Mechanical factors are important determinants in the development of the nervous system (Weiss, 1955). Thus, following closure of the neuropores, the neural tube is the most rapidly expanding element in the relatively enclosed cranial area. This expansion derives from growth, changes in volume attendant upon cellular proliferation, growth in mass, and expansion resulting from increased

because of increased cellular proliferation and intraventricular pressure, the growth rate of the cranial end of the embryonic brain greatly exceeds the growth rate of the mesenchyme condensed to form the skull. This results in the formation of a bend in the neural tube at the level of the mesencephalon, the *mesencephalic* (cephalic) *flexure* (Fig. 6). Increased pressure inside the loop of neural tube tends to displace the mesencephalon caudally, and in this way the mesencephalic flexure contributes to the formation of the dorsal *pontine flexure* (Fig. 6). Rapid expansion of the cerebral hemispheres results in an accentuation of the pontine flexure. In the later stages of development both flexures are less prominent; retention of the mesencephalic flexure, however, provides explanation for the fact that in the adult the telencephalon and diencephalon are of the central nervous system. The spinal cord is initially an unsegmented tube, extending from the caudal end of the rhombencephalon to the tip of the embryonic tail. As the somatic mesoderm lateral to the neural tube segments into somites, a faint segmentation of the myelon becomes apparent. A funda-

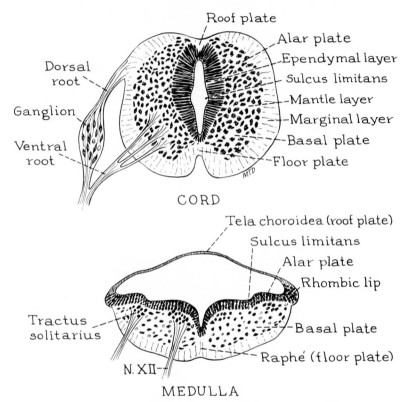

FIG. 7. Transverse sections of embryonic spinal cord and medulla illustrating similarity of organization.

aligned perpendicular to the longitudinal axis of the lower brain stem (Fig. 6). It may also be noted that the approximation of the free edges of the pontine flexure provides a favorable situation for the incorporation of the *rhombic lip* into the developing cerebellum.

The *myelon,* or spinal cord, is the least modified of the primary brain vesicles in the adult; it has value, therefore, in analysis of the fundamental organization mental metamerism is thus imposed upon the myelon by segmentation of the mesoderm, and for each mesodermal somite there is a corresponding *neuromere,* or spinal cord segment (Bergquist and Källen, 1954). Each neuromere gives origin to a pair of spinal nerves which grow out on either side into the surrounding mesoderm and ectoderm. Once established, the relation of a nerve with peripheral structures, *e.g.,* muscle, is thenceforth retained. Thus, although various distortions of the original neural metameric pattern often obscure them, the original neuromere-somite relations remain apparent through patterns of muscle innervation and the strips of cutaneous innervation designated as *dermatomes*. In the latter case the original segmental innervation pattern is modified greatly by the development and torsion of the limb buds and regression of the embryonic tail; the pattern is clearly apparent, however, in the band-like dermatomes of the trunk.

Early in its development the organization of the myelon permits analysis of its functional areas and the structural characteristics of the brain stem. A bilateral longitudinal furrow develops along the inner, luminal surface of the neural tube which is designated as the *sulcus limitans* (Fig. 7). The sulcus limitans divides each half of the neural tube into dorsal and ventral portions. That portion of the lateral wall of the neural tube located dorsal to the sulcus is defined as the *alar plate*; the lateral wall of the neural tube ventral to the sulcus limitans is designated as the *basal plate*. The alar plates are connected across the dorsal midline by the *roof plate,* and the basal plates interconnect through the *floor plate*. These primary regions of the neural tube provide a means for analysis of the early topographic and functional organization of the spinal cord. The alar plate comprises the future sensory area of the spinal cord; the basal plate will give rise to the motor elements of the spinal cord. The roof plate and floor plate generally do not give origin to any prominent neural structures. The roof plate disappears with the formation of the *posterior median septum* of the spinal cord; the floor plate persists above the *anterior median fissure*. The basal and alar plates each differentiate into three layers: an inner *ependymal layer,* an intermediate *mantle layer,* and an outer *marginal layer* (Figs. 4 and 7). The embryonic ependymal layer contains the germinal cells, and in the adult forms the lining of the *central canal* of the spinal cord and the ventricles of the brain. The mantle layer becomes the *gray matter* of the spinal cord as cells accumulate from the proliferating ependymal elements. The marginal layer becomes the *white matter* of the spinal cord; it is formed by ascending and descending processes of nerve cells in the gray matter and nerve fibers entering from the dorsal root ganglia (Sauer, 1935; Sidman *et al.,* 1959). The relationship of the gray and white matter in the adult spinal cord corresponds to that of the mantle and marginal layers in the developing neural tube. There is, however, considerable modification of the arrangement in the brain, as will become apparent in a later discussion of that part of the central nervous system.

As the free edges of the neural folds fuse to close the neural tube and the neural epithelium separates from the superficial ectoderm, the cells comprising the neural crest begin to migrate from the dorsolateral surface of the neural tube. Initially, neural crest cells are aligned as an unsegmented, loosely organized cellular sheet along the dorsolateral border of the myelon in the angle between the neural tube, the ectoderm and the somites (Figs. 3 and 4). The neural crest soon undergoes segmentation into discrete cellular condensations, corresponding to the neuromeres and mesodermal somites (Detwiler, 1936; Hamburger and Levi-Montalcini, 1949). These early cellular condensations are the primordia of the *dorsal root ganglia* of the spinal nerves. In addition to forming the spinal ganglia, neural crest cells also migrate ventrally and medially to contribute to the autonomic ganglia and the medulla of the adrenal gland (Hammond and Yntema, 1947). Neural crest cells also participate in formation of certain cranial nerve ganglia and, by inward migration, the mesencephalic nucleus of the trigeminal nerve (Horstadius, 1950).

The **spinal nerve** develops from cells located inside and outside the neural tube. Those neurons developed in the spinal ganglia develop into pseudounipolar neurons; from the cell body a proximal fiber passes into the alar region of the developing spinal cord, and a distal fiber process proceeds laterally and ventrally to become part of the spinal nerve. The processes of the pseudounipolar neurons with cell bodies located in the spinal ganglia thus form most of the dorsal root of the spinal nerve. The dorsal root of a spinal nerve is thus sensory in nature. The ventral root of the spinal nerve forms as the accumulation of nerve fibers emerging from the basal plate of the neural tube. These fibers represent the axis cylinders of multipolar motoneurons with cell bodies in the future anterior column of the spinal cord gray matter. The ventral root of a spinal nerve is thus motor in nature. The union of the dorsal and ventral roots effects the formation of the spinal nerve (Fig. 4). The *rami communicantes* are formed by nerve fibers emerging from cells located in the *intermediolateral column* of the spinal cord gray matter, the autonomic ganglia, and sensory neurons in the spinal ganglia. The connective tissue sheath of the nerve forms from mesodermal cells.

The organization of the neural tube according to alar and basal plates connected by roof and floor plates, respectively, is apparent in the brain as well as the spinal cord. The *sulcus limitans* is well developed in the myelencephalon (Fig. 7), separating basal plate from the laterally displaced alar plate. The greatly attenuated roof plate participates in formation of the choroid plexus; the floor plate is incorporated into the midline raphé. The distinction of the alar and basal plates according to sensory and motor function is valid also in the brain, and the disposition of sensory and motor nuclear groups in the brain stem may be thus ascertained. The basal plate probably does not extend rostral to the mamillary recess of the diencephalon (Kingsbury, 1922), and the correlation of motor and sensory function according to the embryonic plates is not unreservedly applicable to the derivatives of the prosencephalon. The neural structures associated with the telencephalon and diencephalon appear to originate primarily from the embryonic alar plate.

The *myelencephalon* develops into the medulla oblongata of the adult brain. It is modified only slightly from the fundamental structure of the spinal cord. As in the medulla, the sulcus limitans forms the boundary between the dorsal, sensory region and the ventral, motor region, of the metencephalon. The *tegmentum* of the pons derives from the basal plate; the fibrous portion of the pons is an addition to the primary metencephalon consequent to the development of the cerebrum and cerebellum, and the development of large fiber tracts in the medulla and pons. The cerebellum is of bipartite origin (Larsell, 1947). Part of the cerebellum develops from the rhombic lips located on each side of the fourth ventricle. Each *rhombic lip* is a thickened portion of the alar plate of the rhombencephalon developed at its junction with the roof plate. The pontine flexure causes the approximation of the rhombic lips (Fig. 6), enabling their fusion and growth to form the *flocculonodular lobe* of the cerebellum. The larger, phylogenetically younger, *corpus cerebelli* develops through fusion of the alar plates of the metencephalon cranial to the rhombic lips and the flocculonodular lobe. The *posterolateral fissure* is the line of demarcation between these two, embryologically distinct, portions of the cerebellum. The *tectum,* or *corpora quadrigemina,* of the mesencephalon develops from the alar plates of the embryonic mesencephalon; the tegmentum of the mesencephalon develops from the basal plates. The peduncular portion of the mesencephalon, like the fibrous pons, is added onto the embryonic mesencephalon consequent to the development

ever, whether this region represents the embryonic basal plates. The large cerebral hemispheres develop as lateral evaginations from the telencephalon; they are derived from the alar plates. The *corpus striatum* arises from the inner walls of the telencephalic vesicles; and the *internal capsule* develops at the site where the corpus striatum undergoes a secondary fusion with the lateral walls of the diencephalon.

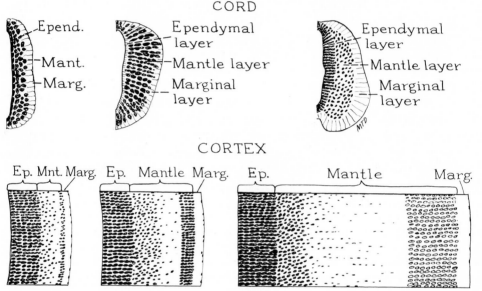

FIG. 8. Diagrams illustrating formation of spinal cord and cerebral cortex in the human embryo.

of large fiber tracts associated with the cerebral hemispheres. The diencephalon develops into three distinct regions. The epithalamus derives from the roof plate and upper ends of the alar plates; the choroid plexus of the third ventricle forms from the roof plate. The (dorsal) thalamus is formed from the alar plates of the diencephalon; its ventral border is defined by the hypothalamic sulcus. Although the *hypothalamic sulcus* is probably not homologous with the sulcus limitans, the hypothalamus nuclei develop inferior to it in the basal portion of the diencephalon. It may be questioned, how-

The **cerebral and cerebellar cortices** develop according to a distinctive pattern. It will be recalled that in the spinal cord proliferation of cells from the ependymal layer results in formation of the cellular mantle layer, and fibers elaborated by cells in the mantle layer accumulate to form an external marginal layer (Fig. 8). In the formation of the cerebral and cerebellar cortices, however, cells derived from germinal elements in the ependymal layer of the telencephalon and metencephalon, respectively, migrate centrifugally to establish a layer of cell bodies (gray matter) near the surface of the vesicle. Thus, in the cerebral cortex, cells migrate external to the mantle layer during the second month of development, establishing thereby a prominent layer of *pyramidal cells*. The primitive cortex thus consists of an ependymal layer, a relatively diffuse intermediate layer, a primitive pyramidal layer and an outer marginal layer. During succeeding months, the innermost portion of the intermediate layer develops into the prominent central white mass of myelinated fibers. The external portion of the intermediate layer, the subdivided pyramidal layer, and the insignificant marginal layer comprise the definitive six-layered cerebral cortex of the adult brain (Fig. 8).

The developing nervous system is influenced by many factors, and its final configurations are the results of external, as well as internal, factors (Weiss, 1955). Thus, the segmentation of the spinal cord and the metameric pattern of spinal nerve ganglia is essentially an imposed pattern, the result of segmentation of the mesoderm into somites (Detwiler, 1936). The size of certain areas of the spinal cord may depend also upon external factors. The cervical and lumbosacral enlargements of the spinal cord are, for example, the direct expression of the large peripheral innervation derived from these segments of the cord and relate to the development of the limb buds at these levels (Detwiler, 1936; Barron, 1948). It should be noted further that an important factor in the final form assumed by the developing nervous system is a result of patterns of cell deaths during ontogeny (Hamburger and Levi-Montalcini, 1949, 1950).

BIBLIOGRAPHY

BARRON, D. H., 1948: Some effects of amputation of the chick wing bud on the early differentiation of the motor neuroblasts in the associated segments of the spinal cord. J. Comp. Neurol., *88*, 93-127.

BERGQUIST, H. and KÄLLÉN, B., 1954: Notes on the early histogenesis and morphogenesis of the central nervous system in vertebrates. J. Comp. Neurol., *100*, 627-659.

DETWILER, S. R., 1936: *Neuroembryology*, The Macmillan Co., New York.

HAMBURGER, V. and LEVI-MONTALCINI, R., 1949: Proliferation, differentiation and degeneration in the spinal ganglia of the chick embryo under normal and experimental conditions. J. Exptl. Zool., *111*, 457-501.

———— 1950: Some aspects of neuroembryology. In *Genetic Neurology*, PAUL WEISS, ed., University of Chicago Press, Chicago, pp. 128-160.

HAMMOND, W. S. and YNTEMA, C. L., 1947: Depletions in the thoraco-lumbar sympathetic system following removal of neural crest in the chick. J. Comp. Neurol., *86*, 237-265.

HORSTADIUS, S., 1950: *The Neural Crest*, Oxford University Press, London.

KINGSBURY, B. F., 1922: The fundamental plan of the vertebrate brain. J. Comp. Neurol., *34*, 461-491.

LARSELL, O., 1947: The development of the cerebellum in man in relation to its comparative anatomy. J. Comp. Neurol., *87*, 85-129.

SAUER, F. C., 1935: Mitosis in the neural tube. J. Comp. Neurol., *62*, 377-405.

SIDMAN, R. L., MIALE, I. L. and FEDER, N., 1959: Cell proliferation and migration in the primitive ependymal zone; an autoradiographic study of histogenesis in the nervous system. Exptl. Neurol., *1*, 322-333.

WEISS, P. A., 1955: Nervous system (neurogenesis). In *Analysis of Development*, WILLIER, B. H., WEISS, P. A. and HAMBURGER, V., eds., W. B. Saunders Co., Philadelphia, pp. 346-401.

Chapter 3

Genesis and Histology of Neural Elements
Degeneration and Regeneration of Nerves

Histogenesis in the nervous system begins in the ependymal layer of the neural tube (Sauer, 1935*a, b*; Kershman, 1938; Sidman *et al.*, 1959). The ependymal layer is composed primarily of columnar epithelial cells, but interspersed throughout the layer are large mitotic stem cells known as *germinal cells.* These germinal cells may not remain stationary, but appear to migrate in and out of the ependymal layer and, while there, undergo division (Sidman *et al.*, 1959). Two primary cell types, *neuroblasts* and *spongioblasts,* arise from the germinal cells. Neuroblasts differentiate into the neurons, or nerve cells; spongioblasts give rise to the several varieties of *neuroglia,* the supportive cells of the nervous system (Fig. 9).

Most of the spongioblasts derived from the germinal cells of the ependyma develop into *astrocytes* and *oligodendroglia.* Some spongioblasts differentiate into the epithelial cells that form the ependymal lining of the central canal and brain ventricles in the adult. Near the end of gestation, mesenchymal cells migrate into the central nervous system and develop into the small *microglial cells*; these cells are sometimes referred to as *mesoglia* on the basis of their supposed mesodermal origin. The structure, distribution and functions of the neuroglia are discussed in a later chapter (Chapter 27).

The **neuroblasts** develop into the neurons of the adult nervous system. Division of neuroblasts is not observed later than the first year after birth, and most neurons differentiate during intrauterine life. A *neuron* consists of a nerve *cell body* and all the processes, designated as *axons* and *dendrites,* which arise from it. There are usually several to many dendrites associated with a nerve cell, whereas most neurons possess a single axon.

A **neuron** may be classified according to various criteria. It may be classified according to the number of its processes as a *pseudounipolar, bipolar* or *multi-*

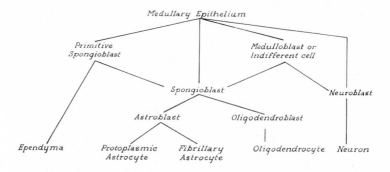

FIG. 9.   Cell lineage in the central nervous system (after Ranson).

polar neuron (Fig. 10). True unipolar neurons, with an axon only, are probably confined to embryonic stages. Bipolar neurons, with one main dendrite and one main axon emerging from opposite ends of a cell body, are of limited occurrence in the adult, where they are

necting them to the cell body. Multipolar neurons possess an axon and two or more dendrites. They are the most numerous variety of neuron in the central nervous system and occur also in the peripheral ganglia of the autonomic nervous system. Multipolar neu-

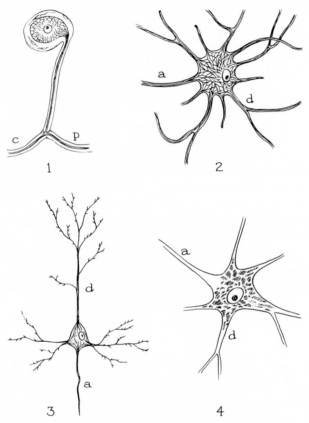

FIG. 10.   Neuron types. (1) pseudounipolar neuron;   (2) multipolar neuron (autonomic nervous system); (3) pyramidal cell, cerebral cortex; (4) multipolar neuron (anterior column, spinal cord gray matter).

restricted to the retina, olfactory organ, and cochlear and vestibular ganglia. In pseudounipolar neurons a single process emerges from the nerve cell body and bifurcates to give rise to an axon and a dendrite. Pseudounipolar neurons occur in the dorsal root ganglia; they develop from bipolar neurons through fusion of the separate axon and dendrite to form the single T-shaped process con-

rons with long axons are designated as Golgi Type I; those with short and freely branching axons are classified as Golgi Type II neurons.

A typical **multipolar motoneuron** demonstrates the cytological characteristics of nerve cells in general (Fig. 11). The cell body, or *perikaryon,* assumes a variety of shapes and may range from 4 to 120 micra in diameter. The prominent

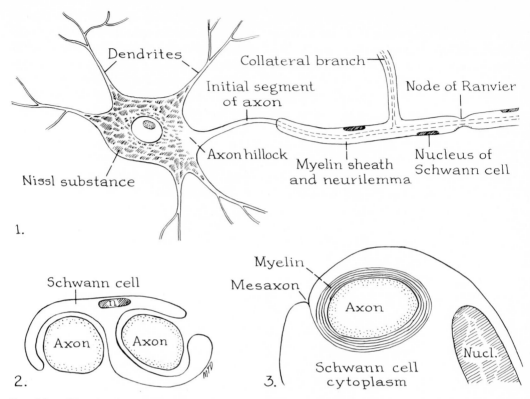

FIG. 11. (1) Diagram of typical neuron, (2) diagram showing relation of Schwann cell to axons, (3) diagram illustrating relation of Schwann cell to myelin sheath and axon.

nucleus is bounded by a membrane which may be as much as 40 mμ in thickness. A *nucleolus* is usually visible; it contains a high concentration of ribonucleic acid (RNA). The cytoplasm of nerve cells contains a variety of intracellular substances such as *neurofibrils, Golgi apparatus, mitochondria* and *pigment*. The *Nissl substance* is associated with the endoplasmic reticulum of the cytoplasm; it is distributed throughout the neuron except in the region of the *axon hillock,* the site of origin of the axon from the perikaryon. The high concentration of nucleoprotein associated with the Nissl substance accounts for the basophilia of Nissl substance and underlies the efficacy of such dyes as thionin as histological stains for nerve cell bodies. A boundary membrane of uniform thickness, approximately 50 Å

encloses the nerve cell cytoplasm. Although its chemical composition is imperfectly understood, this membrane appears to consist of a protein framework associated with a thin, bimolecular layer of phospholipids and cholesterol (Hyden, 1960).

The dendrites of a typical multipolar neuron are numerous branching, tapering processes extending as far as 1 mm. from the cell body; the axon, or axis cylinder, is a single process, generally of uniform diameter, which arises from the axon hillock. The axon, unlike the dendrites, has few branches. Conduction, according to the generally accepted membrane theory, results from the progressive depolarization of the semipermeable membrane enclosing the nerve fiber. The direction of conduction of the nerve impulse relative to the nerve cell body is the criterion for distinguishing dendrites and axons. Thus, despite the relative lengths of the processes associated with the nerve cell, an afferent process is designated as a dendrite and an efferent process is designated as an axon. In peripheral nerves axons emerging from cell bodies in the ventral and intermediolateral columns of the spinal cord gray matter and in brain stem motor nuclei conduct impulses toward effector mechanisms. The peripheral and central processes of pseudounipolar neurons with

The larger myelin sheath which lies internal to the neurilemma develops later and is believed to be an elaboration of the Schwann cells. The myelin sheath is a series of concentric membrane lamellae which actually represents a double-layered infolding of the Schwann cell membrane winding spirally around the axon (Petersen and Murray, 1955; Petersen, 1959; Schmitt, 1958). The so-called *mesaxon* illustrates the continuity of the myelin sheath with the Schwann cell (Fig. 11). The myelin sheath is

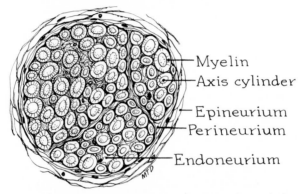

Fig. 12.   Transverse section through peripheral nerve illustrating relations of various sheaths in the nerve.

cell bodies in sensory ganglia, conduct impulses from receptors (sensory end organs) toward the central nervous system.

The first 50 to 100 μ of the axon distal to the axon hillock is referred to as the *initial segment*; beyond the initial segment the axon is ensheathed. The axons of peripheral nerves are traditionally described with two sheaths: a *myelin sheath* immediately surrounding the axon and a *neurilemma* (sheath of Schwann) external to the myelin sheath. The neurilemma is formed by the cytoplasm of the fibroblast-like *Schwann cells*. The Schwann cells appear to derive from embryonic neural crest cells which migrate alongside the growing nerve fibers and wrap around them, thus forming a cytoplasmic investment for the axis cylinder.

interrupted at regular intervals by the *nodes of Ranvier*; at the nodes, the axon is covered only by the cytoplasm of the Schwann cell.

In the central nervous system the nerve fibers may have a myelin sheath. The neurilemma, however, is lacking, and neuroglia, especially the oligodendroglia, serve the same function.

In peripheral nerves each axis cylinder, with its myelin and neurilemmal investments, is enclosed by a thin connective tissue sheath, the *endoneurium*. Groups of axons are held together in fascicles by another connective tissue sheath, the *perineurium*. All the fascicles are bundled together into the nerve by the outermost sheath, the *epineurium* (Fig. 12).

Nerve fibers in peripheral nerves may be classified into three categories on the basis of fiber diameter and, accordingly, conduction rate. The "A" fibers are large myelinated fibers which range in diameter from 1 to 22 μ and have a conduction rate of 30 to 100 meters/second. The "A" fibers are found in all somatic nerves. Most of the lightly myelinated visceral nerve fibers, *e.g.*, postganglionic sympathetic nerve fibers, are "B" fibers. They are 3 μ or less in diameter and conduct at rates of 10 to

tic knobs, boutons terminaux, or *end feet* (Fig. 13). Each synaptic knob is surrounded by a membrane which is a continuation of the cell membrane of its parent cell body; this region of the membrane is referred to as the presynaptic membrane of the synaptic knob. That part of the cell membrane surrounding the dendrite or perikaryon of the postsynaptic neuron with which each synaptic knob is in contact is known as the *subsynaptic membrane*. A gap of 150 to 500 Angstroms, the *synaptic cleft*,

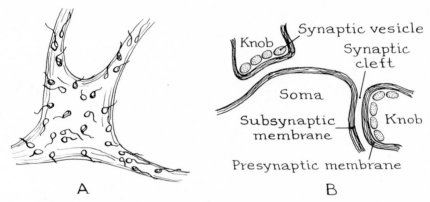

FIG. 13. *A*. Relation of synaptic knobs (*boutons terminaux*) to postsynaptic neuron (after Bremer). *B*. Diagram illustrating relations of presynaptic and postsynaptic membranes at synapse.

20 meters/second. The "C" fibers measure 2 μ or less and conduct at rates of 1.3 to 6 meters/second. They are found in the preganglionic sympathetic nerves and in the dorsal root of spinal nerves.

Neurons are functionally interrelated at the *synapse*. At the synapse the nerve impulse is transferred from the axon of one neuron to the dendrites or perikaryon of another neuron (Palay, 1958). The termination of one neuron in relation to another neuron in a chain is accomplished by the division of a presynaptic fiber into numerous fine filaments which establish contact with the dendrites and/or cell body of the other neuron through terminal expansions designated as *synap-*

separates the presynaptic membrane of the synaptic knob from the subsynaptic membrane of the postsynaptic neuron (Figs. 13 and 14). At the synapse the presynaptic membrane is evaginated by numerous *synaptic vesicles*. The synaptic vesicles, measuring 300 to 500 Å in width, may operate in synaptic transmission of the nerve impulse through the quantal emission of a chemical transmitter. The arrival of a nerve impulse at a synaptic knob presumably causes the vesicles to liberate a chemical mediator, perhaps acetylcholine. This effects a change in the permeability of the subsynaptic membrane, with a resultant membrane de-

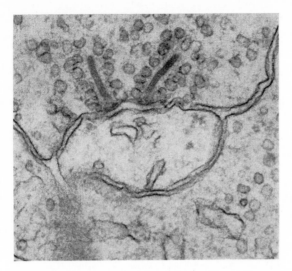

Fig. 14. Electron micrograph of synapse in pineal body illustrating synaptic membranes and vesicles (courtesy of Dr. D. E. Kelly).

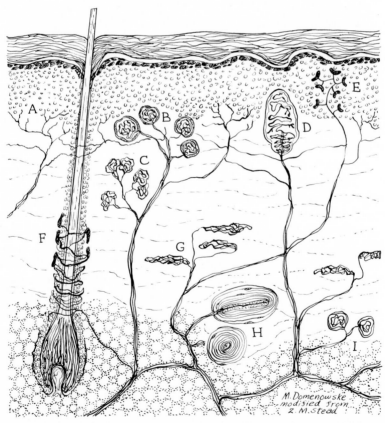

Fig. 15. Composite diagram showing various receptors associated with human skin. Modified from Stead (Wollard, Weddell and Harpmman). *A*, "free" nerve endings; *B*, Krause's end-bulbs; *C*, Ruffini's endings; *D*, Meissner's corpuscles; *E*, Merkel's discs; *F*, nerve fibers and endings on hair follicle; *G*, Ruffini's endings; *H*, Pacinian corpuscles; *I*, Golgi-Mazzoni endings.

polarization and change in electrical potential. If these actions are of sufficient intensity, a nerve impulse is generated in the postsynaptic neuron. Synaptic excitation in one subsynaptic area of a cell membrane can summate with depolarizations at other subsynaptic sites which precede or are concurrent with it (Eccles, 1957).

The detection of sundry stimuli and their transformation into nerve impulses occurs at *receptors*. It has been conventional to ascribe mediation of specific modalities to certain anatomically distinct end-organs. There is, however, good reason to question the strict association of anatomical and functional specificity of receptors (Sinclair, 1955; Weddell *et al.*, 1955; Oppenheimer *et al.*, 1958). Receptors are commonly divided into three groups as *exteroceptors, proprioceptors* and *interoceptors*. Exteroceptors occur in structures of ectodermal origin; proprioceptors are found largely in those structures which develop from mesoderm; interoceptors are associated with structures of endodermal origin. These various receptors may be either *encapsulated* or *unencapsulated,* "free" nerve endings (Fig. 15).

Exteroceptors mediate such sensibilities as touch (tactile sensibility), superficial pain, temperature, tactile discrimination, vision and audition. The receptors concerned with tactile sensibility are usually considered to include the nerve endings around hair follicles, *Merkel's corpuscles, Meissner's corpuscles,* and *Pacinian corpuscles. Tactile discrimination,* the ability to recognize that two or more closely related points on the skin are being stimulated simultaneously, apparently relates to Meissner's corpuscles and "free nerve endings."

Superficial pain does not derive from an encapsulated receptor, but has as its end-organ unencapsulated "free nerve endings" (Weddell and Sinclair, 1953).

Temperature sense has been conventionally ascribed to the *end-bulb of Krause* for cold and *Ruffini nerve endings* for warmth, although these sensibilities may be mediated by other receptors (Sinclair *et al.*, 1952).

Proprioceptors mediate such sensibilities as sense of position, sense of movement, pressure sense and equilibrium. At least four kinds of proprioceptors occur in muscles, tendons and joints. These receptors are the muscle spindle, musculotendinous organ, Pacinian corpuscle and free nerve endings. The latter two, particularly abundant in the superficial fascia, are related to the appreciation of deep pressure. The end-organs subserving sense of position and movement are encapsulated and include muscle spindles, musculo-tendinous endings, Pacinian corpuscles, and Golgi-Mazzoni corpuscles. Muscle spindles are located in, and tend to wind among, the fibers of striated muscles. Musculo-tendinous organs occur at the junction of a muscle and its tendon. Muscle spindles and musculo-tendinous organs consist of a capsule filled with an amorphous material and non-myelinated neurofibrils (Fig. 16). The special proprioceptive sense of equilibrium is associated with the special sensory areas of the vestibular apparatus of the inner ear.

Interoceptors underlie general and special interoceptive (visceral) sensibilities. General interoceptive sensibility includes perception of hunger, thirst, respiratory movements and visceral pain. Many of the receptors are free nerve endings around smooth muscle, underneath the mucosa and beneath the epithelial cells. Specialized and complex sensory endings have been described in visceral structures. These include various spindle-shaped endings in the smooth muscle of the digestive tract, encapsulated endings in the mesentery and club-shaped endings on the surface of the

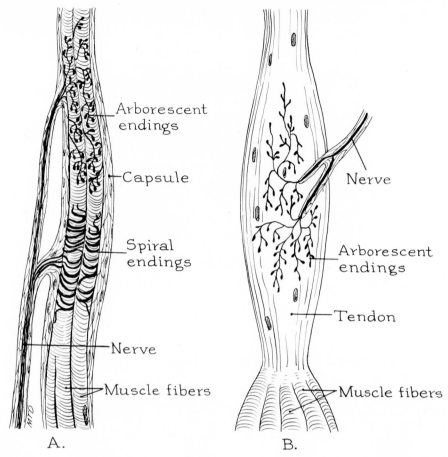

A.   B.

FIG. 16.   *A,* Muscle spindle (after Bremer); *B* musculotendinous organ (after Cajal).

visceral peritoneum of the bladder and stomach. *Special interoceptive sensibilities* include smell and taste. The endings for smell are the dendritic expansions of bipolar olfactory cells located in the nasal olfactory epithelium. The receptors for taste are the flask-shaped taste buds found in the epithelium of the tongue and epiglottis.

Effectors are the structures mediating the motor activity of the nervous system and transforming the nerve impulse into an appropriate response. Somatic and special visceral efferent fibers terminate in *motor end plates* (Fig. 17). Located usually near the midpoints of muscle fibers, the motor end plates account for

the elevated areas on the muscle fibers. The end plates are, like the muscle fibers, covered by sarcolemma. At the end plate the neurilemmal sheaths of the nerve fibers appear to become continuous with the sarcolemma; the myelin sheaths terminate at the sarcolemma. The nerve fibers divide into fibrils which form a network beneath the sarcolemma in close relation to the sarcoplasm. When a nerve impulse reaches the motor end plate in a striated muscle, the acetylcholine or chemical transmitter substance presumably liberated from the synaptic vesicles induces changes in the permeability of the membrane separating the axon from the soleplasm of the muscle cell, thus

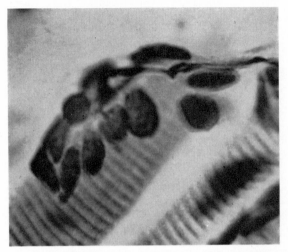

FIG. 17. Motor end plate in striated muscle (courtesy of Dr. C. E. Blevins).

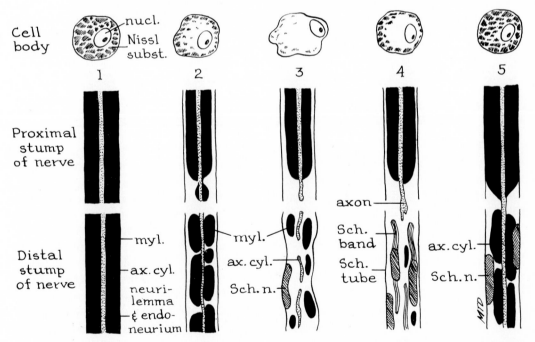

FIG. 18. Diagrams illustrating changes in cell body (*upper*), proximal stump (*middle*) and distal stump (*lower*) during degeneration and regeneration of a peripheral nerve.

permitting flux of potassium ions from and sodium ions into the muscle. The change in permeability of the membrane is accompanied by a change in potential along the sarcolemma which may reach all interior parts of the fiber via the sarcoplasmic reticulum.

Nerves are capable of regeneration following injury (Young, 1950, Weiss, 1955). Traumatization (*e.g.,* cutting, crushing) initiates complex structural and chemical changes in all parts of a peripheral nerve which are both degenerative and regenerative in nature (Fig. 18). Degeneration of that part of the nerve distal to the injury (distal stump) is known as *Wallerian degeneration* and is an important antecedent to regeneration from the proximal part of the nerve (proximal stump). Degeneration of the distal stump begins soon after the constituent nerve fibers are separated from their parent cell bodies. It is first apparent in fragmentation of the myelin sheaths and their enclosed axons. Perhaps as a reflection of altered surface tension the myelin breaks into increasingly smaller fragments, eventually to disappear. Dissolution of the myelin and associated axis cylinders leaves empty channels bounded by the endoneurium and neurilemmal remnants; these channels and the sheaths are designated as *Schwann tubes.* Degeneration of the myelin and nerve fibers is accompanied by an increased incidence of macrophages in the distal stump. These cells invade the Schwann tubes during the period of myelin disintegration, and when this latter process is complete the macrophages disappear.

During the period of fiber and myelin dissolution the Schwann cells associated with the degenerating fibers increase in size and begin to undergo mitosis. The cytoplasmic separation between the products of these Schwann cell mitoses are not always distinct, and the cells thus appear as small, apparently syncytial multinucleated *band fibers* (bands of von Büngner). The band fibers dissociate from the linings of the Schwann tubes and migrate into their lumina along with the macrophages; when the macrophages disappear each Schwann tube contains many band fibers. The walls of the tube, composed of endoneurium and neurilemma, remain unchanged throughout, although the diameter of the tube shrinks considerably after complete degeneration of the original fiber and myelin sheath.

The myelin sheath undergoes chemical degradation as it fragments. During the chemical degradation of myelin to neutral fat it is transformed into simpler intermediate substances. These intermediate compounds may be demonstrated by the Marchi staining procedure, often used for degenerating nervous tissue. The Nauta technique, on the other hand, relies upon the staining characteristics of degenerating axis cylinders. Both the Marchi and Nauta staining techniques provide a means for studying the location and distribution of fibers and fiber tracts within the central nervous system. The disposition of degenerating myelin and/or axis cylinders following a lesion allows insight into the paths followed by fibers emanating from cell bodies in the area of the lesion.

Transection of a nerve causes degenerative changes in the proximal stump which are comparable with the degeneration manifest in the distal stump. This *retrograde degeneration* is normally limited to the terminal parts of the proximal stump and is normally limited in extent and time. The cell bodies of the neurons subjected to trauma also reveal a series of reactions which is designated as *chromatolysis.* During chromatolysis the cell body becomes quite turgid, the Nissl substance undergoes dissolution, and the nucleus assumes an eccentric position within the cell. Profound changes in the metabolism of the cell occur, including altered enzyme concentration, nucleic acid concentration and oxygen consumption. The extent of these changes in the cell body depends upon the proximity of the damage to the neuron; if the axis cylinder is transected close to the cell body chromatolysis is more excessive than it is when the cut is more distant from the perikaryon, and if the damage is too close to the cell body, the neuron may die. If the neuron survives, the injury *regeneration* of a new axis cylinder may occur; turgidity of the cell body disappears, the Nissl substance is again prominent, and the cell returns to normal. Regeneration of the nerve occurs from the end of the proximal stump (Fig. 18). The tips of the axons within the nerve become swollen with axoplasm flowing distally from its generation site in the cell body. Growth of the fibers occurs through pseudopodial extensions which traverse the gap between the proximal stump and the degenerating distal stump. The regenerating axons enter the empty Schwann tubes in the distal stump and thenceforth grow along the interface of the walls and the band fibers to attain their destination. The Schwann tubes thus play a most important role in nerve regeneration; they determine the direction of growth of regenerating nerve fibers (Weiss, 1955; Windle, 1955). The regenerated fibers grow in diameter and become myelinated after acquiring their peripheral connections.

Within the spinal cord and brain Wallerian degeneration proceeds in the same manner as in peripheral nerves, with the exception of those phenomena attributed to the neurilemmal sheath cells, since nerve fibers in the central nervous system lack neurilemmal sheaths. The proximal portions of central nervous system axons regenerate; they seldom retrace their course effectively, however, and often wander aimlessly to create a *neuroma*. If conditions are such that the direction of growth of regenerative fibers in the central nervous system is guided, these fibers may effect an anatomical regeneration (Scott and Clemente, 1955; Campbell *et al.*, 1957a,b) and at least a partial functional regeneration (Sugar and Gerard, 1940; Windle, 1955).

BIBLIOGRAPHY

CAMPBELL, J. B., BASSETT, C. A. L., HUSBY, J. and NOBACK, C. R., 1957a: Regeneration of adult mammalian spinal cord. Science, *126*, 929.

————, 1957b: Axonal regeneration in the transected adult feline spinal cord. Surg. Forum, *8*, 528-532.

ECCLES, J. C., 1957: *The Physiology of Nerve Cells*, Johns Hopkins Press, Baltimore.

HYDEN, H., 1960: The neuron. *In The Cell*, BRACHET, JEAN and MIRSKY, ALFRED E., eds., Academic Press, New York, Vol. 4, pp. 215-323.

KERSHMAN, J., 1938: The medulloblast and the medulloblastoma. A study of human embryos. A.M.A. Arch. Neurol. Psychiat., *40*, 937-967.

LELE, P. P. and WEDDELL, G., 1956: The relationship between neurohistology and corneal sensibility. Brain, *79*, 119-154.

OPPENHEIMER, D. R., PALMA, E. and WEDDELL, G., 1958: Nerve endings in the conjunctiva. J. Anat., *92*, 321-352.

PALAY, S. L., 1958: The morphology of synapses in the central nervous system. Exptl. Cell Res., *Suppl. 5*, 275-293.

PETERSEN, E. R., 1959: Growth, development and myelinization in cultures of fetal rat dorsal root ganglia. Anat. Rec., *133*, 322.

PETERSEN, E. R. and MURRAY, M. R., 1955: Myelin sheath formation in cultures of avian spinal ganglia. Am. J. Anat., *96*, 319-355.

SAUER, F. C., 1935a: Mitosis in the neural tube. J. Comp. Neurol., *62*, 377-405.

———— 1935b: The cellular structure of the neural tube. J. Comp. Neurol., *63*, 13-23.

SCHMITT, F. O., 1958: Axon-satellite cell relationships in peripheral nerve fibers. Exptl. Cell Res., *Suppl. 5*, 33-37.

SCOTT, D., JR. and CLEMENTE, C. D., 1955: Regeneration of spinal cord fibers in the cat. J. Comp. Neurol., *102*, 633-669.

SIDMAN, R. L., MIALE, I. L. and FEDER, N., 1959: Cell proliferation and migration in the primitive ependymal zone; an autoradiographic study of histogenesis in the nervous system. Exptl. Neurol., *1*, 322-333.

SINCLAIR, D. C., 1955: Cutaneous sensation and the doctrine of specific energy. Brain, *78*, 584-614.

SINCLAIR, D. C., WEDDELL, G. and ZANDER, E., 1952: The relationship of cutaneous sensibility to neurohistology in the human pinna. J. Anat., *86*, 402-411.

SUGAR, O. and GERARD, R. W., 1940: Spinal cord regeneration in the rat. J. Neurophysiol., *3*, 1-19.

WEDDELL, G. and SINCLAIR, D. C., 1953: The anatomy of pain sensibility. Acta Neurovegat., *7*, 135-146.

WEDDELL, G., PALMER, E. and PALLIE, W., 1955: Nerve endings in mammalian skin. Biol. Rev., *30*, 159-195.

WEISS, P. A., 1955: Nervous system (neurogenesis). In *Analysis of Development*, WILLIER, B. H., WEISS, P. A. and HAMBURGER, V., eds., W. B. Saunders Co., Philadelphia, pp. 346-401.

WINDLE, W. F. (ed.), 1955: *Regeneration in the Central Nervous System*, Charles C Thomas, Springfield.

YOUNG, J. Z., 1950: The determination of the specific characteristics of nerve fibers. In *Genetic Neurology*, WEISS, PAUL, ed., University of Chicago Press, Chicago, pp. 92-104.

Chapter 4

The Spinal Cord

THE spinal cord is contained within the spinal canal. It begins at the level of the foramen magnum and its average caudal extent in the adult is to the level of the disc between the first and second lumbar vertebrae (Fig. 19). The range of variation reported is from the twelfth thoracic to the third lumbar vertebrae (Fig. 19). It is surrounded by three meningeal coverings which, from within outward, are designated as pia mater, arachnoid mater, and dura mater (Fig. 20). The *pia mater* very closely invests the spinal cord and is reflected into it along the courses of the blood vessels which supply it. The *arachnoid mater,* as its name implies, is spider-web-like in character; it is separated from the pia mater by the *subarachnoid space* which is normally filled with cerebrospinal fluid. The *dura mater* is the outermost covering and it is separated from the arachnoid mater by the *subdural space.* The dura mater is surrounded by a thick layer of *epidural fat* containing the epidural plexus of veins. It should be noted that the spinal cord is quite small as compared with the size of the spinal canal and that the extra space is occupied by the several protective elements de-described above.

The dura mater extends caudally beyond the lower limit of the spinal cord, or to the level of the disc between the second and third sacral vertebrae, and thereby forms the *dural cul-de-sac* (Fig. 19). The cul-de-sac is lined by arachnoid mater and contains cerebrospinal fluid. Lumbar puncture needles are usually introduced into the dural cul-de-sac for the purpose of withdrawing cerebrospinal fluid for diagnostic examination, and for the injection of therapeutic solutions or spinal anesthetics. This area is obviously chosen because the needle can be introduced without danger of damaging the spinal cord.

The **filum terminale** is a pia-glial process which begins at the lower end of the spinal cord and extends downward through the dural cul-de-sac and spinal canal; it is attached inferiorly to the dorsal surface of the coccyx and thus serves to anchor the spinal cord. Within the cul-de-sac the filum is surrounded by the lower lumbar and sacral nerves as they pass from the spinal cord to their foramina of exit. The lumbar and sacral nerves, surrounding the filum terminale and conus medullaris, constitute the *cauda equina.*

In cross-section the spinal cord is seen to have an H-shaped, centrally placed area of gray matter which is surrounded by white matter (Fig. 21). The two halves of the gray matter are connected across the midline by the ventral and dorsal *gray commissures*—so named because of their relationships to the central canal. Dorsally, division of the cord into right and left halves is indicated by the *dorsal median septum* which is continuous with the pia mater. On the ventral side the two halves are separated by the *ventral median fissure.* The position of the dorsal median septum is indicated on the surface by a longitudinal groove called the *dorsal median sulcus.* Each lateral surface of the spinal cord presents a *dorsolateral* and a *ventrolateral sulcus.*

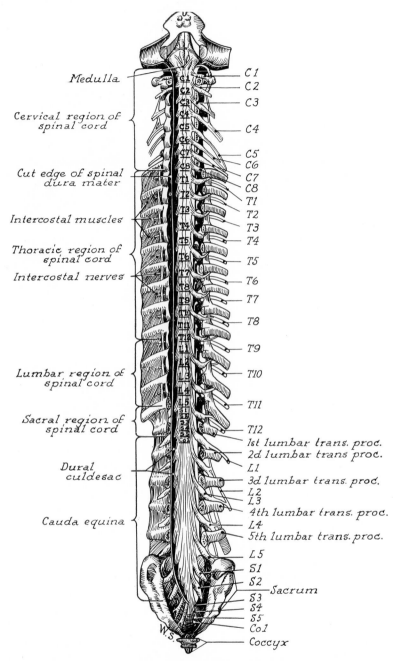

Medulla

Cervical region of
spinal cord

Cut edge of spinal
dura mater

Intercostal muscles

Thoracic region of
spinal cord

Intercostal nerves

Lumbar region of
spinal cord

Sacral region of
spinal cord

Dural
culdesac

Cauda equina

C 1
C 2
C 3
C 4
C 5
C 6
C 7
C 8
T1
T2
T3
T4
T5
T6
T7
T8
T9
T10
T11
T12
1st lumbar trans. proc.
2d lumbar trans proc.
L1
3d lumbar trans. proc.
L2
L3
4th lumbar trans. proc.
L4
5th lumbar trans. proc.
L 5
S1
S2
Sacrum
S3
S4
S5
Co1
Coccyx

Fig. 19. Dorsal view of the spinal cord *in situ* (vertebral laminae removed) to show the relation of the spinal cord segments to the vertebral column (after Tilney and Riley).

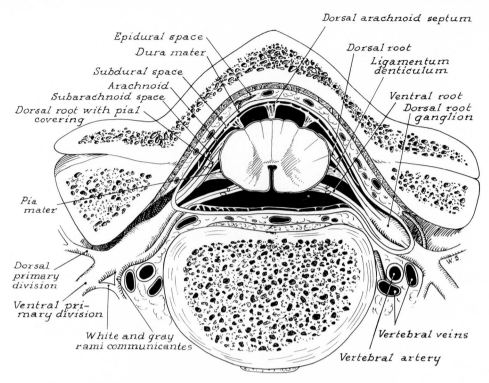

FIG. 20.   Cross-section of spinal cord in the spinal canal showing its meningeal coverings and the manner of exit of the spinal nerves (after Rauber).

The dorsal roots of the spinal nerves enter the cord in the region of the dorsolateral sulcus and the anterior roots emerge from it at the ventrolateral sulcus (Fig. 20).

Each lateral half of the *gray matter* presents dorsal and ventral projections which are respectively designated as *dorsal* and *ventral gray columns*. The thoracic and upper lumbar levels present, in addition, a third column of gray matter located laterally and midway between the dorsal and ventral columns—the *lateral gray column* (Fig. 23); it contains the cell bodies of general visceral efferent neurons. The cell bodies of somatic efferent neurons are found in the ventral gray columns. Cervical and lumbosacral enlargements of the spinal cord appear at the levels which, respectively, give origin to the brachial and lumbo-

sacral plexuses (Figs. 22, 24 and 25). The increases in size at these levels are due to the increased number of neurons required for the innervation of the limbs.

The neurons whose cell bodies are located in the dorsal gray columns are of two functional types and are designated as *internuncial* (or *association*) and *tract cells*. The internuncial neurons receive impulses from the dorsal root fibers; their axons are distributed to other cells in the gray matter, particularly in the ventral gray columns, and thus complete spinal reflex arcs (Fig. 26). The axons of some internuncial neurons are distributed to ventral gray column cells within their own segment of the spinal cord; others reach those of higher or lower levels; both intra- and intersegmental reflex arcs are thus made possible. They may connect with cells

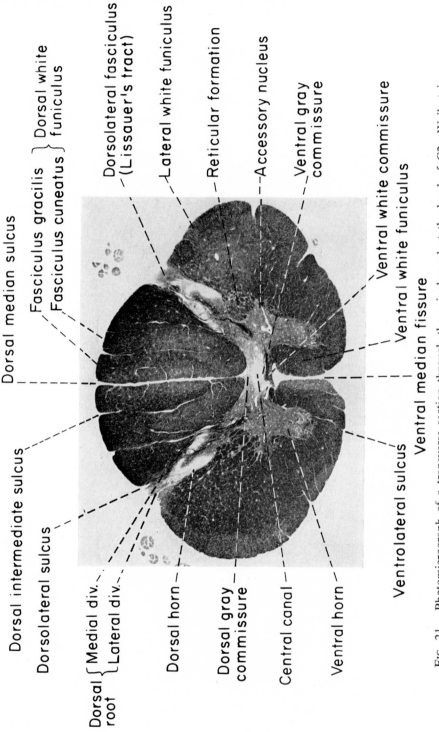

Dorsal median sulcus

Fasciculus gracilis ⎫ Dorsal white
Fasciculus cuneatus ⎬ funiculus

Dorsolateral fasciculus (Lissauer's tract)

Lateral white funiculus

Reticular formation

Accessory nucleus

Ventral gray commissure

Ventral white commissure

Ventral white funiculus

Ventral median fissure

Dorsal intermediate sulcus

Dorsolateral sulcus

Dorsal root { Medial div.
{ Lateral div.

Dorsal horn

Dorsal gray commissure

Central canal

Ventral horn

Ventrolateral sulcus

Fig. 21. Photomicrograph of a transverse section through the spinal cord at the level of C2. Weil stain.

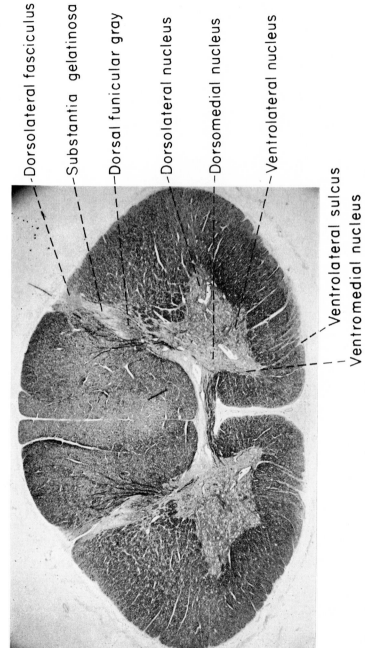

Dorsolateral fasciculus

Substantia gelatinosa

Dorsal funicular gray

Dorsolateral nucleus

Dorsomedial nucleus

Ventrolateral nucleus

Ventrolateral sulcus

Ventromedial nucleus

FIG. 22.   Photomicrograph of a transverse section of the spinal cord through the cervical enlargement. Weil stain.

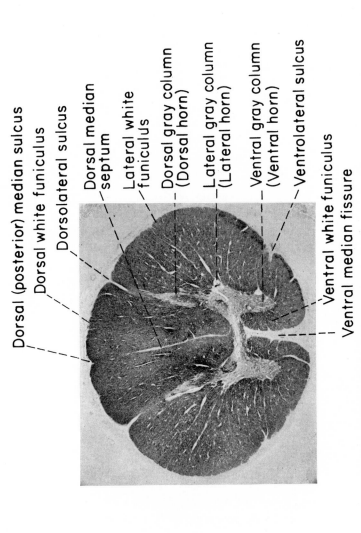

Dorsal (posterior) median sulcus

Dorsal white funiculus

Dorsolateral sulcus

Dorsal median septum

Lateral white funiculus

Dorsal gray column (Dorsal horn)

Lateral gray column (Lateral horn)

Ventral gray column (Ventral horn)

Ventrolateral sulcus

Ventral white funiculus

Ventral median fissure

FIG. 23.   Photomicrograph of a transverse section of the spinal cord through the midthoracic region.   Weil stain.

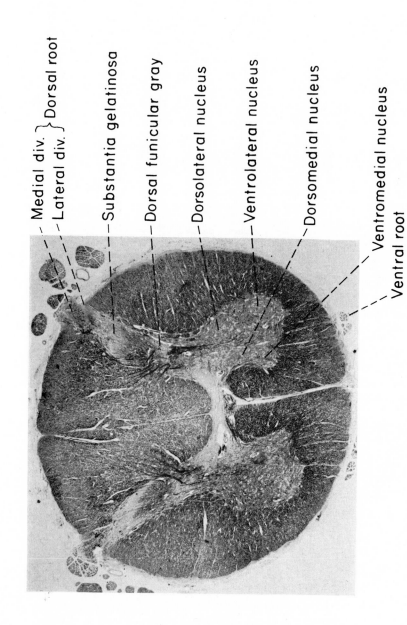

Medial div. ⎱
Lateral div. ⎰ Dorsal root

Substantia gelatinosa

Dorsal funicular gray

Dorsolateral nucleus

Ventrolateral nucleus

Dorsomedial nucleus

Ventromedial nucleus

Ventral root

FIG. 24. Photomicrograph of a transverse section of the spinal cord through the lumbar enlargement. Weil stain.

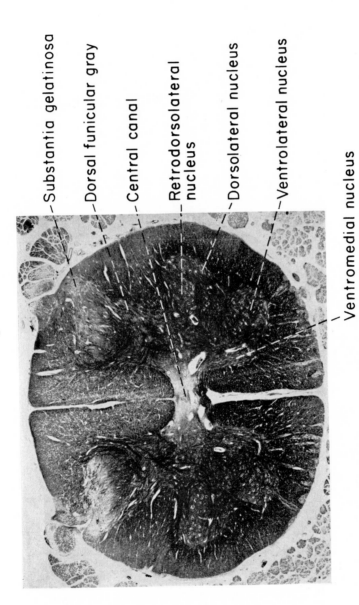

Substantia gelatinosa

Dorsal funicular gray

Central canal

Retrodorsolateral nucleus

Dorsolateral nucleus

Ventrolateral nucleus

Ventromedial nucleus

FIG. 25. Photomicrograph of a transverse section of the spinal cord through the level of S2. Weil stain.

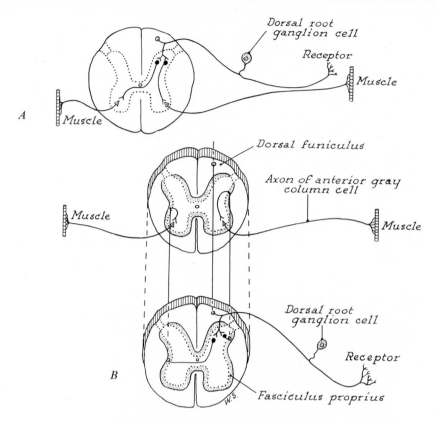

FIG. 26. Reflex arcs. *A*, Crossed and uncrossed intrasegmental arcs. *B*, Crossed and uncrossed intersegmental arcs with intersegmental connections by way of the fasciculus proprius.

in the ventral gray column on the same side as that of their origin or they may cross to those of the opposite side; through such crossed and uncrossed connections, as many muscles are brought into action on one or both sides as are necessary for a given reflex act (Fig. 26).

The tract cells also receive impulses from the periphery over the dorsal roots of the spinal nerves; their axons course upward in the white matter and eventually terminate in the brain. The ascending *fiber tracts* of the spinal cord are made up of these axons and each tract is concerned with the conduction of relatively specific types of impulses to the brain.

The *white matter* in each lateral half of the spinal cord is divided into three columns or *funiculi* (Fig. 21). The *dorsal funiculus* is between the dorsal median septum and the dorsal gray column. The *lateral funiculus* occupies the area between the dorsal and ventral gray columns and the *ventral funiculus* is between the lateral funiculus and the ventromedian fissure. Each funiculus is composed of a number of fiber tracts, which occupy relatively circumscribed and constant positions within it. The more detailed considerations of the individual tracts are contained in following chapters.

That part of each funiculus which is in immediate relationship to the gray matter is designated as the fasciculus proprius (Fig. 26). There are, then, dorsal, lateral and ventral fasciculi

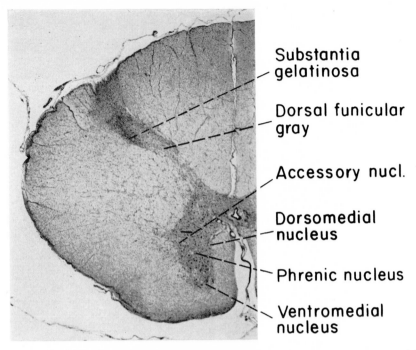

Substantia
gelatinosa

Dorsal funicular
gray

Accessory nucl.

Dorsomedial
nucleus

Phrenic nucleus

Ventromedial
nucleus

FIG. 27. Photomicrograph of a transverse section of the spinal cord at C3. Cresyl violet stain.

proprii. The fasciculi are made up of the ascending and descending processes of internuncial neurons whose cell bodies are in the gray matter. They are therefore important in intersegmental reflex arcs (Fig. 26).

Appropriately stained transverse sections of the spinal cord show the three major gray columns to be composed of more or less distinct cell groups or nuclei (Figs. 27-31). The various cell groups of the dorsal gray column are the *substantia gelatinosa, dorsal funicular gray, dorsal nucleus of Clarke* and the *secondary visceral gray* (Figs. 27-30). The substantia gelatinosa consists primarily of small neurons (Golgi Type II) and extends through the length of the spinal cord. This column of cells receives primarily the terminals of small dorsal root ganglion cells which mediate pain and temperature sensibilities. The dorsal funicular gray column is composed of larger cells as well as of small neurons.

This column, which likewise extends through the length of the spinal cord, receives incoming tactile and proprioceptive fibers. Pain and temperature impulses are also received directly by cells in this column, and after relay in the substantia gelatinosa. The larger neurons of the dorsal funicular gray column give rise to secondary ascending fibers.

The dorsal nucleus of Clarke (dorsal nucleus) (Fig. 29) is comprised of large neurons and extends approximately from cord segment C8 to L2. The dorsal spinocerebellar tract (Chapter 18) takes origin from cells in this nucleus.

The secondary visceral gray (Fig. 29) is an indistinct column of small neurons which extends through the thoracic and upper lumbar levels. It lies at the base of the dorsal horn, above the cells of lateral horn gray and is believed to receive incoming visceral afferent fibers.

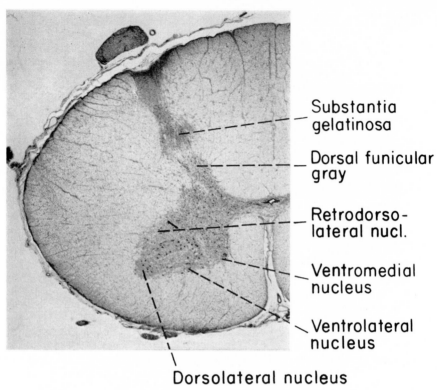

Substantia gelatinosa

Dorsal funicular gray

Retrodorso-lateral nucl.

Ventromedial nucleus

Ventrolateral nucleus

Dorsolateral nucleus

FIG. 28. Photomicrograph of a transverse section of the spinal cord through the cervical enlargement. Cresyl violet stain.

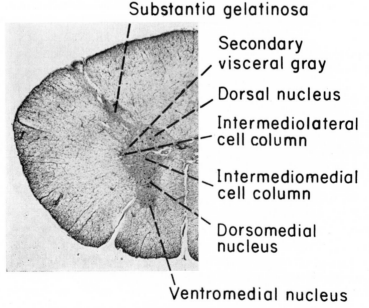

Substantia gelatinosa

Secondary visceral gray

Dorsal nucleus

Intermediolateral cell column

Intermediomedial cell column

Dorsomedial nucleus

Ventromedial nucleus

FIG. 29. Photomicrograph of a transverse section of the spinal cord at midthoracic region. Cresyl violet stain.

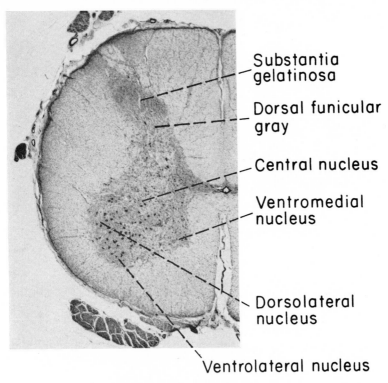

Substantia
gelatinosa

Dorsal funicular
gray

Central nucleus

Ventromedial
nucleus

Dorsolateral
nucleus

Ventrolateral nucleus

FIG. 30.   Photomicrograph of a transverse section of the spinal cord through the lumbar
enlargement. Cresyl violet stain.

The lateral gray column (intermediate gray column) is composed of preganglionic neurons which are directly lateral to the central canal. From T1 to L3 levels of the cord two divisions of the lateral column are recognized, the *intermediolateral* and *intermediomedial* (Fig. 29). These give rise to the preganglionic sympathetic fibers. The intermediate column is represented at levels S2 to S4 by the *parasympathetic* cell column. Fibers from these cells are the preganglionic efferents to the pelvic viscera (Chapter 21).

The ventral gray column, is composed of relatively large multipolar neurons which give origin to somatic efferent fibers that innervate skeletal muscle fibers of somite origin. The column may be divided into 3 major subdivisions, the medial, lateral and central. The medial division, represented at all levels of the cord, consists of the *ventromedial* and *dorsomedial* cell columns or nuclei which supply fibers to the axial musculature (Figs. 23, 27 and 29). The lateral division is present in the cervical and lumbar enlargements and serves as the origin for fibers to muscles of the limbs. This division may be subdivided into *ventrolateral, dorsolateral* and *retrodorsolateral* nuclei which relate respectively to the innervation of the proximal, intermediate and distal limb musculature (Figs. 23, 25, 28, 30 and 31). It is to be emphasized that there are differences in the longitudinal extent of these nuclei (for further details see Elliott, 1942; Crosby *et al.,* 1962).

The central division of the ventral gray column includes the *phrenic, lumbosacral* and *accessory nuclei* (Figs. 27

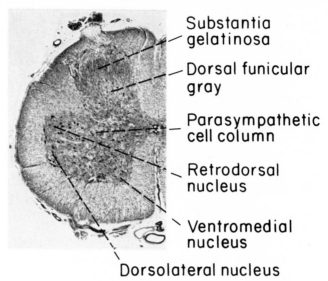

Substantia gelatinosa

Dorsal funicular gray

Parasympathetic cell column

Retrodorsal nucleus

Ventromedial nucleus

Dorsolateral nucleus

FIG. 31. Photomicrograph of a transverse section of the spinal cord at midsacral level. Cresyl violet stain.

and 30). The phrenic nucleus which extends from about segment C3 to C6 gives origin to fibers that innervate the skeletal muscle of the diaphragm. There is no general agreement relative to the mediolateral location of this nucleus (Keswani and Hollinshead, 1956). The lumbosacral (central) nucleus extends from upper lumbar to upper sacral levels. The peripheral distribution of its axons is unknown. The accessory nucleus extends through segments C1 to C6 and gives origin to fibers that form the spinal part of the accessory nerve which innervates the trapezius and sternomastoid muscles. The fibers, after emerging from the spinal cord, ascend in the spinal canal, pass through foramen magnum and join the bulbar portion of the accessory nerve.

BIBLIOGRAPHY

CROSBY, E. C., HUMPHREY, T. and LAUER, E. W., 1962: *Correlative Anatomy of the Nervous System*. Macmillan Co., New York.

ELLIOTT, H. C., 1942: Studies on the motor cells of the spinal cord. I. Distribution in the normal human cord. Am. J. Anat., *70*, 95-117.

KESWANI, N. H. and HOLLINSHEAD, W. H., 1956: Localization of the phrenic nucleus in the spinal cord of man. Anat. Rec., *125*, 683-700.

Chapter 5

Somatic Tactile, Proprioceptive, Pain and Thermal Pathways; Visceral Afferent Pathways

THE **tactile impulses** set up by stimulation of tactile receptors are conducted to the spinal cord over the peripheral and central divisions of the processes of spinal ganglion cells. The centrally directed fibers from these ganglion cells traverse the dorsal root through its medial division and enter the dorsal funiculus of the spinal cord (Figs. 32 and 33). Here they divide into short, descending branches and much longer ascending ones. The descending branches aggregate into small tracts known as the *fasciculus septomarginalis* adjacent to the posterior median septum and the *fasciculus interfascicularis* between the gracile and cuneate fasciculi (Fig. 33). Both the ascending and descending branches distribute collaterals to cells in the dorsal gray column and thus facilitate spinal reflexes in response to tactile stimuli (Figs. 26, 32 and 33). The collaterals also terminate in relation to tract cells whose axons cross the midline through the gray or white commissure and help to form the ventral spinothalamic tract of the contralateral ventral funiculus (Fig. 32).

A pathway of major importance in the mediation of tactile sensibility is formed by the many ascending divisions of dorsal root fibers which continue their upward course through the dorsal funiculus of the same side and finally synapse upon cells in the nuclei gracilis and cuneatus in the medulla (Fig. 36). Axons from the cells in these nuclei cross to the opposite side and course upward to the thalamus in the fiber tract known as the *medial lemniscus* (Fig. 32). In the medulla the paired lemnisci are adjacent and appear as vertical columns of longitudinally running fibers near the midline. In the pons the lemnisci are more horizontally disposed in the ventral part of the tegmentum, and in the midbrain they migrate to a ventrolateral tegmental position. Tactile impulses reaching the thalamus by the medial lemnisci are synaptically relayed by thalamic neurons to the cerebral cortex. The axons of the thalamic neurons project upward through the internal capsule (Fig. 32) to sensory receiving areas of the cortex. The internal capsule (Chapter 9) consists of nerve fibers which relay information from lower levels of the nervous system to the cerebrum and of fibers which project motor and regulatory information from the cerebrum to the lower centers.

An alternate pathway for the mediation of tactile sensibility is the ventral spinothalamic tract (Fig. 32). The fibers in this tract course upward through the spinal cord and brain stem and finally terminate by synapsing upon neurons in the thalamus. In its course through the brain stem the fibers in the ventral spinothalamic tract are incorporated into the medial lemniscus (Fig. 32) and like other lemniscal fibers, are synaptically relayed at the thalamus to the cerebral cortex.

Hence, both the pathway over the ventral spinothalamic tract and that via the dorsal funiculus and medial lemnis-

(47)

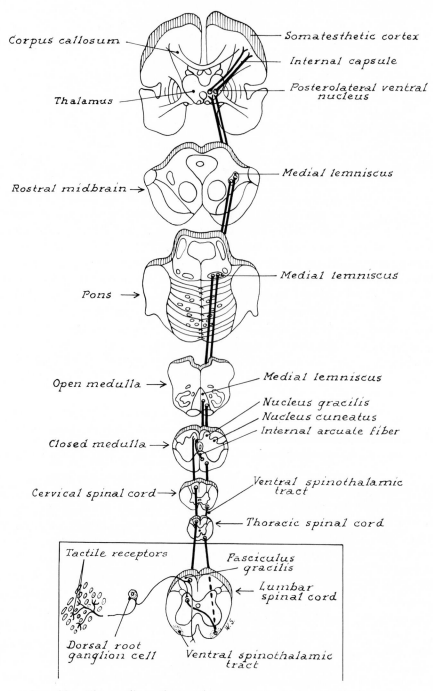

FIG. 32. The tactile pathways from receptor to somatesthetic cortex.

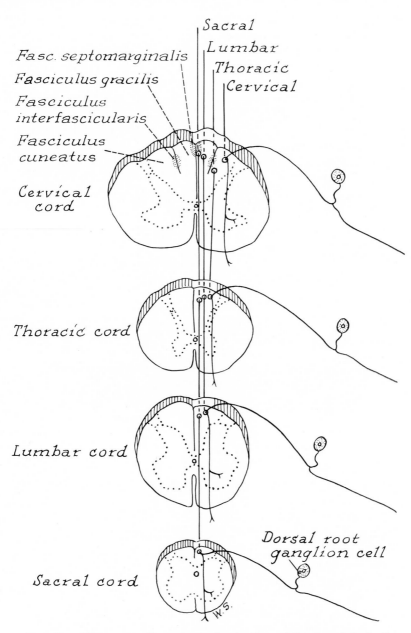

Fasc. septomarginalis

Fasciculus gracilis

Fasciculus
interfascicularis

Fasciculus
cuneatus

Cervical
cord

Sacral

Lumbar

Thoracic

Cervical

Thoracic cord

Lumbar cord

Dorsal root
ganglion cell

Sacral cord

W.S.

FIG. 33.   Diagram to illustrate the lamination of the dorsal funiculi.

cus ultimately reach the cerebral cortex and the conscious level.

The pathway over the dorsal funiculus and medial lemniscus is primarily concerned with the finer localizing and discriminatory aspects of tactile sensibility. Its discriminatory capabilities depend upon a synaptic ratio approaching 1:1 among the three levels of afferent conduction which intervene between receptor and cerebral cortex—dorsal root ganglia, nuclei gracilis and cuneatus, and

laminated; fibers coming into the funiculus at successively higher levels are more and more laterally placed. Those which enter below the midthoracic level constitute the *fasciculus gracilis* and those entering above that level make up the *fasciculus cuneatus* (Fig. 33). In the cervical levels of the spinal cord the two fasciculi are separated from one another by the *dorsal intermediate septum* whose position is indicated on the surface by the *dorsal intermediate* sulcus. It and the

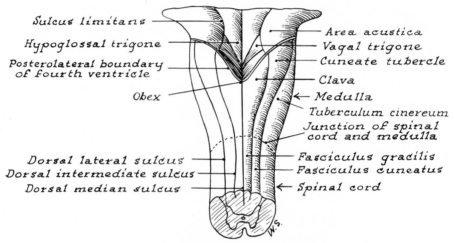

Fig. 34. Dorsal view of medulla oblongata and cervical spinal cord showing continuity of spinal cord sulci with those on the dorsal aspect of the closed part of the medulla.

thalamus. In contrast, the ventral spinothalamic pathway is concerned with less localized, more general tactile sensibility. This decreased specificity is indicative of the fact that more than one primary afferent neuron synapses upon a given tract cell, and several tract cells, in turn, synapse upon one thalamic neuron. It is evident from this that some tactile sensibility will remain if either the dorsal funiculi or the ventral spinothalamic tracts are not functioning, but that discrete tactile capabilities will be lost if the dorsal funiculi are not operating.

The **dorsal funiculus** of the spinal cord is chiefly composed of the ascending rami of dorsal root fibers and is specifically

other sulci on the surface of the cervical part of the cord are continued upward on to the medulla oblongata (Fig. 34).

The **medulla oblongata** consists of a caudal closed portion and of a rostral open portion. At the point of junction of the two portions the central canal opens out into the fourth ventricle. The open portion is so designated because of failure of approximation of the alar laminae, in this region, to form a central canal such as exists in the closed portion.

Between the dorsal median and dorsal intermediate sulci of the medulla, and in immediate relationship to the fourth ventricle, there is a swelling that is referred to as the *clava* (Fig. 34). Just lateral to the dorsal intermediate sulcus, and extending to a more rostral level, is a similar swelling called the *cuneate tubercle*. The clava and cuneate tubercle, respectively, indicate the positions beneath the surface, of the nucleus gracilis and the nucleus cuneatus. The fasciculus gracilis terminates in the former and

section of the closed portion of the medulla which cuts through the clava and cuneate tubercle; they are covered on their dorsal sides by the terminal portions of the fasciculi gracilis and cuneatus (Fig. 35). In sections through this caudal level of the medulla it can be appreciated that nucleus gracilis and nucleus cuneatus are extensions of the

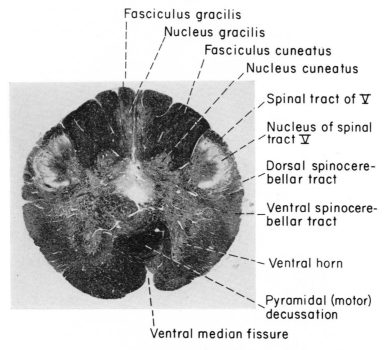

Fasciculus gracilis
Nucleus gracilis
Fasciculus cuneatus
Nucleus cuneatus
Spinal tract of Ⅴ
Nucleus of spinal tract Ⅴ
Dorsal spinocere-bellar tract
Ventral spinocere-bellar tract
Ventral horn
Pyramidal (motor) decussation
Ventral median fissure

FIG. 35.   Photomicrograph of a transverse section of the neuraxis at the level of transition from spinal cord to medulla. Weil stain.

the fasciculus cuneatus in the latter nucleus. The term "nucleus" as it is used with reference to the central nervous system, denotes a compact collection of nerve cells having more or less specific functions; the cells in a given nucleus are concerned with the reception of nervous impulses from certain neurons elsewhere in the nervous system and with the relay of those impulses to other centers or to effectors.

The **nucleus gracilis** and the **nucleus cuneatus** are clearly visible in a cross-

dorsal gray columns of the cervical spinal cord (Fig. 35). Fibers from the fasciculi can be traced into the nuclei where they synapse upon cells whose axons course ventrally and medially to enter the contralateral medial lemniscus (Figs. 36 and 37). The decussating fibers from the nuclei, because of their arched course, are called *internal arcuate fibers*. The decussation, formed by the fibers from both sides, is known as the *sensory decussation* or, sometimes, as the *decussation of the medial lemniscus*.

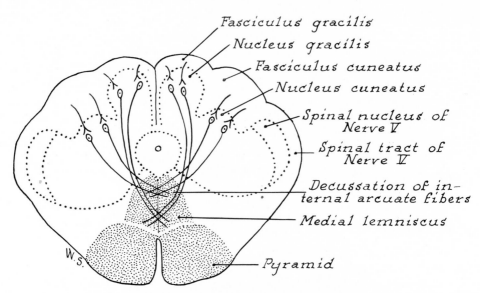

FIG. 36.   Cross-section of medulla at the level of the decussation of the internal arcuate fibers.

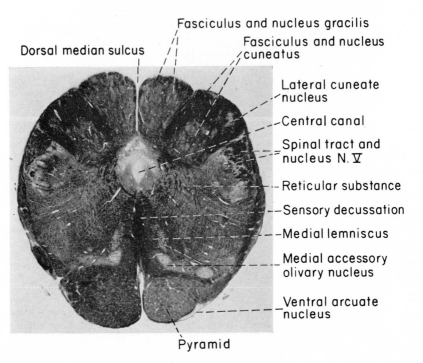

FIG. 37.   Photomicrograph of transverse section of the medulla at the level of the sensory decussation.   Weil stain.

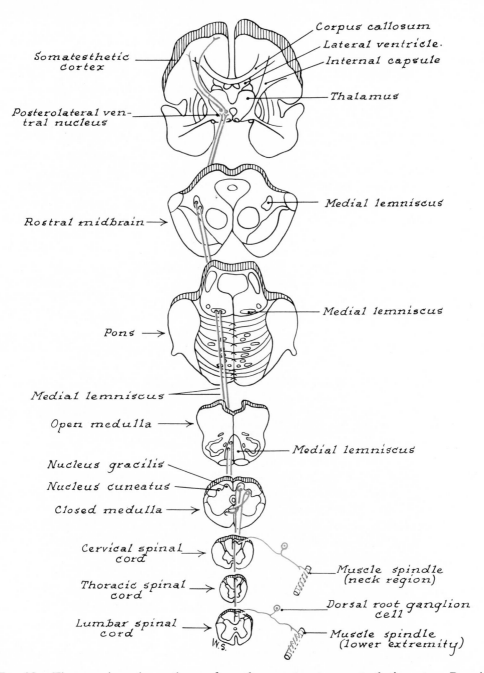

Fig. 38.   The proprioceptive pathways from the receptors to somatesthetic cortex. Proprioceptive impulses entering the spinal cord below the midthoracic level are shown utilizing the fasciculus gracilis while those entering above that level course upward in the fasciculus cuneatus.

The **medial lemniscus,** as was previously stated, can be traced rostrally through the medulla, pons, and mesencephalon to its termination in relation to cells in the thalamus whose axons end in the sensory area of the cerebral cortex. As will become apparent in subsequent discussions, the medial lemniscus contains some descending fibers (Chapter 13). The fact that the ventral spinothalamic tract joins the lemniscus in the medulla has also been mentioned.

Pathways from receptor endings to the cerebral cortex require a minimum of three neurons. The first (*primary* or of the *first order*) has its cell body in a peripheral ganglion (with some exceptions). The second neuron (*secondary* or of the *second order*) has its cell body in the dorsal gray column of the spinal cord or in some nucleus of the brain stem and, with few exceptions, is a decussating neuron, *i.e.,* its axon crosses to the opposite side. The cell body of the third neuron (*tertiary* or of the *third order*) is in the thalamus and its axon courses upward to terminate in the cerebral cortex. A given sensory impulse, due to the decussation of the secondary neuron, is delivered to the side of the brain opposite that of its origin, in most instances. The exceptions to these general rules that exist in some of the pathways from the head region will be pointed out as the cranial nerves are considered. The nucleus in the thalamus in which the medial lemniscus terminates, is situated laterally, posteriorly and ventrally; it is, therefore, designated as the posterolateral ventral nucleus (Figs. 32 and 69).

Destruction of the medial lemniscus on one side results in loss of all tactile perception on the opposite side of the body. The loss of ordinary tactile sense in conjunction with tactile discrimination is readily explained by the fact that the ventral spinothalamic tract joins the medial lemniscus in the medulla. If either dorsal funiculus of the spinal cord is interrupted there is loss of tactile discrimination on the side of, and below the level of, the lesion without loss of ordinary tactile sense.

Position, pressure and *vibratory sense,* the *sense of movement* and *stereognosis* are, like tactile discrimination, functions of the dorsal funiculi. The neurons of the first order, in the dorsal root ganglia, distribute peripheral processes to proprioceptive receptors and insofar as vibratory sense and stereognosis are concerned, to exteroceptors as well. Exteroceptors may also be concerned in pressure sense. Central processes enter the dorsal funiculi over the medial divisions of the dorsal roots and their long ascending divisions end in the nucleus gracilis or cuneatus, depending upon the level of the spinal cord at which they entered (Fig. 38). The further course of proprioceptive impulses over the internal arcuate fibers and medial lemniscus to the thalamus and from the thalamus to the cortex is the same as that described for tactile discriminatory impulses.

Collaterals from the central processes of the primary neurons in the proprioceptive pathway terminate in relation to internuncial neurons in the dorsal gray column and thus contribute to the formation of proprioceptive spinal reflex arcs. The knee jerk is an example of a reflex that utilizes such an arc (Fig. 39). Tapping the patellar tendon effects a sudden stretch of the quadriceps muscle and stimulates the muscle spindles and musculotendinous endings therein. The impulses thus set up reach the spinal cord by way of the femoral nerve and the dorsal roots of the second, third, and fourth lumbar nerves; through the medium of intrasegmental internuncial neurons they are conducted to, and serve to activate, anterior gray column cells in the corresponding lumbar segments. Through the axons of the latter cells, efferent impulses are conducted to the quadriceps muscle and account for its sudden reflex contraction. In this instance, the stimulus is an artificial one, but it illustrates the connections which facilitate proprioceptive reflexes as they normally occur in response to changes in length and tension of muscles.

It is now apparent that destruction of

spinal cord and interruption of either medial lemniscus may result from thrombosis of one or more branches of the anterior spinal artery (Fig. 40).

Pernicious anemia, undiagnosed and untreated, results in pathology of the spinal cord in the form of degeneration in the dorsal and lateral funiculi—so-called *subacute combined degeneration*

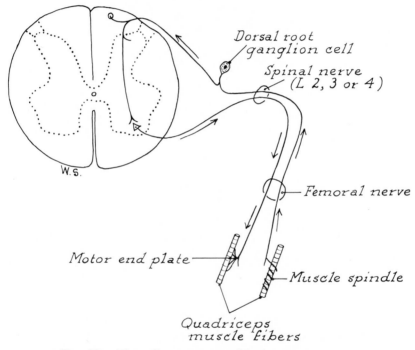

Fig. 39.   The reflex arc responsible for the knee jerk.

either dorsal funiculus at any given level will result in loss of position sense, sense of movement, pressure and vibratory sense, and stereognosis, as well as of tactile discrimination, on the same side as the lesion and caudal to it (Figs. 32 and 38). Interruption of one medial lemniscus will cause contralateral loss of all these types of sensibility and ordinary tactile sense (the latter because the ventral spinothalamic tract joins the medial lemniscus). Unilateral interruption of a dorsal funiculus may occur as a result of intra- or extramedullary tumor of the

or sclerosis (Fig. 149). This is a bilateral condition which, so far as the degeneration in the dorsal funiculi is concerned, accounts for bilateral reduction and eventual loss of all types of sensibility carried by the fasciculi gracilis and cuneatus.

The dorsal funiculi also exhibit degeneration with marked loss of myelin in *tabes dorsalis*. The degeneration in this condition, is secondary to *radiculitis* (inflammatory involvement of the dorsal roots). The spirochete of syphilis attacks the dorsal roots whose component fibers

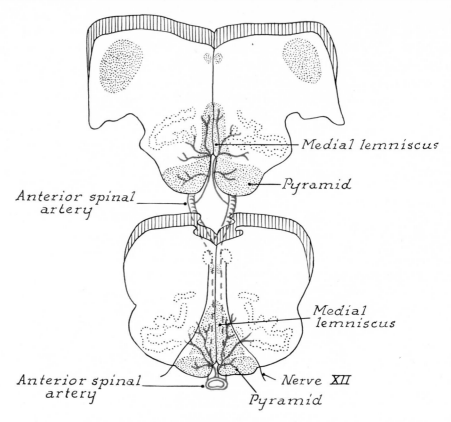

FIG. 40.   Diagram showing the distribution of the branches of the anterior spinal artery to the ventral and medial areas of the medulla.

are degenerated throughout their intramedullary course; proprioceptive sensibility is therefore diminished or completely abolished. As should be expected, the radiculitis also results in some reduction of tactile, pain and thermal sensibility. Degeneration is not found in the ventral and lateral spinothalamic tracts since they are formed by axons of secondary neurons; only the primary neurons are involved. Since the dorsal roots are the afferent limbs of proprioceptive reflex arcs, the knee jerk and other deep reflexes are diminished or absent in tabes dorsalis.

The lumbar and sacral nerves are the first to be attacked by the radiculitis of syphilis; therefore, loss of vibratory and position sense and diminution of reflexes occur in the lower extremities first. Degeneration in the dorsal funiculi, if there is opportunity to examine the spinal cord from a tabetic patient in the earlier stages of the disease, will be more marked in the fasciculus gracilis than in the fasciculus cuneatus.

Sensory loss similar to that of tabes has been occasionally reported in uncontrolled diabetics. Post-mortem examinations in such individuals have revealed similar changes in the spinal cord (Griggs and Olsen, 1937).

Pain and thermal sensibilities may be discussed together since they utilize the same pathway through the spinal cord and brain stem. The dorsal root ganglion cells concerned with pain and thermal sense are smaller than those which con-

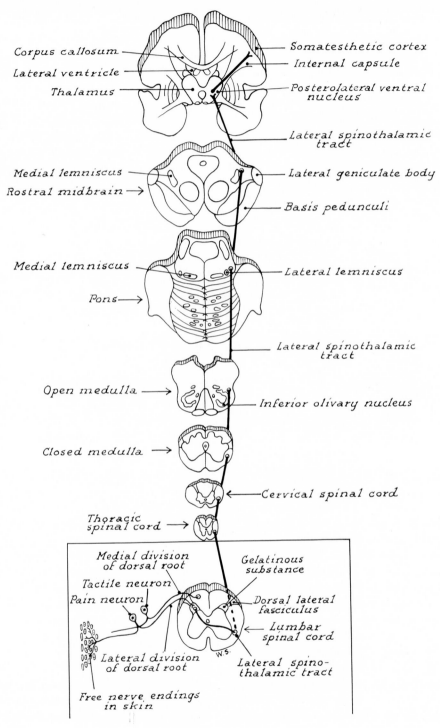

FIG. 41.   The pain and thermal pathway from receptor to somatesthetic cortex.

duct tactile and proprioceptive impulses. The processes of the cells are also of smaller caliber and are lightly myelinated; their central divisions enter the spinal cord in the region of the dorsolateral sulcus and are then directed laterally as compared with the course of the tactile fibers; for that reason they have been considered to form the *lateral division of the dorsal root* in contradistinction to the *medial division* which enters

cord sections, stained with iron-hematoxylin, the dorsal lateral fasciculus appears much lighter in color than the white matter of the adjacent dorsal and lateral funiculi. This is due to the relative lack of myelin in this fasciculus. The intensity of the blue color produced in the white matter when such sections are stained with hematoxylin (Pal-Weigert or Weil methods) varies in proportion to the amount of myelin present.

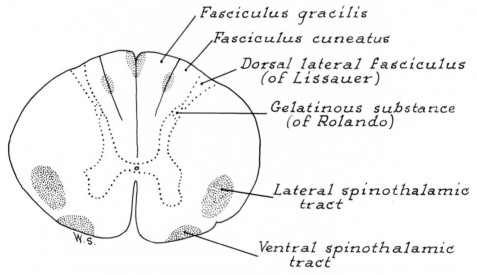

FIG. 42.   Cross-section of thoracic spinal cord showing the locations of the ventral and lateral spinothalamic tracts.

the dorsal funiculus (Fig. 41). It is important to understand that these are divisions of the dorsal root as a whole and not of the individual root fibers.

The **dorsal lateral fasciculus** (of Lissauer) is found in the interval between the dorsal and lateral funiculi (Fig. 21). It is formed by the short ascending and descending divisions of the pain and thermal fibers which constitute the lateral divisions of the dorsal roots. Although this tract is present throughout the length of the spinal cord, the individual fibers are distributed to no more than a total of 3 or 4 segments. In the standard preparations of spinal

The **gelatinous substance** (of Rolando), forming the apex of the dorsal gray column, lies immediately beneath the dorsal lateral fasciculus (Figs. 23, 27 and 42). It contains the cell bodies of the secondary neurons in the pain and thermal pathways. Collaterals from the ascending and descending fibers in the fasciculus and, eventually, the fibers themselves terminate through synapses upon these secondary neurons. Prior to the investigations of Pearson (1952), it was generally believed that axons of cells in the gelatinous substance crossed to the opposite lateral funiculus through the commissures and coursed upward through the spinal cord and brain stem as components of the **lateral spinothalamic tract.** It now appears that cells in the gelatinous substance relay their impulses through one or more intercalated neurons to cells in the extragelatinous part of the dorsal gray column which then give rise to the lateral spinothalamic tract; this tract terminates in relation to neurons of the third (or fourth) order in the thalamus (Fig. 41). The lateral spinothalamic tract, like the medial lemniscus, terminates in the postero-lateral ventral thalamic nucleus (Figs. 41 and 69). Glees (1953) speculated on why these two tracts terminate in the same thalamic nucleus and suggested that the localization of painful stimuli may be improved thereby, because pain impulses must be accompanied by simultaneous tactile impulses. Pain and thermal impulses are then presumably conducted to the cerebral cortex over the axons of the thalamic neurons. Clinical observations and experimental studies indicate that conscious recognition of pain occurs at thalamic level. This is supported by the failure of cortical stimulation to elicit the sensation of pain. Nevertheless, it is likely that pain has a cortical representation which is necessary for its quantitative, qualitative, and topographic assessment.

Spinal reflexes in response to pain and thermal stimuli are facilitated by direct or indirect connections from the gelatinous substance to ventral gray column cells. These reflexes are classified as *nociceptive.*

In **syringomyelia** there is, as the name implies, cavitation of the spinal cord. Such cavitation may result from degeneration of tumors arising in the ependymal lining of the central canal. It eventually destroys the gray and white commissures of the cord and thus interrupts the decussating axons of the second (or third) order neurons in the pain and thermal pathway. The cavity tends to extend longitudinally through several segments of the spinal cord and its presence is manifested by bilateral loss of pain and thermal sensibility, localized to those areas whose sensory innervation depends upon the spinal cord segments involved. Thus, a syringomyelia of the cervical and upper thoracic segments of the cord gives rise to a "jacket" type of anesthesia (shoulders, upper extremities and upper part of the thoracic wall). There may be preservation of all other types of sensibility, since they are conducted to the brain over spinal cord pathways which are uncrossed. It is typical of syringomyelia that the cavity expands to such an extent as to involve the ventral gray columns. This causes weakness localized in those muscles innervated by the same cord levels in which there is a loss of cutaneous pain and thermal sense.

The **lateral spinothalamic tract** is situated in the ventral half of the lateral funiculus of the spinal cord (Fig. 42). Damage to the tract results in loss of pain and thermal perception on the opposite side, below the level of the lesion. Practical application is made of the knowledge of the location and course of the lateral spinothalamic tract in the procedure known as cordotomy.

Cordotomy entails the surgical severance of the lateral spinothalamic tract, at an appropriate level of the spinal cord, for the relief of otherwise intractable pain. If the pain-producing disease process is unilateral the tract must, of course, be severed on the opposite side. If it is bilateral (a classic example is the gastric crisis of tabes dorsalis) it becomes necessary to cut the tract on both sides.

The **dentate ligament** is an important landmark in cordotomy. It consists of eighteen to twenty-one tooth-like projections of the pia mater. The serrations arise from the lateral midline of the spinal cord (Fig. 43), pierce the arachnoid mater, and attach to the inner surface of the dura mater. If the surgeon inserts his knife into the cord ventral to the dentate ligament he can cut the lateral spinothalamic tract without danger of damage to the main motor pathway (lateral corticospinal tract) which is also in the lateral funiculus, but lies dorsal to the plane of the dentate ligaments. White (1954) has re-emphasized that the lateral

spinothalamic tract is not confined to a small bundle of fibers and that analgesia cannot be obtained by a "3-millimeter deep" incision between the dentate ligament and the emerging ventral roots of spinal nerves. He, and others, advocated a ventromedial incision to include almost the entire anterior quadrant of the spinal cord (Fig. 43).

It has been noted that the ascending divisions of the dorsal root fibers carry-

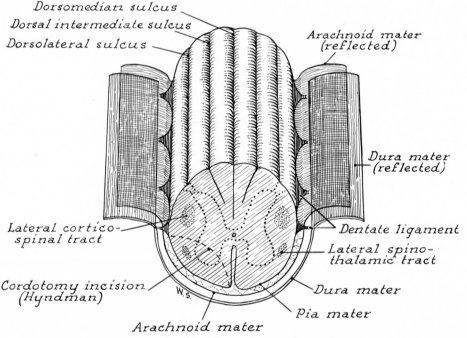

FIG. 43.   Diagram to show the relationship of the dentate ligament to the spinal cord and its coverings and to indicate its importance as a landmark in cordotomy.

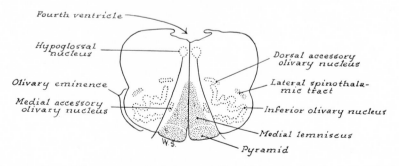

FIG. 44.   Cross-section of the open part of the medulla oblongata showing the relationship of the lateral spinothalamic tract to the inferior olivary nucleus and to the olivary eminence.

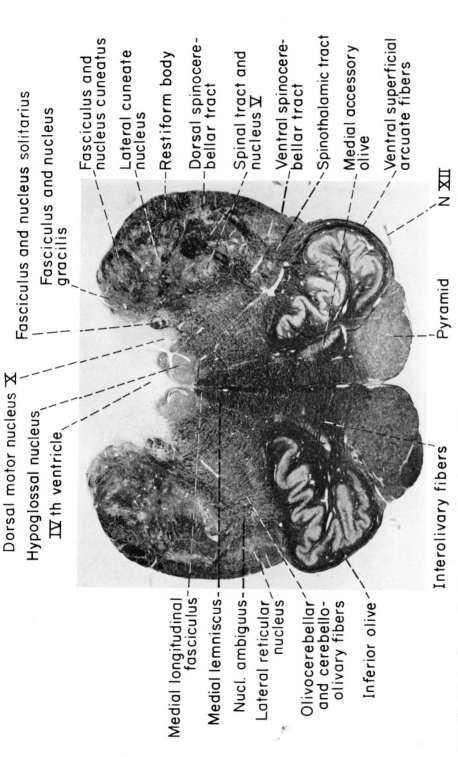

Fig. 45. Photomicrograph of transverse section of the medulla at the caudal part of the fourth ventricle. Weil stain. Note the reduced pyramid on the right which is due to partial degeneration of pyramidal tract fibers resulting from hemorrhage into the internal capsule (see Chapters 15 and 17).

ing pain impulses course upward in the dorsal lateral fasciculus for a variable number of segments, usually 1 to 3. It is therefore necessary to section the lateral spinothalamic tract at a level rostral to that which represents the upper limit of the painful process.

In the medulla the lateral spinothalamic tract is situated dorsolateral to the inferior olivary nucleus (Chapter 6) which for the present, will remain just a landmark. The nucleus has been described as having the shape of a crumpled purse; it is located in the ventrolateral area of the medulla (Figs. 44 and 45). Damage to the lateral spinothalamic tract in the medulla results in complete loss of pain and thermal sense from the head down on the side opposite that of the lesion. The tract can be cut surgically in the medulla as well as at other levels in the brain stem (Glees, 1953).

The **olivary eminence** provides an important landmark for section of the lateral spinothalamic tract at the level of the medulla (Fig. 44). The eminence consists of an elongated swelling on the lateral surface of the medulla which is due to the underlying olivary nucleus. If the surgeon inserts his knife immediately dorsal to the eminence and to a measured depth (about 4½ mm.), he can completely sever the tract (Schwartz and O'Leary, 1941). Crawford and Knighton (1953) have described, in considerable detail, the techniques utilized and the results obtained in their series of medullary spinothalamic tractotomies. They obtained high cervical levels of contralateral analgesia and some sensory changes indicating injury to the trigeminal pathways. The latter will be discussed at a later time (Chapter 7).

The lateral spinothalamic tract is more or less specifically laminated, like the fasciculi gracilis and cuneatus; its lamination differs from that of those fasciculi, however, in that the fibers entering it at successively higher levels assume a more and more medial and ventral position in the lateral funiculus (Yoss, 1953; White, 1954; Poirier and Bertrand, 1955).

Yoss (1953) investigated the conduction of impulses resulting from stimulation of pain-sensitive receptors in tendons and concluded that the conduction of "deep pain" is exactly like that of "superficial pain." In the monkey, impulses set up by painful stimulation of exposed tendons ascend in the lateral spinothalamic tract on the side opposite their origin. No impulses from tendons, interpreted as pain by the monkey, were found to ascend in the homolateral dorsal white column of the spinal cord; this is in conflict with conclusions arrived at by White (1954) who considered the pain from muscle spasm to be conducted over dorsal columns.

Interoceptive nervous impulses reach the conscious level but those classified as *general visceral afferent* are neither accurately localized with reference to the area of stimulation nor as accurately interpreted as are exteroceptive and proprioceptive impulses. The *special visceral afferent impulses* are more accurately interpreted.

The cell bodies of the *primary visceral afferent neurons* are in the spinal ganglia, in the ganglia associated with the glossopharyngeal, vagus, and facial nerves, and in the olfactory mucous membrane. The peripheral processes of those in the spinal ganglia pass from the spinal nerves to the ganglia of the sympathetic chain through the *white rami communicantes* (Fig. 46). They pass through the chain ganglia without any synapse therein and may rejoin the spinal nerves by way of the *gray rami communicantes,* in which event they are distributed to vascular and glandular structures outside the body cavities. Other visceral afferent fibers are distributed from the chain

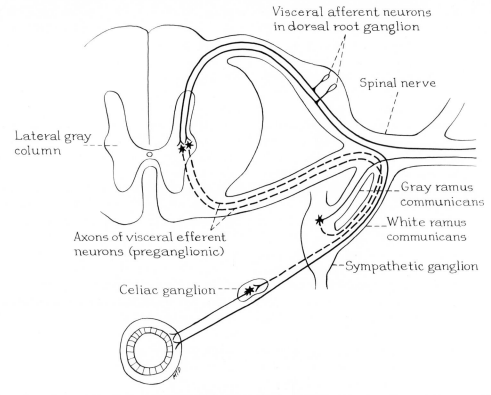

FIG. 46.   The origin and manner of distribution of visceral afferent and efferent fibers from the lower thoracic region.

ganglia to thoracic and abdominal viscera by way of the cardiac, pulmonary, and splanchnic nerves. Visceral afferent fibers to the heart and lungs arise from the upper thoracic spinal ganglia. Those to the digestive tract, liver, kidneys, ureters, bladder, gonads, and peritoneum arise from the lower thoracic ganglia and course to the celiac and other plexuses of the abdomen by way of the splanchnic nerves (Fig. 46). They eventually reach the visceral structures, in association with visceral efferent fibers, through these plexuses.

Caudal analgesia, as used in obstetrics, represents a practical application of the knowledge that the visceral afferent fibers of the eleventh and twelfth thoracic nerves, via the splanchnics, are particularly concerned with the sensory innerva-

tion of the uterus. The analgesic agent is introduced into the spinal canal through the sacral hiatus in just sufficient quantity that it diffuses upward in the epidural fat to a level which includes the eleventh thoracic nerves. Thus the pain impulses from the uterus are blocked without interfering with the visceral efferent impulses to the musculature of its upper segment which come from the intermediolateral gray column in thoracic segments above the eleventh (Hingson and Edwards, 1943). The somatic afferent impulses from the perineum are also blocked and the pain which is otherwise associated with the marked dilatation of this region is eliminated (Bonica, 1964).

General visceral afferent fibers of the vagus nerve, arising from cells in the *nodose ganglion* (Chapter 1), are also distributed to thoracic and abdominal viscera. The nodose ganglion is a sensory ganglion which is functionally and structurally analogous to spinal ganglia and whose neurons function as the afferent limbs of visceral reflex arcs; experiments have indicated, however, that these neurons are of less importance in the conscious perception of visceral sensations than those whose cell bodies are in the spinal ganglia (Fulton, 1949).

The **interoceptive pathway** to the conscious level is not as well defined as are the exteroceptive and proprioceptive pathways. It is usually considered to consist of a series of several neurons, with cell bodies in the dorsal gray columns, whose axons course upward in the fasciculi proprii through a few segments and synapse upon the dendrites or cell bodies of the next higher group of neurons in the chain. If this were the only pathway for visceral impulses, section of the lateral spinothalamic tract should be without effect upon visceral pain. Experiments have shown, however, that the pain pathway from the renal pelvis can be interrupted by cordotomy (Hyndman and Wolkin, 1943). The gastric crises of tabes dorsalis may be due to irritation of pain receptors in the viscera and peritoneum; as previously mentioned, this type of pain is often relieved by bilateral cordotomy (Hyndman and Jarvis, 1940). White (1954) has stated, on the basis of surgical results, that visceral pain is eliminated by extensive transection of the anterolateral quadrant of the spinal cord, carried out contralateral to the painful focus. It appears, therefore, that *visceral pain impulses* are carried upward in or near the lateral spinothalamic tract and additional evidence in support of this concept has been presented by Nathan and Smith (1953) who studied a large series of cordotomies for relief of pain from the rectal region. Other types of impulses arising in the viscera may be conducted by a chain of neurons with cell bodies in the dorsal gray column.

It is generally believed that visceral sensations reach the conscious level in the thalamus. Somatic pain is also believed to reach consciousness in the thalamus but localization of the point of stimulation and differentiation between varying intensities of stimulation are functions of the cerebral cortex (see page 59).

Visceral reflex arcs are completed within the spinal cord; the central processes of visceral afferent neurons may synapse directly upon visceral efferent neurons in the intermediolateral gray column (Fig. 47, *A*) or upon internuncial neurons in the dorsal gray column (secondary visceral gray) whose axons are distributed in such a manner as to account for both intra- and intersegmental arcs.

Internuncial neurons also facilitate *viscerosomatic reflexes*. An example of such a reflex is the rigidity of the muscles of the anterior abdominal wall in the presence of acute appendicitis. Pain impulses from the regional peritoneum are conducted to the spinal cord by the splanchnic nerves and the dorsal roots of the lower thoracic nerves. Within the cord, connections are made, through internuncial cells, with the anterior gray column cells which innervate the abdominal muscles (Fig. 47 *B*).

The existence of *somatovisceral reflexes* may be appropriately mentioned at this point although the consideration of visceral efferent impulses will be left until later (Chapter 22). The *pilomotor reflex* is an example of this type; it is manifested by the appearance of goose flesh in response to the application of cold to the skin. Thus, exteroceptors for cold and somatic afferent neurons are responsible for the afferent portion of a reflex in which the effectors are smooth muscles that are innervated by general visceral efferent fibers (Fig. 47, *C*).

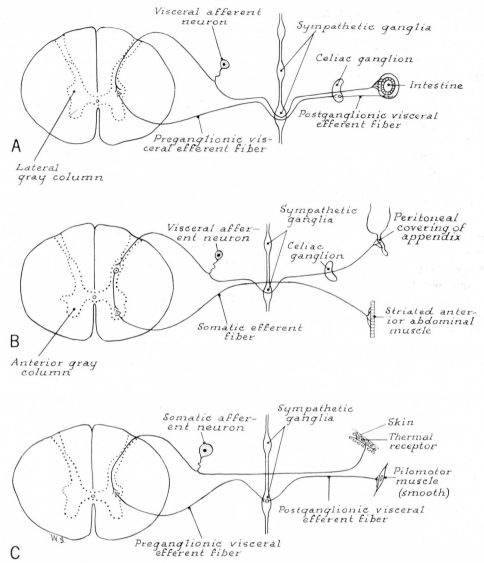

FIG. 47.   Visceral reflex arcs. *A,* Viscerovisceral arc. *B,* Viscerosomatic arc responsible for abdominal rigidity in appendicitis. *C,* Somatovisceral arc involved in the pilomotor reflex.

Referred pain (pain referred to the body wall or extremities) may result from visceral disease. Visceral pain may be due to over-distention of the walls of a viscus as in cases of ureteral or biliary stone, by inflammation as in appendicitis, or by impaired blood supply (ischemia). Instead of being localized in the diseased viscus, the pain is referred to definite skin areas which become hyperalgesic to

stimuli while the patient is experiencing the pain or in the interims between acute attacks of pain. The location of the skin areas to which visceral pain is referred is determined by the fact that the visceral afferent fibers reach the same segment of the spinal cord that innervates the particular skin zone (Brock, 1945). Apparently, the spinal receptive neurons within the cord segments corresponding to the dermatomes involved in the referred pain are activated (facilitated) by the stream of painful impulses from the viscus and, for this reason, have a lower threshold for impulses from the skin (Hinsey and Phillips, 1940). An alternative explanation of referred pain has been advanced by supposing that visceral afferents converge with cutaneous afferents to end upon the *same* neuron at the cord (or higher) level in the pain pathway. This neuron could then be activated by either visceral or cutaneous stimuli and presumably would relay similar information to the brain in either case. The possibility of the brain misinterpreting the source of the stimuli would then be obvious. This explanation for the mechanism of referred pain is known as the convergence-projection theory (Ruch, 1961).

Pain arising as the result of spasm of the coronary arteries (cardiac ischemia) is referred to the precordium and to the ulnar side of the arm, forearm, and hand. Pain from gallbladder disease is commonly referred to the region around the inferior angle of the right scapula. Subdiaphragmatic pain is referred to the skin of the shoulder (area supplied by the supraclavicular nerves).

Collaterals from the pain pathways which end in brain stem nuclei caudal to the classical relay nuclei in the thalamus have long been recognized. Recently, Bowsher (1962) has shown that after anterolateral cordotomy in humans many degenerating fibers may be found in reticular nuclei of the medulla and pons, descending vestibular nuclei, and nuclei of the solitary and spinal trigeminal tracts. The nuclei which receive these projections form a diffuse, multisynaptic medial or extralemniscal corticipetally conducting system in the brain stem. This system has been studied in the brain stem of monkeys by French *et al.* (1953a, b), and has been compared with the lateral (classical lemniscal) system.

Slow conduction and prolonged response to stimulation indicated the presence in the medial system of numerous relays. Functionally, it appeared that the lateral system is essential for perception, recognition and localization of stimuli while the medial system, through its slower transport of all sensory modalities, initiates and maintains the conscious state and thus provides a background of nervous activity without which integrated sensory motor and adaptive functions would be impossible. These investigators proposed, further, that the medial system is involved in the process of concentration superimposed upon inattentive wakefulness (Magoun, 1958). Direct stimulation of the medial system induced alert attention while its depression or destruction rendered the subject unconscious. The effect of anesthesia on potentials conducted in the medial and lateral systems gave support to the conclusions regarding consciousness (French *et al.*, 1953b); impulses propagated over the medial system were blocked by administration of ether or sodium pentobarbital to the animal while laterally conducted impulses reached the sensory cortex with unimpaired or augmented intensity. This evidence suggests that the multisynaptic medial system is more susceptible to anesthetic blocking than the paucisynaptic lateral pathway. Anatomically the extralemniscal sensory system can be located only in a general manner, based upon sites from which electrical activity has been recorded. These sites are found in pontile and mesencephalic tegmenti, in the reticular formation and periaqueductal gray matter and in the subthalamus and hypothalamus, adjacent to the third ventricle. Certain thalamic nuclei were also found to be concerned in the final relay to cerebral cortex. These include the *intralaminar* and/or *reticular nuclei* (Chapter 6).

BIBLIOGRAPHY

BONICA, J. J., 1964: *An Atlas on Mechanisms and Pathways of Pain in Labor*. F. A. Davis Co., Philadelphia. (In Press)

BOWSHER, D., 1962: The topographical projection of fibers from the anterolateral quadrant of the spinal cord to the subdiencephalic brain stem in man. Psychiat. Neurol., Basel, *143*, 75-99.

BROCK, S., 1945: *The Basis of Clinical Neurology*, 2nd Ed., Williams & Wilkins Co., Baltimore.

CRAWFORD, A. S. and R. S. KNIGHTON, 1953: Further observations on medullary spinothalamic tractotomy. J. Neurosurg., *10*, 113-121.

FRENCH, J. D., VERZEANO, M. and MAGOUN, H. W., 1953a: An extralemniscal sensory system in the brain. A.M.A. Arch. Neurol. Psychiat., *69*, 505-518.

———— 1953b: A neural basis of the anesthetic state. A.M.A. Arch. Neurol. Psychiat., *69*, 519-529.

FULTON, J. F., 1949: *Physiology of Nervous System*, 3rd Ed., Oxford University Press, New York.

GLEES, P., 1953: The central pain tract (tractus spino-thalamicus). Acta Neuroveget., *7*, 160-174.

GRIGGS, D. E. and OLSEN, C. W., 1937: Changes in the spinal cord in diabetes mellitus. A.M.A. Arch. Neurol. Psychiat., *38*, 564-571.

HINGSON, R. A. and EDWARDS, W. B., 1943: Continuous caudal analgesia in obstetrics. J. Am. Med. Assoc., *121*, 225-229.

HINSEY, J. C. and PHILLIPS, R. A., 1940: Observations upon diaphragmatic sensation. J. Neurophysiol., *3*, 175-181.

HYNDMAN, O. R. and JARVIS, F. J., 1940: Gastric crisis of tabes dorsalis: treatment by anterior chordotomy in eight cases. Arch. Surg., *40*, 997-1013.

HYNDMAN, O. R. and WOLKIN, J., 1943: Anterior chordotomy: further observations on physiologic results and optimum manner of performance. A.M.A. Arch. Neurol. Psychiat., *50*, 129-148

MAGOUN, H. W., 1958: *The Waking Brain*. Charles C Thomas, Springfield.

NATHAN, P. W. and SMITH, M. C., 1953: Spinal pathways subserving defaecation and sensation from the lower bowel. J. Neurol., Neurosurg. Psychiat., *16*, 245-256.

PEARSON, A. A., 1952: Role of gelatinous substance of spinal cord in conduction of pain. A.M.A. Arch. Neurol. Psychiat., *68*, 515-529.

POIRIER, L. J. and BERTRAND, C., 1955: Experimental and anatomical investigation of the lateral spino-thalamic and spino-tectal tracts. J. Comp. Neurol., *102*, 745-757.

RUCH, T. C., 1961: Pathophysiology of pain. In *Neurophysiology*, RUCH, T. C., PATTON, H. D., WOODBURY, J. W. and TOWE, A. L., Chapter 15, W. B. Saunders Company, Philadelphia, pp. 350-368.

SCHWARTZ, H. G. and O'LEARY, J. L., 1941: Section of the spinothalamic tract in the medulla with observations on the pathway for pain. Surgery, *9*, 183-193.

WHITE, J. C., 1954: Conduction of pain in man; observations on its afferent pathways within the spinal cord and visceral nerves. A.M.A. Arch. Neurol. Psychiat., *71*, 1-23.

YOSS, R. E., 1953: Studies of the spinal cord. III. Pathways for deep pain within the spinal cord and brain. Neurology, *3*, 163-175.

Chapter 6

External and Internal Configurations of the Brain Stem: Relations Within the Brain Stem of the General Sensory Pathways; the Thalamus

THE **brain stem,** as previously stated, consists of thalamus, midbrain, pons and medulla oblongata. It has already been observed that the medulla oblongata is a direct and expanded upward continuation of the spinal cord and that it consists of closed and open portions. The floor of the fourth ventricle, often called the *rhomboid fossa,* occupies the dorsal surface of the open portion and extends rostrally to assume the same relationship to the pons (Fig. 48).

The **fourth ventricle** is bounded inferolaterally, on either side, by the inferior cerebellar peduncle or restiform body, the cuneate tubercle and the clava (Fig. 48). The rostrolateral walls of the ventricle are formed by the superior cerebellar peduncles or brachia conjunctiva. The inferior peduncles curve dorsally from the medulla to enter the cerebellum. The superior peduncles course rostrally from the cerebellum to the midbrain and, as they pass forward, sink into the teg-

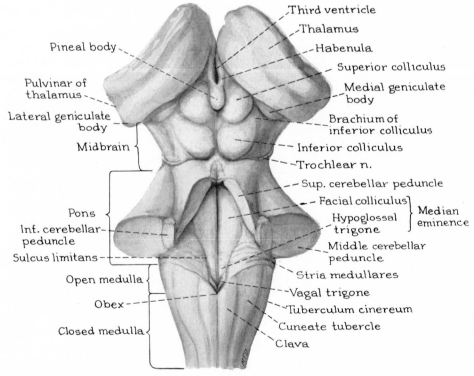

FIG. 48. Drawing of the brain stem, dorsal view.

mentum (dorsal area) of the pons. The functions of the cerebellar peduncles will not be considered at this time.

On the **ventral aspect of the medulla** the *pyramids* appear as longitudinal prominences on either side of the ventromedian fissure (Fig. 49). The ventromedian fissure terminates at the

the spinal accessory, vagus and glossopharyngeal nerves which emerge from the medulla through the dorsolateral sulcus (Fig. 50).

Cross sections through the medulla at the level of the glossopharyngeal (IX) and vestibulocochlear (VIII) nerves traverse the widest part of the fourth

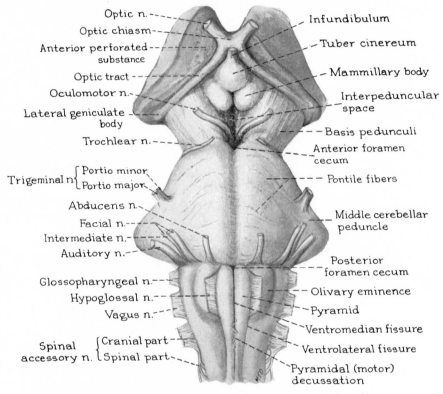

FIG. 49.   Drawing of the brain stem, ventral view.

junction of the medulla and pons as the *posterior foramen cecum*. Its termination at this point is due to the superimposition on the ventral surface of the brain stem of a broad band of transversely coursing fibers. These are the *pontile fibers* and they can be seen to become concentrated laterally and dorsally into bilateral bundles—the brachia pontis or middle cerebellar peduncles—which enter the cerebellum.

The **lateral view of the brain stem** shows to good advantage the rootlets of

ventricle (Figs. 51 and 52). It may be noted that the *lateral spinothalamic tracts* and *medial lemnisci* occupy the same relative positions as at more caudal medullary levels. In sections through the most caudal region of the pons (Fig. 53) the transversely cut bundles of fibers which comprise the medial lemnisci are oriented somewhat obliquely. This orientation reflects the rotation which the medial lemnisci undergo in passing through the transition zone of medulla to pons. This rotation, approximately

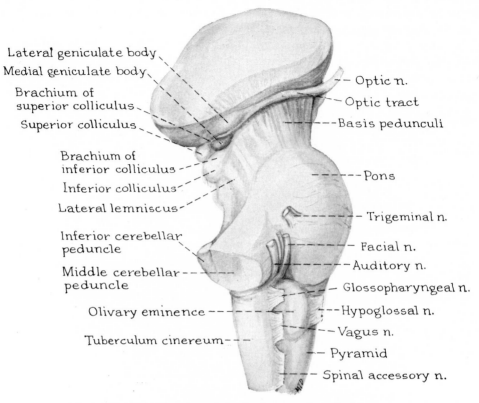

Lateral geniculate body
Medial geniculate body
Brachium of
superior colliculus
Superior colliculus

Brachium of
inferior colliculus
Inferior colliculus
Lateral lemniscus

Inferior cerebellar
peduncle

Middle cerebellar
peduncle

Olivary eminence

Tuberculum cinereum

Optic n.
Optic tract
Basis pedunculi

Pons

Trigeminal n.

Facial n.
Auditory n.
Glossopharyngeal n.
Hypoglossal n.
Vagus n.
Pyramid
Spinal accessory n.

Fig. 50. Drawing of the brain stem, lateral view.

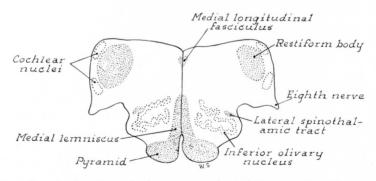

Medial longitudinal
fasciculus
Restiform body
Cochlear
nuclei
Eighth nerve
Lateral spinothal-
amic tract
Medial lemniscus
Inferior olivary
nucleus
Pyramid

Fig. 51. Section through the open portion of the medulla oblongata.

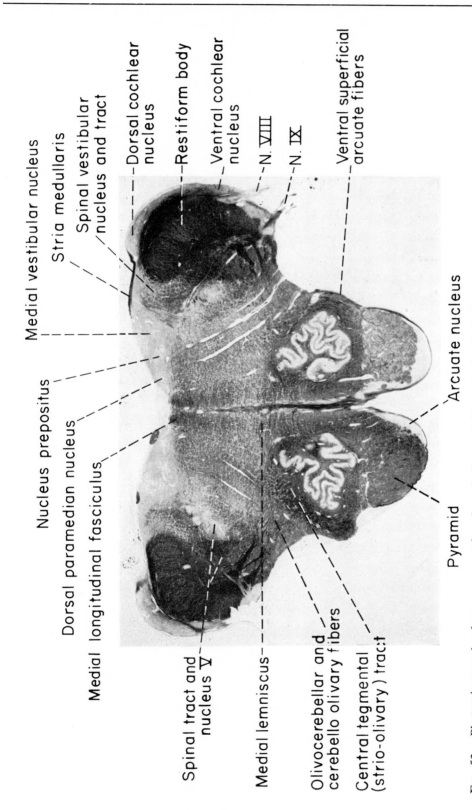

Medial vestibular nucleus

Stria medullaris

Spinal vestibular nucleus and tract

Dorsal cochlear nucleus

Restiform body

Ventral cochlear nucleus

N. VIII

N. IX

Ventral superficial arcuate fibers

Nucleus prepositus

Dorsal paramedian nucleus

Medial longitudinal fasciculus

Arcuate nucleus

Pyramid

Spinal tract and nucleus V

Medial lemniscus

Olivocerebellar and cerebello olivary fibers

Central tegmental (strio-olivary) tract

FIG. 52. Photomicrograph of transverse section through the medulla at the level of the glossopharyngeal (IX) and cochlear division of N. VIII. Weil stain. Note the reduced pyramid on the right. (See explanation, Figure 45, which is a section from the same brain stem.)

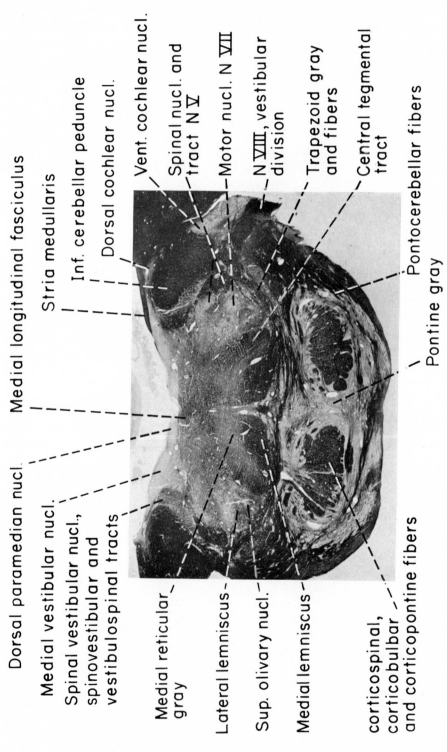

Dorsal paramedian nucl.

Medial vestibular nucl.

Spinal vestibular nucl.,
spinovestibular and
vestibulospinal tracts

Medial longitudinal fasciculus

Stria medullaris

Inf. cerebellar peduncle

Dorsal cochlear nucl.

Vent. cochlear nucl.

Spinal nucl. and
tract N V

Motor nucl. N VII

N VIII, vestibular
division

Trapezoid gray
and fibers

Central tegmental
tract

Pontocerebellar fibers

Pontine gray

Medial reticular
gray

Lateral lemniscus

Sup. olivary nucl.

Medial lemniscus

corticospinal,
corticobulbar
and corticopontine fibers

FIG. 53.   Photomicrograph of transverse section through the caudal pons at the level of the nuclei of the facial (VII) and vestibulocochlear nerves (VIII).

90°, brings the medial lemnisci into the transverse position at the intermediate levels of the pons (Figs. 54 and 55). The rotation occurs in such a way as to bring the original dorsal or cuneate component medially and the more ventral or gracile component laterally. In more rostral sections (Figs. 56 and 57) the medial lemnisci are seen to have migrated laterally from the median raphé and are in relation to the spinothalamic tracts.

the medulla (Figs. 49 and 51); they will be discussed later. The cells of the nuclear masses, or *pontile nuclei,* give origin to the pontile or pontocerebellar fibers (Figs. 53, 54 and 57).

The **lateral lemniscus**—another, smaller, bundle of longitudinally coursing fibers—lies dorsolateral to the medial lemniscus in the tegmentum of the pons (Figs. 54 and 55). It is an important link in the central auditory pathway and

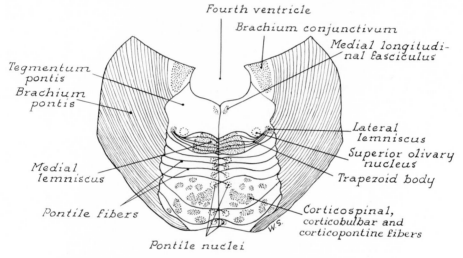

FIG. 54. Frontal section through the caudal third of the pons.

Frontal sections of the pons (sections cut at right angles to its rostrocaudal axis) reveal that it consists of dorsal and ventral portions which are quite different from one another in appearance (Figs. 54 and 55). The dorsal part, or *tegmentum,* is continuous with that portion of the medulla dorsal to the pyramids (Fig. 51). The *basis pontis,* or ventral part, is composed, in great part, of the transversely coursing *pontile fibers* already referred to. Intermingled with the pontile fibers are bundles of longitudinally coursing fibers and numerous nuclear masses. The corticospinal fibers which are included in the longitudinal group continue caudally into the pyramids of

is readily identified in Weil-stained sections of the pons; it becomes important at this point in the discussion because the *lateral spinothalamic tract* is located just dorsolateral to it. Its presence in this location has been demonstrated by Rasmussen and Peyton (1941) who studied the brain from a patient who died nineteen days after section of his lateral spinothalamic tract at the fourth or fifth thoracic level of the spinal cord. Through the use of the Marchi staining technique (Swank-Davenport modification, 1935) they were able to trace the lateral spinothalamic tract upward through the medulla, pons and midbrain to its termination in the thalamus. Glees (1953) has

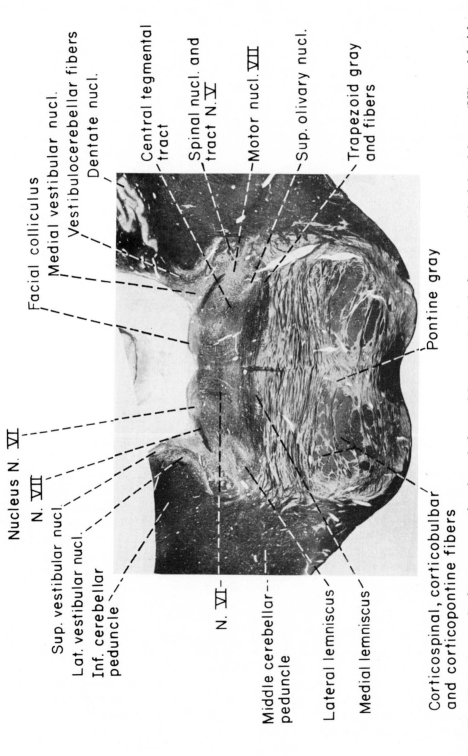

Facial colliculus

Medial vestibular nucl.

Vestibulocerebellar fibers

Dentate nucl.

Central tegmental tract

Spinal nucl. and tract N. V

Motor nucl. VII

Sup. olivary nucl.

Trapezoid gray and fibers

Pontine gray

Nucleus N. VI

N. VII

Sup. vestibular nucl.

Lat. vestibular nucl.

Inf. cerebellar peduncle

N. VI

Middle cerebellar peduncle

Lateral lemniscus

Medial lemniscus

Corticospinal, corticobulbar and corticopontine fibers

Fig. 55. Photomicrograph of transverse section through the caudal pons at the level of motor nuclei of the abducens (VI) and facial nerve (VII). Weil stain.

confirmed the above-described course of the lateral spinothalamic tract through the brain stem, including its association with the lateral lemniscus. More recently, Poirier and Bertrand (1955) have also confirmed the observations of Rasmussen and Peyton, using similar techniques.

The *lateral lemniscus,* at the extreme rostral limit of the pons (Figs. 58 and 59), moves into a more dorsal position; it lies immediately lateral to the lower half of the brachium conjunctivum which

point where the bases pedunculi disappear under cover of the pontile fibers (Fig. 49).

In **frontal sections through the midbrain** (Figs. 60-63) the original cavity of the embryonic neural tube is represented by the *cerebral aqueduct* (or *aqueduct of Sylvius*) which connects the third and fourth ventricles (Fig. 66). The *central gray matter,* within the ventral area of which the oculomotor and trochlear nuclei are found, surrounds the cere-

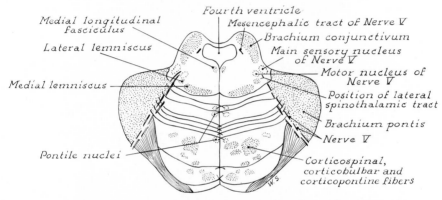

Medial longitudinal fasciculus
Lateral lemniscus
Medial lemniscus
Pontile nuclei
Fourth ventricle
Mesencephalic tract of Nerve V
Brachium conjunctivum
Main sensory nucleus of Nerve V
Motor nucleus of Nerve V
Position of lateral spinothalamic tract
Brachium pontis
Nerve V
Corticospinal, corticobulbar and corticopontine fibers

FIG. 56.   Section through the pons at the level of the trigeminal nerve.

is here completely submerged in the tegmentum of the pons. The *lateral spinothalamic tract,* at this level, according to Rasmussen and Peyton, lies in the interval between the brachium conjunctivum and the periphery of the pons and just dorsal to the lateral lemniscus.

The midbrain, on its dorsal surface, presents four rounded eminences or *colliculi* (Fig. 48). The two rostral eminences are usually termed the *superior colliculi* and the two caudal ones are referred to as the *inferior colliculi.* The colliculi are also called *quadrigeminal bodies.* The two *bases pedunculi,* separated from one another by the *interpeduncular space* are seen on the ventral aspect of the midbrain (Fig. 49). The interpeduncular space terminates caudally as the *anterior foramen cecum* at the

bral aqueduct. That part of the midbrain that lies dorsal to the level of the aqueduct, and including the quadrigeminal bodies, is called the *quadrigeminal lamina* or *tectum.* The *tegmentum* of the midbrain lies between the quadrigeminal lamina and the *bases pedunculi.* Its contact with the bases pedunculi, on either side, is marked by a pigmented layer of gray matter designated as the *substantia nigra.* The tegmentum is continuous with the correspondingly named area of the pons and the bases pedunculi continue caudally into the basis pontis. The corticospinal, corticobulbar, and corticopontine fibers which constitute the bases pedunculi account for the longitudinally coursing bundles of fibers previously noted in the basilar part of the pons.

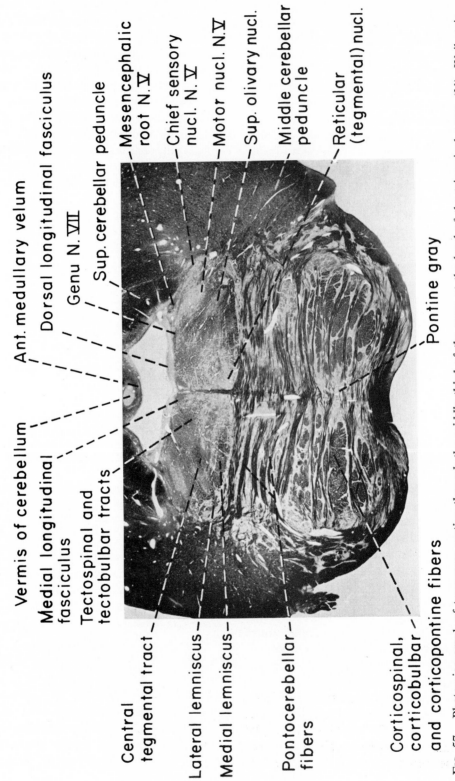

Vermis of cerebellum

Ant. medullary velum

Medial longitudinal
fasciculus

Dorsal longitudinal fasciculus

Tectospinal and
tectobulbar tracts

Genu N. VII

Sup. cerebellar peduncle

Mesencephalic
root N. V

Chief sensory
nucl. N. V

Motor nucl. N. V

Sup. olivary nucl.

Middle cerebellar
peduncle

Reticular
(tegmental) nucl.

Central
tegmental tract

Lateral lemniscus

Medial lemniscus

Pontocerebellar
fibers

Corticospinal,
corticobulbar
and corticopontine fibers

Pontine gray

Fig. 57. Photomicrograph of transverse section through the middle third of the pons at the level of the trigeminal nerve (V). Weil stain.

The *medial lemniscus,* in the midbrain, is forced into a more lateral and dorsal position by the *decussation of the brachia conjunctiva* and by the *red nucleus*; the former is seen at the level of the inferior colliculi and the latter at the level of the superior ones (Figs. 60-63). The brachia cross the midline and distribute large proportions of their component fibers to the red nuclei. The red nuclei are so-called because they are pinkish in appearance in freshly cut sections.

Rasmussen and Peyton suggested that it should be relatively easy to sever the lateral spinothalamic tract at midbrain levels because of its superficial position in the tegmentum. Glees (1953) found the spinothalamic tract to be quite superficial at the level of the superior colliculus where it was "accessible to the surgical procedure of *mesencephalic tractotomy.*" Walker (1942) has treated intractable pain in this manner without surgical complications and has found the pro-

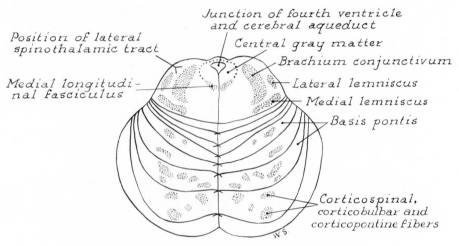

Fig. 58.   Section through the rostral part of the pons.

The *lateral lemniscus,* at the level of the inferior colliculi, is actually dorsomedial to the medial lemniscus. Most of its fibers terminate in the *nucleus of the inferior colliculus* (Figs. 60 and 61). At the level of the superior colliculi the *inferior quadrigeminal brachium* (peduncle of the inferior colliculus), composed of axons originating in the inferior collicular nucleus, occupies a superficial position, dorsolateral to the medial lemniscus (Figs. 62 and 63). The *lateral spinothalamic tract* intermingles with the terminal fibers of the lateral lemniscus at the level of the inferior colliculi, and lies medial to the inferior quadrigeminal brachium at the superior collicular level.

cedure to be effective in the relief of pain. His incisions (at the level of the superior colliculi) were extensive enough that they also severed the secondary trigeminal pathway and thus served to relieve pain originating in the head region. The course of the trigeminothalamic fibers from the spinal nucleus of the trigeminal nerve will be described in Chapter 7.

The **diencephalon** is so completely and intimately surrounded by the cerebral hemispheres as to appear to be a part of them (Fig. 64). Only its ventral surface can be observed in the intact brain (Fig. 65). Two rounded prominences at the caudal limit of its ventral surface are known as *mammillary bodies*. The *tuber*

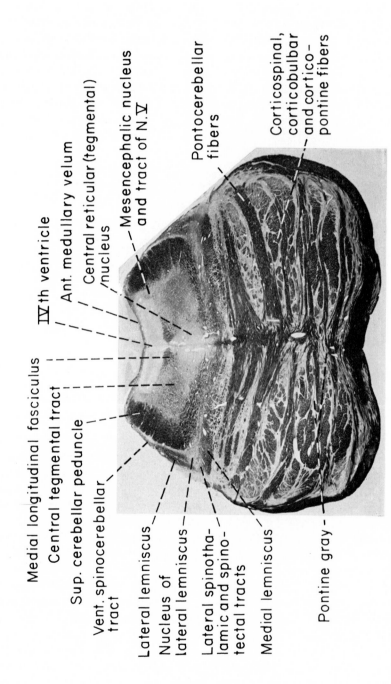

Medial longitudinal fasciculus

Central tegmental tract

Sup. cerebellar peduncle

Vent. spinocerebellar tract

Lateral lemniscus

Nucleus of lateral lemniscus

Lateral spinotha-lamic and spino-tectal tracts

Medial lemniscus

Pontine gray

IVth ventricle

Ant. medullary velum

Central reticular(tegmental) nucleus

Mesencephalic nucleus and tract of N. V

Pontocerebellar fibers

Corticospinal, corticobulbar and cortico-pontine fibers

FIG. 59. Photomicrograph of a transverse section through the rostral third of the pons (Isthmus region). Weil stain.

cinereum, from which the *hypophysis* is suspended, is immediately rostral to the mammillary bodies and the *optic chiasm* is rostral to it.

The **third ventricle** appears as a slit-like cavity in sections of the diencephalon (Fig. 64). It communicates, as previously stated, with the fourth ventricle by way of the cerebral aqueduct. It communicates rostrally, through the paired *inter-*

two thalami and by the pia mater overlying the ependyma. The pia mater constitutes the *tela choroidea* of the third ventricle (Fig. 64).

The **thalami,** when observed from above following removal of the cerebral hemispheres and corpus callosum, are seen to consist of ovoid masses of gray matter on either side of the third ventricle (Fig. 48). Each is considerably

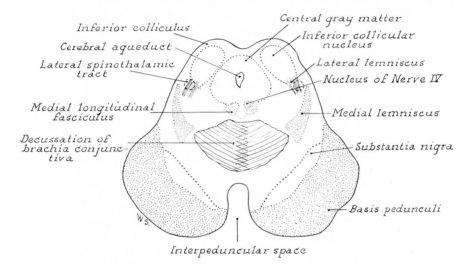

Inferior colliculus

Cerebral aqueduct

Lateral spinothalamic tract

Medial longitudinal fasciculus

Decussation of brachia conjunctiva

Central gray matter

Inferior collicular nucleus

Lateral lemniscus

Nucleus of Nerve IV

Medial lemniscus

Substantia nigra

Basis pedunculi

Interpeduncular space

F**IG**. 60.   Section through the midbrain at the level of the inferior colliculi.

ventricular foramina, with the right and left lateral ventricles in the cerebral hemispheres (Fig. 66). The floor of the third ventricle is formed by the *hypothalamus* which includes the structures previously mentioned as being visible on the ventral surface of the diencephalon as well as several nuclei and fiber tracts which will be discussed later (Chapter 20). The lateral walls of the ventricle are formed by the medial surfaces of the right and left *thalami*. The *massa intermedia* (not always present) bridges the ventricle and connects the two thalami with each other (Fig. 67). The roof of the third ventricle is formed by a thin layer of ependyma which stretches between the dorsomedial borders of the

expanded at its caudal limit; the expansion is termed the *pulvinar*. The dorsal and lateral surfaces of the thalamus are covered by thin layers of white matter (Fig. 67). That on the dorsal surface is called the *stratum zonale* and that on the lateral surface the *external medullary lamina*. A Y-shaped reflection from the stratum zonale into the substance of the thalamus, as seen in sections, is termed the *internal medullary lamina*. It divides the thalamus into *medial, lateral,* and *anterior parts*. The anterior part, in frontal sections through the middle third of the thalamus, is dorsally placed; the reason for its being called anterior is, however, quite obvious in horizontal sections (Fig. 68).

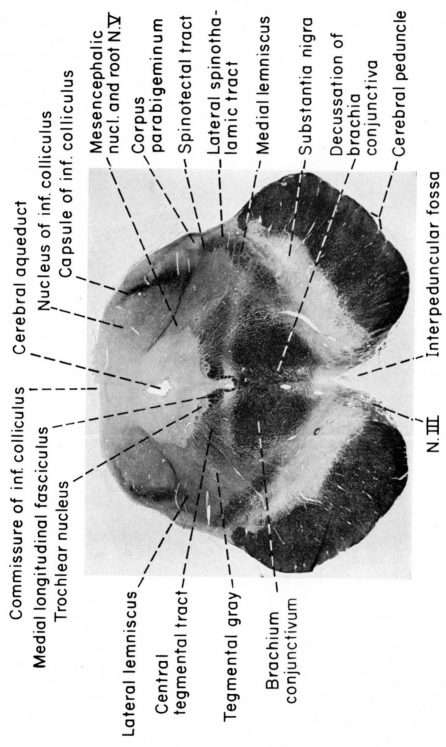

Commissure of inf. colliculus

Medial longitudinal fasciculus

Trochlear nucleus

Cerebral aqueduct

Nucleus of inf. colliculus

Capsule of inf. colliculus

Mesencephalic nucl. and root N. V

Corpus parabigeminum

Spinotectal tract

Lateral spinotha- lamic tract

Medial lemniscus

Substantia nigra

Decussation of brachia conjunctiva

Cerebral peduncle

Interpeduncular fossa

N. III

Lateral lemniscus

Central tegmental tract

Tegmental gray

Brachium conjunctivum

Fig. 61. Photomicrograph of transverse section through the inferior collicular level of the midbrain. Weil stain.

Each of the three parts of the thalamus contains a number of nuclei which have more or less specific functions. The nucleus in which the medial lemniscus and lateral spinothalamic tract terminate, is ventrally and caudally placed in the lateral part (Fig. 69) and, as previously noted, is designated as the *posterolateral ventral nucleus*. Medial to it is the posteromedial ventral nucleus in which impulses from the head region are

The regions of the external and internal medullary laminæ (Figs. 67 and 68) contain the reticular and/or intralaminar nuclei which play an important role in the conduction of nonspecific sensory impulses to the cerebral cortex. These impulses reach the intralaminar nuclei by way of the extralemniscal sensory system (Chapter 5) and, through this thalamic relay, contribute to the "arousal" of the cerebrum, making it

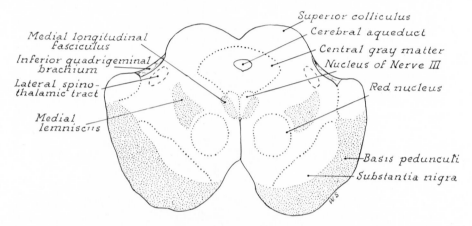

FIG. 62. Section through the midbrain at the level of the superior colliculi.

received. Mountcastle and Henneman (1952) described these two nuclei as being a "ventrobasal complex." Within the posterolateral portion they found the body segments represented in an orderly fashion with cervical segments most medial and the sacral most lateral. The posteromedial portion contains representation of contralateral head, face and intra-oral structures with mouth and face most medially located. Cohen and Grundfest (1954) refuted these investigators' interpretations of electrical responses and maintained that the "thalamus does not separate the reports of sensory activity from different areas into discrete trains of messages to higher levels."

receptive to visual, auditory and general sensory impulses.

The **internal capsule**—so-called because it appears to form the inner part of a capsule of white matter surrounding the lentiform nucleus—lies immediately lateral to the external medullary lamina of the thalamus (Figs. 64 and 67). It is composed of axons of cells in the thalamus which are proceeding to the cerebral cortex and of axons of cells in the cortex which are distributed to lower levels of the central nervous system. The *thalamocortical fibers* include those which carry general sensory impulses from the posterolateral ventral nucleus to the sensory area of the cortex (Fig. 69).

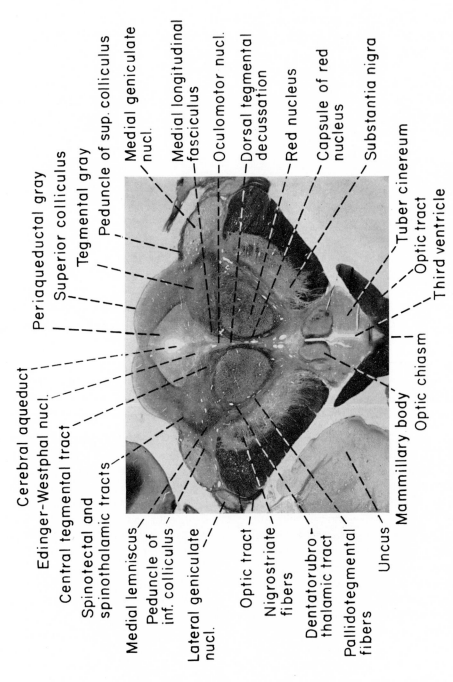

Cerebral aqueduct

Edinger-Westphal nucl.

Central tegmental tract

Spinotectal and
spinothalamic tracts

Periaqueductal gray

Superior colliculus

Tegmental gray

Peduncle of sup. colliculus

Medial geniculate
nucl.

Medial longitudinal
fasciculus

Oculomotor nucl.

Dorsal tegmental
decussation

Red nucleus

Capsule of red
nucleus

Substantia nigra

Tuber cinereum

Optic tract

Third ventricle

Medial lemniscus

Peduncle of
inf. colliculus

Lateral geniculate
nucl.

Optic tract

Nigrostriate
fibers

Dentatorubro-
thalamic tract

Pallidotegmental
fibers

Uncus

Mammillary body

Optic chiasm

Fig. 63.   Photomicrograph of a transverse section through the superior collicular level of the midbrain.   Weil stain.

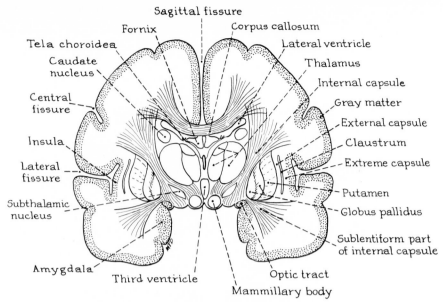

FIG. 64. Diagram of a frontal section through the brain at the diencephalic level.

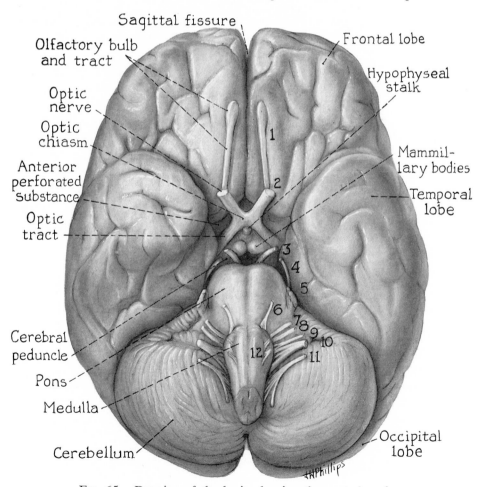

FIG. 65. Drawing of the brain showing the ventral surface.

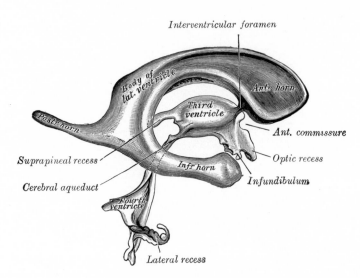

FIG. 66.   Drawing of a cast of the ventricular system of the brain as seen from the side (Retzius in Gray's Anatomy).

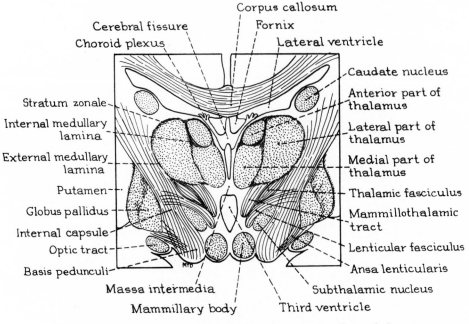

FIG. 67.   Diagram of a frontal section through the diencephalon.

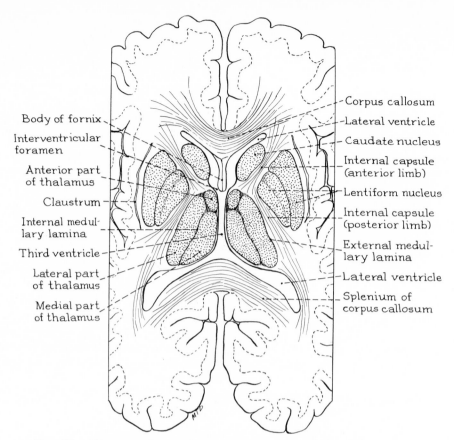

FIG. 68. Diagram of a horizontal section through the diencephalon.

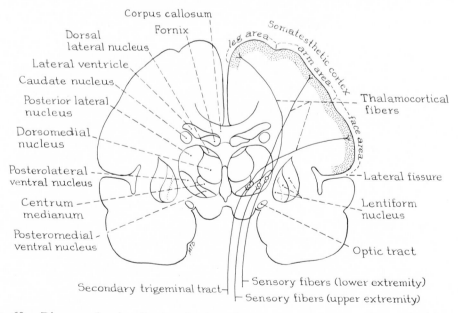

FIG. 69. Diagram showing the termination of sensory tracts in the nuclei of the lateral part of the thalamus and the projection of these nuclei upon the somatesthetic cortex by way of the internal capsule (modified from Ranson).

(85)

BIBLIOGRAPHY

Cohen, S. M. and Grundfest, H., 1954: Thalamic loci of electrical activity initiated by afferent impulses in cat. J. Neurophysiol., *17*, 193-297.

Glees, P., 1953: The central pain tract (tractus spino-thalamicus). Acta Neurovegat., *7*, 160-174.

Mountcastle, V. B. and Henneman, E., 1952: The representation of tactile sensibility in the thalamus of the monkey. J. Comp. Neurol., *97*, 409-439.

Poirier, L. J. and Bertrand, C., 1955: Experimental and anatomical investigation of the lateral spino-thalamic and spino-tectal tracts. J. Comp. Neurol., *102*, 745-757.

Rasmussen, A. T. and Peyton, W. T., 1941. The location of the lateral spinothalamic tract in the brain stem of man. Surgery, *10*, 699-710.

Swank, R. L. and Davenport, H. A., 1935: Chlorate-osmic-formalin method for staining degenerating myelin. Stain Technol., *10*, 87-90.

Walker, A. E., 1942: Relief of pain by mesencephalic tractotomy. A.M.A. Arch. Neurol. Psychiat., *48*, 865-883.

Chapter 7

The Pathways Concerned in the Conduction of General Afferent Impulses From the Head Region to the Thalamus

THE pathways to the thalamus traversed by afferent impulses originating in the trunk and extremities have now been described in considerable detail. Before discussing their further course through the internal capsule and their manner of termination in the cerebral cortex, we shall trace the pathways concerned in the conduction of afferent impulses from the head region to the thalamus.

General somatic afferent fibers are contained in the *trigeminal, facial, glossopharyngeal, vagus, oculomotor, trochlear and abducens nerves*. Since the trigeminal is the most extensive, it will be considered first.

The **semilunar** or **Gasserian ganglion,** like the spinal ganglia, is developed from the neural crest. Like the spinal ganglia it contains unipolar neurons. It is located in Meckel's cave, between the two layers of the cranial dura mater, on the anterior surface of the petrosa of the temporal bone. The peripheral processes of the ganglion cells are distributed to exteroceptive endings throughout the head region by way of the *ophthalmic, maxillary,* and *mandibular divisions* of the trigeminal nerve. The central processes form the *portio major* of the nerve which crosses the superior border of the petrosa and enters the pons at a point approximately midway between its rostral and caudal borders and in the region where the pontile fibers enter into, and form, the brachium pontis (Figs 49 and 50).

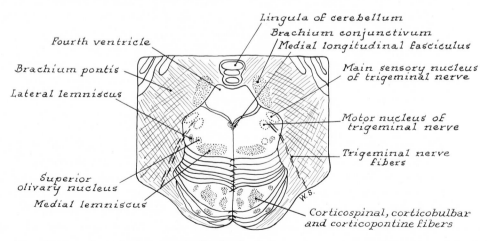

FIG. 70.   Section through the pons at the level of the main sensory and motor nuclei of the trigeminal nerve.

(87)

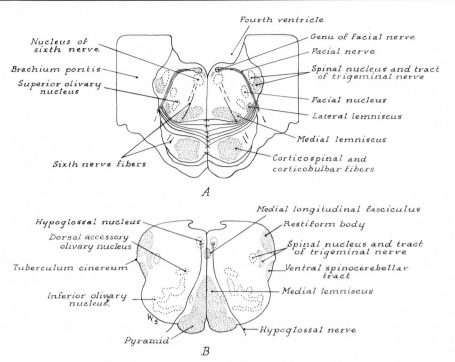

FIG. 71.   *A,* Section through the pons at the level of the abducens nucleus. *B,* Section through the medulla near the caudal end of the fourth ventricle.

The *portio minor* of the trigeminal emerges from the pons immediately anterior (rostral) to the entering fibers of the portio major; it is chiefly motor in function but also contains proprioceptive fibers which are distributed to the muscles of mastication.

Some of the **fibers of the portio major** terminate in the *main sensory nucleus* of the trigeminal which, in frontal sections through the middle third of the pons, is seen in the dorsolateral area of the pontile tegmentum (Figs. 70 and 57). The nucleus is ventral to the brachium conjunctivum, medial to the brachium pontis, and dorsolateral to the motor nucleus of the trigeminal. The motor and sensory nuclei are separated from one another by a layer of trigeminal nerve fibers. The fibers that terminate in the main sensory nucleus are concerned only with tactile sensibility.

Other central fibers of the trigeminal turn caudally to form its *descending* or *spinal tract;* this continues downward through the caudal third of the pons and through the entire length of the medulla (Fig. 71). In the pons it lies in the lateral part of the tegmentum and in intimate relation to the brachium pontis (Fig. 71, *A*). In the medulla the tract is relatively superficial and, together with its nucleus, accounts for a narrow longitudinal prominence, observable on the surface and known as the *tuberculum cinereum;* it lies considerably dorsal to the inferior olivary nucleus and immediately ventral to the restiform body (Figs. 71, *B* and 37). Throughout its course the tract distributes fibers to the *spinal nucleus* of the trigeminal; the spinal nucleus extends caudally from the main sensory nucleus in the pons to the level of the junction of medulla and spinal cord and lies just medial to the tract (Fig. 72). The spinal tract and nucleus are chiefly con-

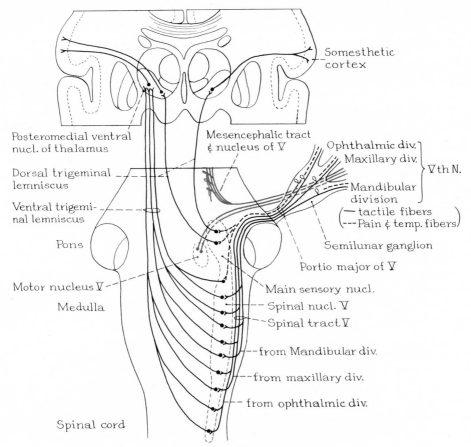

Posteromedial ventral nucl. of thalamus

Dorsal trigeminal lemniscus

Ventral trigeminal lemniscus

Pons

Motor nucleus V

Medulla

Spinal cord

Mesencephalic tract & nucleus of V

Somesthetic cortex

Ophthalmic div.
Maxillary div.
} V th N.
Mandibular division
(— tactile fibers)
(---Pain & temp. fibers)

Semilunar ganglion

Portio major of V

Main sensory nucl.
Spinal nucl. V
Spinal tract V
from Mandibular div.
from maxillary div.
from ophthalmic div.

FIG. 72. Diagram of the central connections of the trigeminal nerve superimposed upon a dorsal view of the brain stem.

cerned with pain and thermal impulses. Crawford and Knighton (1953), following medullary spinothalamic tractotomy (Chapter 5), observed ipsilateral analgesia of the face which they attributed to destruction of, or injury to, the spinal tract and nucleus of the trigeminal nerve. On the basis of the order in which recovery of pain sense occurred, they concluded that the fibers in the spinal tract are arranged, from dorsal to ventral, in the following order: mandibular, maxillary and ophthalmic. This arrangement of fibers in the spinal tract was similarly described by Szentagothai and Kiss (1949) following experiments with cats. The ventralmost fibers concerned with projection to the spinal nucleus of pain impulses from the ophthalmic region, according to Crawford and Knighton, appeared to lie close to the lateral spinothalamic tract. In addition to the dorsoventral arrangement, there is a cephalocaudal pattern within the spinal tract which reflects the differences in caudal extent of pain and temperature fibers from the three main divisions of the fifth nerve. The ophthalmic fibers terminate upon cells in the most caudal part of the spinal nucleus; some reach the level of the second or third cervical segment. The mandibular fibers end upon cells in the more cephalic part of the nucleus and those of the maxillary nerve synapse with cells in the intermediate region (Fig. 72). There is some overlap in the termination of descending spinal tract fibers as well as variation in caudal extent. Significantly, complete facial analgesia may be obtained by section of the spinal tract at the level of the obex.

Some tactile impulses are also conducted through the spinal tract to its nucleus. A considerable number of the central processes of semilunar ganglion cells concerned with the transmission of tactile impulses divide into ascending branches which terminate in the main sensory nucleus and descending branches which end in the spinal nucleus.

It should be noted that the spinal tract and nucleus are, in effect, upward extensions into the brain stem of the dorsolateral fasciculus of Lissauer and the gelatinous substance of the dorsal gray column (Figs. 73 and 35). The spinal nucleus, moreover, has a gelatinous appearance similar to that of its counterpart in the spinal cord. The fact that the nucleus and tract are primarily concerned with pain and thermal sensibility is also

of interest in view of the exclusive pain and thermal function of the analogous spinal cord structures.

It will be remembered that the cell bodies of secondary neurons in sensory pathways to the cerebral cortex from levels served by the spinal nerves were found in the dorsal gray columns—so-called tract cells. Cells similar in function are found in the sensory nuclei of cranial nerves and are responsible for transmission of sensory impulses upward to the thalamus (Fig. 72). There are also association or internuncial cells in the sensory nuclei; they connect, through the reticular formation, with efferent neurons in the brain stem and thus enter into reflex arcs (Fig. 73). The efferent neurons may have their cell bodies in motor nuclei of cranial nerves or in the reticular formation.

The term, **reticular formation,** is applied to the network of gray and white matter in the medulla (Fig. 79) and in the tegmental areas of the pons and midbrain. The rather large cells scattered

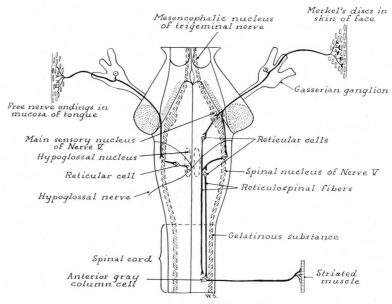

FIG. 73. Diagram showing (left side) a reflex arc through the spinal nucleus of the trigeminal nerve, reticular formation, and hypoglossal nucleus and (right side) trigemino-reticulospinal arcs.

through the formation contribute to numerous reflex arcs within the brain stem and also give rise to *reticulospinal fibers*. As their name implies, the reticulospinal fibers descend into the spinal cord where they come into direct or indirect relationship with anterior gray column cells to complete reflex arcs (Fig. 73) whose effectors are striated muscles of the trunk and extremities.

A third sensory nucleus is associated with the trigeminal nerve. It is concerned with proprioceptive impulses from the muscles of mastication and, because it extends rostrally into the midbrain, it is called the *mesencephalic nucleus* (Figs. 61 and 74). Proprioceptive impulses from the extrinsic muscles of the eye may also enter this nucleus (Corbin, 1940). The *mesencephalic root* (or tract) of the trigeminal is associated with the nucleus and both are found at the periphery of the central gray matter surrounding the cerebral aqueduct and in the ventrolateral angle of the rostral part of the fourth ventricle (Figs. 74, *B* and *C* and 57).

While the cells in the main sensory and spinal nuclei of the trigeminal, like those in the dorsal gray columns of the spinal cord, are multipolar in type, those in the mesencephalic nucleus are unipolar with axons that divide into peripheral and central processes. The peripheral processes are distributed to proprioceptive endings in the muscles of mastication by way of the mesencephalic root and portio minor of the trigeminal (Fig. 72); others may course to the eye muscles with the oculomotor, trochlear, and abducens nerves. The central processes may enter the trigeminal lemnisci and, through them, may proceed upward to the thalamus. The fact that the cells in the mesencephalic nucleus are of the unipolar variety leads to the assumption that this nucleus is developed from the rostral limit of the neural crest and that

it failed to separate from the neural tube as did those portions which developed into true sensory ganglia.

The **secondary afferent pathways of the trigeminal** are usually designated as *ventral* and *dorsal trigeminal lemnisci* (Fig. 74). The *ventral lemniscus* is chiefly composed of crossed fibers arising in the opposite spinal and main sensory nuclei (Fig. 72). In the medulla it is closely associated with the lateral spinothalamic tract; this relationship was thought by Crawford and Knighton (1953) to account for contralateral analgesia, limited to the ophthalmic distribution of the fifth nerve, subsequent to medullary spinothalamic tractotomy. The ventral lemniscus, in the pons, forms a flattened bundle on the dorsal aspect of the medial lemniscus. The ventral trigeminal lemniscus terminates in the *posteromedial ventral thalamic nucleus* (Fig. 69).

Walker (1942) produced a lesion in the spinal nucleus of the trigeminal nerve in a monkey and was thus able to determine, through the subsequent application of the Marchi staining method, the position of *trigeminothalamic fibers* in the midbrain. Degenerating fibers, with their origin in the spinal nucleus, were intermingled, at the level of the superior colliculi, with the dorsolateral fibers of the medial lemniscus and with those of the lateral spinothalamic tract (Fig. 74, *A*). The fact that the operation designated as *mesencephalic tractotomy* accomplishes interruption of both the lateral spinothalamic tract and the ventral trigeminal lemniscus has already been mentioned (Chapter 6).

The *dorsal trigeminal lemniscus* is generally considered to be situated ventrolateral to the central gray matter surrounding the cerebral aqueduct in the mesencephalon and just ventral to the floor of the fourth ventricle in the pons (Fig. 74, *B* and *C*). Its fibers have also been said to terminate in the postero-medial ventral nucleus of the thalamus. Russell (1954) was unable to demonstrate a dorsal trigeminothalamic tract, either crossed or uncrossed, in cats following lesions limited to the sensory nuclei of the trigeminal nerve. He concluded that those fibers previously described as forming such a tract are actually lateral reticulothalamic fibers. In view of the uncertainty which has always existed relative to origin, function and termination of a dorsal trigemino-thalamic tract, Russell's findings seem

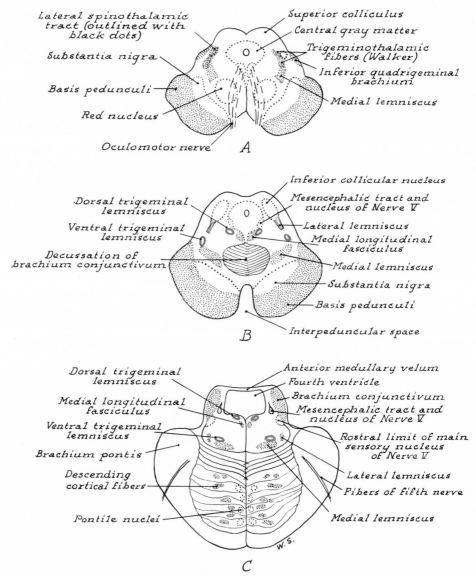

FIG. 74. *A*, Section through the midbrain at the level of the superior colliculi showing intermingling of trigeminothalamic fibers with those of the medial lemniscus and lateral spino-thalamic tract (Walker). *B*, Section through the midbrain at the inferior collicular level showing the locations of the trigeminal lemnisci and of the mesencephalic tract and nucleus of the trigeminal nerve. *C*, Section through the rostral part of the pons with locations of trigeminal lemnisci and mesencephalic tract and nucleus indicated.

quite logical and would indicate that some of the impulses reaching the main and mesencephalic nuclei of the trigeminal nerve are relayed upward to the thalamus by reticular neurons which are projected upon by the nuclei.

General somatic afferent fibers of the vagus, glossopharyngeal and facial nerves are distributed to skin in the region of the external ear. These cutaneous fibers of the vagus, auricular branch (Arnold's nerve), arise from cells in the jugular ganglion. Those of the glossopharyngeal nerve arise from cells in the superior ganglion (Woodburne, 1961) and are distributed peripherally through the auricular branch of the vagus. Those of the facial nerve are from cell bodies in

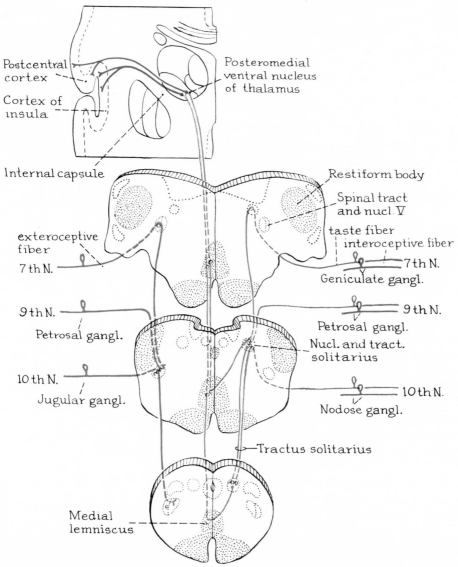

Fig. 75. Diagram showing the central connections of the sensory fibers in the facial, glossopharyngeal and vagus nerves. The general and special visceral afferent components are shown in blue and red respectively on the right. The general somatic afferent components are shown in green on the left.

the geniculate ganglion and their distribution to the ear is through the auricular branch of the vagus and through the posterior auricular branch of the facial. The central processes of these fibers enter the medulla and pons, join the spinal tract of the trigeminal and terminate in the spinal nucleus (Fig. 75).

Sjöqvist (1938) developed an operative procedure for eliminating trigeminal neuralgia by cutting the fibers of the descending tract of the trigeminal nerve, immediately caudal to the level of the lowest filaments of the vagus nerve. Brodal (1947) studied the ensuing sensory loss in four cases of trigeminal neuralgia in which the tractotomy of Sjöqvist was performed. In addition to analgesia, with retained tactile sensibility in the trigeminal area of the face and mouth, he found similar sensory changes in other regions. These regions included the concha of the auricle, the posterior one-third of the tongue, the tonsil and the pharynx, all on the side of operation. In one case, a similar area behind the ear was included, and in two cases, the analgesia extended to the posterior, upper and anterior walls of the external auditory meatus. From these observations, since the regions mentioned are innervated by the seventh, ninth and tenth cranial nerves, Brodal concluded that the fibers conducting pain impulses in the facialis-intermedius complex, the glossopharyngeal and the vagus, join the pain fibers of the trigeminal nerve and accompany them in the descending tract of the trigeminal nerve. The inclusion of the facialis-intermedius complex in the sensory innervation of this region was based on Brodal's belief that somatic sensory fibers, originating in the geniculate ganglion, are distributed to the concha by way of the facial nerve.

The **somatic afferent fibers of the oculomotor, trochlear and abducens nerves,** as was implied in the discussion of the mesencephalic nucleus of the trigeminal, may arise from unipolar cells located in that nucleus and be distributed to proprioceptive endings in the extrinsic eye muscles. Corbin (1940) suggested that the somatic afferent fibers to the extrinsic eye muscles might be largely unmyelinated and arise from the small cell component of the mesencephalic nucleus at the level of the oculomotor nucleus. Corbin and Oliver (1942) found the origin of afferent fibers to grape-like endings in the extra-ocular muscles to be in the oculomotor and trochlear nuclei. Further evidence in favor of the latter statement was obtained by Corbin and Harrison (1942) when they traced nervous impulses from the inferior oblique muscle to the oculomotor nucleus and were unable to trace any afferent impulses from this muscle to the mesencephalic nucleus. Despite the fact that complete information as to the origin of these fibers is still lacking, it is obvious that they have a very important function in coördination of the extra-ocular muscles. A very delicate balance among all the extrinsic muscles of both eyes is essential to accurate binocular vision.

General visceral afferent fibers are present in the *glossopharyngeal* and *vagus nerves.* Those of the glossopharyngeal have their cell bodies in the *petrosal ganglion.* Peripheral processes are distributed to the pharynx, to the posterior third of the tongue, and to the carotid sinus. Central processes enter the medulla in the region of the dorsolateral sulcus and through the tractus solitarius, synapse upon cells in the nucleus solitarius (Figs. 75 and 45). The tract is surrounded by the nucleus and both, in the open part of the medulla, are located somewhat medial to the restiform body, in the reticular formation. They extend throughout almost the entire length of the medulla and at their caudal limit are in the gray matter surrounding the central canal.

The **general visceral afferent fibers of the vagus nerve** arise from cells in the *nodose ganglion*. Peripheral processes are distributed to the pharynx, larynx, trachea, esophagus and to the thoracic and abdominal viscera. The central processes, like those from the petrosal ganglion of the glossopharyngeal and the jugular ganglion of the vagus, enter the medulla through the dorsolateral sulcus. They are then distributed to cells in the *nucleus solitarius* in the same manner as those from the petrosal ganglion (Fig. 75).

The *facial nerve* contains afferent fibers classified as *general visceral afferent* (Ranson-Clark, 1959). They arise from cells in the *geniculate ganglion* and are distributed peripherally to proprioceptive endings in the face. The central processes of the cells in the geniculate ganglion traverse the *nervus intermedius* and may end in the nucleus solitarius or in the spinal nucleus of the trigeminal. Although usually classified as *general visceral afferent* there appears, on the bases of distribution and probable termination, to be good reason for classifying these fibers as *general somatic afferent*. Other *general visceral afferent fibers*, originating in the geniculate ganglion and distributed to the nose and soft palate by way of the *greater (superficial) petrosal* branch of the nervus intermedius have been described by Foley and DuBois (1943).

The **axons of cells in the nucleus solitarius,** upon which the general visceral afferent fibers of the glossopharyngeal and vagus nerves synapse, make numerous indirect and direct connections with efferent neurons in visceral and somatic motor nuclei and with neurons in the reticular formation and so complete important visceral and viscerosomatic reflex arcs. The carotid sinus reflex (reflex for control of blood pressure), the respiratory reflexes, the cough reflex and the vomiting reflex are dependent upon such intramedullary connections (Chapter 22). The secondary pathway to the thalamus for general visceral afferent impulses conducted to the nucleus solitarius by the vagus and glossopharyngeal nerves is incorporated into the medial lemniscus of the opposite side (Fig. 75).

BIBLIOGRAPHY

BRODAL, A., 1947: Central course of afferent fibers for pain in facial glossopharyngeal and vagus nerves. A.M.A. Arch Neurol. Psychiat., *57*, 292-306.

CORBIN, K. B., 1940: Observations on the peripheral distribution of fibers arising in the mesencephalic nucleus of the fifth cranial nerve. J. Comp. Neurol., *73*, 153-177.

CORBIN, K. B. and HARRISON, F., 1942. Further attempts to trace the origin of afferent nerves to the extrinsic eye muscles. J. Comp. Neurol., *77*, 187-190.

CORBIN, K. B. and OLIVER, R. K., 1942: The origin of fibers to the grape-like endings in the insertion third of the extra-ocular muscles. J. Comp. Neurol., *77*, 171-186.

CRAWFORD, A. S. and KNIGHTON, R. S., 1953: Further observations on medullary spinothalamic tractotomy. J. Neurosurg., *10*, 113-121.

FOLEY, J. O. and DuBois, F. S., 1943: An experimental study of the facial nerve. J. Comp. Neurol., *79*, 79-105.

RANSON, S. W. and CLARK, S. L., 1959: *The Anatomy of the Nervous System*, 10th Ed., W. B. Saunders Co., Philadelphia.

RUSSELL, G. V., 1954: The dorsal trigeminothalamic tract in the cat reconsidered as a lateral reticulo-thalamic system of connections. J. Comp. Neurol., *101*, 237-263.

SJÖQVIST, O., 1938: Eine neue Operationsmethode bei Trigeminusneuralgie: Durchschneidung des Tractus spinalis trigemini. Zentr. Neurochir., *2*, 274-281.

SZENTAGOTHAI, J. and KISS, T., 1949: Projection of dermatomes on the substantia gelatinosa. A.M.A. Arch. Neurol. Psychiat., *62*, 734-744.

WALKER, A. E., 1942: Somatotopic localization of spinothalamic and secondary trigeminal tracts in mesencephalon. A.M.A. Arch. Neurol. Psychiat., *48*, 884-889.

WOODBURNE, R. T., 1961: *Essentials of Human Anatomy*, 2nd Ed., Oxford University Press, New York.

Chapter 8

The Special Senses of Taste, Hearing, Equilibrium, Sight, and Smell

Taste is classified as a *special visceral afferent* sense. The receptors are the *taste buds* which develop during fetal life from local thickenings of the lingual epithelium. The cells in these thickenings elongate and reach the surface; the epithelial mass thus produced differentiates into taste cells and columnar supporting cells and eventually assumes its characteristic flask shape (Fig. 76). Recent evidence indicates that cells of the taste buds undergo renewal and that the so-called supporting cells are precursors of the more differentiated neuroepithelial taste cells. The taste cells end at the surface in hair-like receptive tips. The *taste fibers* of the *facial, glossopharyngeal,* and *vagus nerves* ramify upon the surfaces of the cells. In the adult, according to Arey (1946) taste buds persist on the surfaces of the vallate and foliate papillae and on a few fungiform papillae of the tongue, on the soft palate, and on the laryngeal surface of the epiglottis.

Taste fibers to the anterior two-thirds of the tongue are components of the facial nerve and arise from unipolar cells in the *geniculate ganglion* (Fig. 75). The peripheral processes reach the tongue by way of the *chorda tympani nerve*. The nerve leaves the facial canal through an opening in its anterior wall, traverses

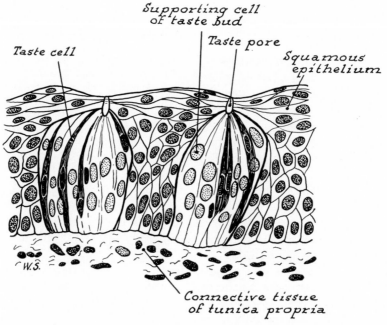

FIG. 76. Taste buds in the mucosa of the tongue (after Schaffer).

the tympanic cavity and the petrotympanic fissure, and joins the lingual nerve with which it proceeds to the tongue. The central processes course inward through the facial and internal auditory canals and enter the brain stem at the junction of the pons and medulla. Within the medulla the fibers enter the *tractus (fasciculus) solitarius* (Figs. 75 and 45) through which the taste impulses are conducted to the *nucleus solitarius* (Allen, 1923a, b).

Taste fibers to the posterior third of the tongue are from the *glossopharyngeal nerve.* The fibers originate as the peripheral processes of cells in the *petrosal ganglion.* The central processes of petrosal ganglion cells, as previously described, enter the medulla and terminate in the *nucleus solitarius* (Fig. 75).

The **taste buds of the epiglottis** are innervated by *vagus nerve fibers* whose cells of origin are in the *nodose ganglion* (Fig. 75). Central processes terminate in the *nucleus solitarius.* If there are taste buds in the epithelium of the soft palate, as stated by Arey (1946), they may receive special visceral afferent fibers from the nodose ganglion by way of the pharyngeal plexus or from the geniculate ganglion by way of the greater (superficial) petrosal nerve. In either case taste impulses from the soft palate would be conducted to the nucleus solitarius.

The **secondary afferent pathway for taste** (from nucleus solitarius to thalamus) is apparently incorporated into the contralateral *medial lemniscus* (Fig. 75). Upon reaching the thalamic level such secondary fibers terminate in the *posteromedial ventral nucleus* (Figs. 75 and 69) along with the other secondary afferent fibers from the head region (Patton *et al.,* 1944). From this nucleus tertiary taste fibers apparently project to the inferior part of the postcentral gyrus and adjacent insular cortex (Börnstein, 1940; Patton *et al.,* 1946; Penfield

and Rasmussen, 1950; Bagshaw and Pribram, 1953). As is true of the general visceral afferent fibers which terminate in the nucleus solitarius, the taste fibers also serve as the afferent limbs of numerous visceral and viscerosomatic reflex arcs.

Before proceeding to the description of the other special visceral afferent pathway—that for the special sense of smell—the special somatic senses of hearing, equilibrium and vision are considered. This is done in order that those sensory pathways which utilize the brain stem in their course to the cerebral cortex may be studied consecutively. The olfactory pathway to the cortex does not traverse the brain stem.

The auditory portion of the eighth nerve is made up of the central processes of axons of bipolar cells in the *spiral ganglion* (Fig. 77). The peripheral processes, or dendrites, of these cells are distributed to the *spiral organ of Corti* in the cochlea.

The **cochlea** consists of a bony canal which spirals forward around a central core; the core is termed the *modiolus* and the canal completes approximately two and one-half turns around it. The *cochlear duct,* often referred to as the *scala media,* occupies a median position in the bony canal; it is separated from the *scala vestibuli* on the one side by the *vestibular* (Reissner's) *membrane* and from the *scala tympani* on the other side by the bony *spiral lamina, spiral ligament* and *basilar membrane*; the last-named structure stretches between the spiral ligament and lamina. The scala tympani ends at the *round window (fenestra rotunda)* in the base of the cochlea (Fig. 78, *A*). The round window is a deficiency in the bony wall between the tympanic cavity and the internal ear which is normally closed by the *secondary tympanic membrane.* The scala vestibuli and the scala tympani, which are

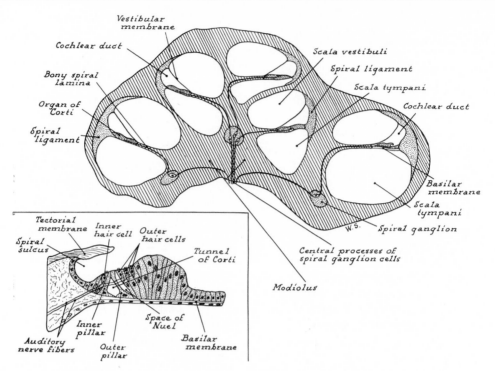

FIG. 77. Longitudinal section of the cochlea (after Schaffer). Inset showing details of the organ of Corti (after Held).

normally filled with perilymph, communicate with one another at the apex of the cochlea (helicotrema).

The cochlear duct, saccule, utricle and membranous semicircular canals are developed from the otic vesicle. The vesicle, as described in Chapter 2, comes from a thickened ectodermal plate known as the *auditory placode* which develops alongside the rhombencephalon; invagination of the placode gives origin to the *auditory pit*; this closes to form the vesicle which then migrates inward and comes to occupy a position in the mesenchyme between the ectoderm and the hind-brain. The cochlear duct, as finally developed, ends blindly at the apex of the cochlea; it contains the spiral organ of Corti and is filled with endolymph. At its basal limit it communicates with the saccule through the *ductus reuniens* (Fig. 78, *B*).

The **spiral organ of Corti**—the end

organ for auditory stimuli—extends throughout the length of the cochlear duct where it rests upon the basilar membrane. In cross-section it is seen to have a triangular tunnel running through it, known as the tunnel of Corti (Fig. 77, inset). On either side of the tunnel, and contributing to its formation, are the inner and outer rods or pillars of Corti. A single row of hair cells lies on the inner side of the inner rod; on the outer side of the outer rod there are three or four rows of similar cells. Each hair cell is surmounted by about twenty hair-like processes. Both the inner and outer hair cells are supported by rows of columnar cells. A space medial to the organ of Corti is known as the internal spiral sulcus; the tectorial membrane overhangs the sulcus and the organ of Corti.

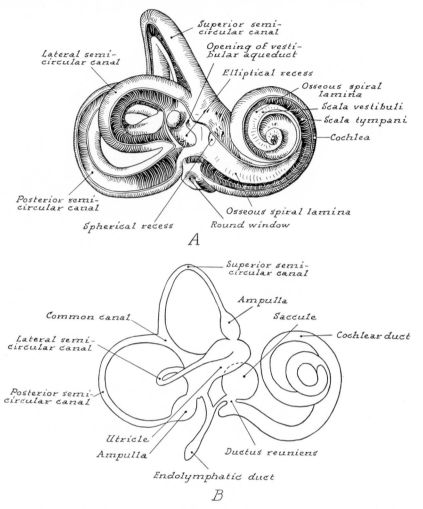

FIG. 78. *A*, The bony labyrinth of the ear (after Sobotta-McMurrich). *B*, The membranous labyrinth (after Gray).

Sound waves strike the tympanic membrane and cause it to vibrate; the vibrations are transmitted to the perilymph of the vestibule by the ossicular chain whose final component is the stapes with its footplate in the oval window. The waves set up in the perilymph cause the basilar membrane to vibrate; since the organ of Corti rests upon the membrane it, too, is set into vibration and the processes of the hair cells are moved about in the endolymph or against the under surface of the tectorial membrane.

The nerve impulses thus set up in the hair cells are transferred to the dendrites of the spiral ganglion cells. Although not usually demonstrable in fixed sections of the cochlea, it is frequently stated that the processes of the hair cells are actually embedded in the under surface of the tectorial membrane. A dampening effect upon the hair cells is ascribed to the tectorial membrane by some investigators.

The basilar membrane appears to be specifically segmented as to the frequencies to which it will respond maximally. That this is true appears to have been proven in animal experiments in which certain segments of the membrane and organ of Corti have been removed. Animals thus treated are found to be deaf to certain frequency ranges (Eyster *et al.*, 1935). These observations are in support of the "place theory" of hearing and there is, in fact, good evidence that the part of the basilar membrane evidencing the most pronounced response to stimulation, changes with changes of frequency (Stevens *et al.*, 1935). The

and 52). Experiments have indicated that the various levels of the cochlear spiral are topically represented in the cochlear nuclei (Lewy and Kobrak, 1936; Rose *et al.*, 1957).

The **cochlear nuclei** are applied to the external surface of the restiform body. They contain the cell bodies of the *secondary neurons* in the *auditory pathway*. Axons of these cells enter the tegmentum of the pons where they either decussate in, and form, a transverse band of fibers known as the *trapezoid body* (Figs. 80 and 53) or end in the homolateral

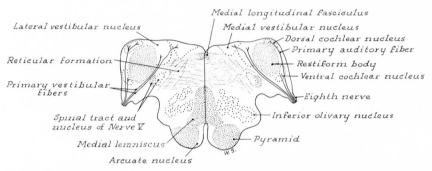

FIG. 79.   Section through the rostral limit of the medulla showing the manner of termination of the auditory and vestibular fibers of the eighth nerve.

response of the basilar membrane to different sound frequencies has been explained by the traveling wave theory (Békésey, 1951).

The **spiral ganglion** is situated within the bony spiral lamina at its point of attachment to the modiolus (Fig. 77). The dendrites of its bipolar cells course outward through the spiral lamina and basilar membrane and terminate in relation to the hair cells of the organ of Corti. The central processes, or axons, enter the modiolus and emerge through the lamina cribrosa at its base to form the auditory portion of the eighth nerve which then traverses the internal auditory canal and terminates in the *dorsal* and *ventral cochlear nuclei* at the junction of the medulla and pons (Figs. 79

superior olivary nucleus (Stotler, 1953). The *superior olivary nucleus* is dorsal to the trapezoid body and in the angle formed between the medial and lateral lemnisci (Figs. 80 and 53). As components of the trapezoid body the secondary auditory fibers are intermingled with the longitudinally coursing fibers of the medial lemnisci. In their course to the trapezoid body they form *dorsal* and *ventral striae* (Fig. 80); the former originates in the dorsal cochlear nucleus and passes dorsal to the restiform body while the latter originates in both dorsal and ventral nuclei and passes ventral to the restiform body. After decussating in the trapezoid body some of the fibers turn rostrally in the *lateral lemniscus,* the further course of which, through the

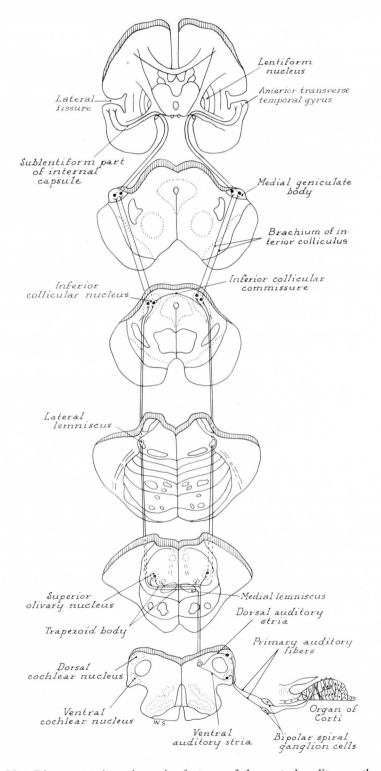

FIG. 80.   Diagram to show the major features of the central auditory pathway.

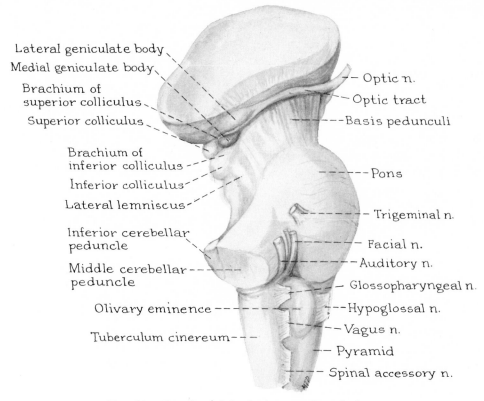

Lateral geniculate body
Medial geniculate body
Brachium of superior colliculus
Superior colliculus
Brachium of inferior colliculus
Inferior colliculus
Lateral lemniscus
Inferior cerebellar peduncle
Middle cerebellar peduncle
Olivary eminence
Tuberculum cinereum

Optic n.
Optic tract
Basis pedunculi
Pons
Trigeminal n.
Facial n.
Auditory n.
Glossopharyngeal n.
Hypoglossal n.
Vagus n.
Pyramid
Spinal accessory n.

FIG. 81.   Drawing of the brain stem, lateral view.

pons, was observed in connection with the study of the lateral spinothalamic tract (Figs. 56, 58 and 59). Others, after traversing the dorsal stria and trapezoid body, end in the contralateral superior olivary nucleus (Stotler, 1953).

The **lateral lemniscus,** as shown by degeneration experiments of Barnes *et al.* (1943) and Stotler (1953), terminates in the nucleus of the inferior colliculus; the brachium of the inferior colliculus is formed by axons of cells in this nucleus (Figs. 80 and 61).

The **brachium (peduncle) of the inferior colliculus** courses rostrally and ventrally across the lateral aspect of the mesencephalon and terminates in the *medial geniculate body* (Fig. 81). The latter structure is a posterior thalamic nucleus located just dorsal to the lateral limit of the basis pedunculi at the level

of the superior colliculi. Axons from cell bodies therein course through the sublentiform portion of the internal capsule and terminate in the auditory area of the cerebral cortex (Fig. 80).

It appears, therefore, that the *auditory pathway* to the cortex consists of a series of at least *four neurons* instead of the usual three. The first has its cell body in the *spiral ganglion,* the second in one of the *cochlear nuclei,* the third in the *inferior collicular nucleus,* and the fourth in the *medial geniculate body* (Fig. 80).

The **conduction of auditory impulses** is further complicated by the existence along the pathway of other relay stations; these include the superior olivary nucleus (Figs. 80 and 53) and the nucleus of the lateral lemniscus (Fig. 59). The *nucleus of the lateral lemniscus* consists of numerous cells scattered among the fibers of the lemniscus in its pontile portion. Secondary auditory fibers from the cochlear nuclei end in the superior olivary nuclei of the same and of the opposite side as noted above; others terminate in or send collaterals to the nucleus of the lateral lemniscus. The axons of the cells in these nuclear structures, in turn, course rostrally in the lateral lemniscus and, for the most part, terminate in the nucleus of the inferior colliculus; those from the superior olivary nucleus may enter the lemniscus of the same side or they may decussate through the trapezoid body and enter the contralateral one. Some of the fibers of the lateral lemniscus cross to the inferior collicular nucleus of the opposite side through the *commissure of the inferior colliculi* (Figs. 80 and 61). According to Stotler (1953) the nucleus of the lateral lemniscus projects, to some extent, to adjacent reticular formation. This suggests a mechanism for cerebral arousal through the extralemniscal system, resulting in "attention" to auditory impulses (Chapter 5).

It becomes evident that there are a number of possibilities for auditory impulses arising in either ear to be projected upon the auditory areas of both cerebral hemispheres. These possibilities include the termination in the superior olivary nuclei of both sides of axons of cells in the cochlear nuclei, the contribution of fibers to the lateral lemnisci of both sides by either superior olivary nucleus, and the decussation of some of the fibers of the lateral lemniscus at the level of the inferior colliculi (Fig. 80). That the ear is bilaterally represented in the cortex is indicated by the clinical observation that unilateral destruction of the lateral lemniscus, medial geniculate body, internal capsule, or auditory area of the cortex may exist without detectable deafness in either ear.

Auditory reflexes are effected through connections in the inferior colliculi (Fig. 82). The oval *nucleus of the inferior colliculus,* in which the lateral lemniscus terminates, has already been referred to. The area dorsomedial to the nucleus presents a laminated appearance and contains several large cells which give origin to some of the fibers of the *tectobulbar* and *tectospinal tracts.* At this point attention should be called again to the fact that the *quadrigeminal lamina* is also spoken of as the *tectum* of the mesencephalon. It is worthy of note that Pearce and Glees (1953) failed to describe tectospinal fibers, in the cat, originating at the inferior collicular level, but stated that they do originate from the superior colliculi; this observation does not exclude tectobulbar and tectospinal fibers from participation in auditory reflexes since there are internuncial connections between inferior and superior collicular regions of the mesencephalon. *Tectobulbar* and *tectospinal fibers* cross to the opposite side through the *dorsal tegmental decussation* (Fig. 82) and course downward through the brain stem and cervical portion of the spinal cord; the former terminate in relation to cells in the motor nuclei of cranial nerves and the latter in relation to anterior gray column cells of the cervical cord. Pearce and Glees (1953) found both crossed and uncrossed fibers in the tectospinal tracts. The observations indicated further that fibers which could be classified as tectobulbar ended in the reticular formation rather than in direct relation to the nuclei of cranial nerves. Connections are made with the cells of origin of the tectospinal and tectobulbar tracts through collaterals from the lateral lemniscus or through the medium of internuncial cells in the collicular nuclei. Subcortical auditory reflexes which utilize the muscles of the head, neck, and upper extremities are facilitated by tectobulbar, tectospinal and reticulospinal

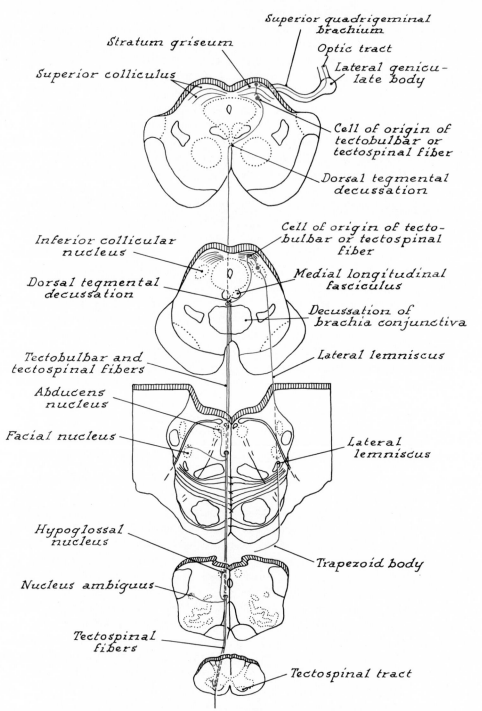

F<small>IG</small>. 82.   Diagram illustrating the function of tectobulbar and tectospinal fibers in visual and auditory reflexes.

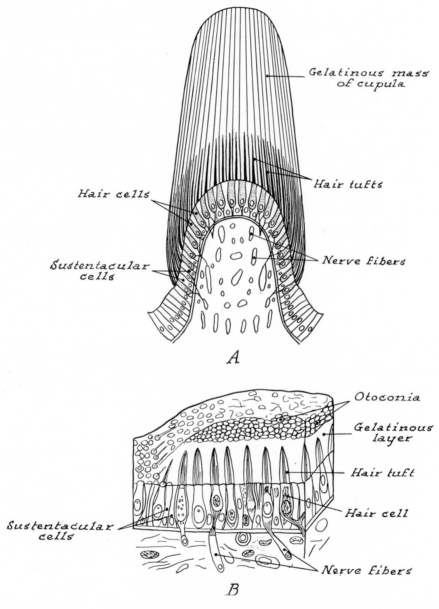

Fig. 83.   *A*, Diagram of a section of crista ampullaris (in part after Kolmer). *B*, Diagram of a section of macula (after Kolmer).

connections. In addition, reflexes involving turning of the eyes and head are facilitated by direct projections from the superior olivary nuclei to the abducens nuclei and the medial longitudinal fasciculi. Such reflexes would include turning of head and eyes toward a sudden noise or elevating the hands before the face as protection against injury which is likely to be a concomitant of a blast or explosion.

The **special somatic sense of equilibrium** involves the vestibular portion of the eighth nerve. The cells of origin of the *vestibular nerve* are in the *vestibular ganglion* which is found in the internal auditory canal. Like those in the spiral ganglion of the cochlea, these neurons are of the bipolar type. Their peripheral processes pierce the lamina cribrosa at the outer limit of the internal auditory canal and are distributed to the *cristae ampullares* of the membranous semicircular canals and to the *maculae* of the utricle and saccule.

The **membranous semicircular canals** are located within the bony canals and are completely surrounded by perilymph. The **utricle and saccule,** within the bony vestibule of the internal ear, are also surrounded by perilymph. The perilymph spaces of the semicircular canals and vestibule are continuous with the scala vestibuli of the cochlea (Fig. 78).

The **cristae** develop from the epithelium lining the ampullae of the membranous semicircular canals. A curved ridge, transverse to the long axis of the canal, appears in each ampulla; within it two types of cells are differentiated— sensory and supporting (Fig. 83). The sensory cells have bristle-like hairs at their free surfaces. It has been suggested that the supporting cells secrete the jelly-like substance which is seen on the surface of the crista and which forms its so-called cupula. The **maculae** develop within the utricle and saccule in the same

manner as described for the development of the cristae and are considerably larger. Their surfaces are covered by a gelatinous membrane within which are calcareous bodies called *otoconia* or *otoliths.*

The hair cells of the cristae are stimulated by currents set up in the endolymph which fills the membranous canals, utricle and saccule. Such currents result from movement of the head in the planes of the respective canals. The hair cells of the maculae are stimulated by the effect of gravity upon the otoliths embedded in the gelatinous masses surmounting them. The former have to do, therefore, with dynamic equilibrium and the latter with static equilibrium.

The **axons of the vestibular ganglion cells** accompany the auditory portion of the eighth nerve through the internal auditory canal and enter the brain stem at the junction of the pons and medulla. They pass ventral to the restiform body and, for the most part, terminate in the vestibular nuclei; some vestibular fibers, however, continue past the nuclei and enter the cerebellum by way of the inferior cerebellar peduncle (restiform body) (Fig. 85).

Four pairs of vestibular nuclei are found in the medullary and pontile portions of the brain stem (Figs. 52, 55 and 85). The *inferior or spinal vestibular nucleus* is limited to the medulla where it lies just medial to the restiform body. This nucleus is continuous rostrally with the *lateral vestibular nucleus (Deiters)* which extends through the rostral part of the medulla and into the caudal part of the pons. The most rostrally placed of the nuclei is the *superior vestibular nucleus* which is located entirely within the pons. The *medial vestibular nucleus* is bounded laterally and rostrally by the other three. It extends forward into the pons and its caudal extremity is near the caudal limit of the fourth ventricle. Its medial border is near the midline of the brain stem. All the vestibular nuclei are immediately beneath the floor of the fourth ventricle and they account for a prominence in the floor that is called the *area vestibularis*.

The vestibular nuclei are concerned mainly with the completion of vestibular reflex arcs. All the nuclei give origin to *vestibulospinal fibers* which course caudally into the spinal cord in the *medial longitudinal fasciculi* (Figs. 84, 85 and 53); in the cord they enter the *sulco-*

upon postural muscles have been demonstrated by stimulation or destruction, unilaterally, of the lateral vestibular nucleus. Stimulation is responsible for postural asymmetry of the entire body consisting of ipsilateral extension, contralateral flexion, deviation of the head toward the opposite side and, in cats, a tendency to fall toward the contralateral side; destruction of the lateral vestibular nucleus results in postural asymmetry which is the exact reciprocal of that produced by stimulation. Cutting the vestib-

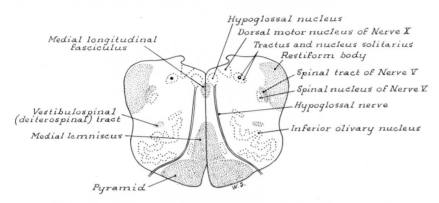

Fig. 84.   Section through medulla showing the positions of the medial longitudinal fasciculi and vestibulospinal tracts.

marginal fasciculi (Fig. 86). The medial longitudinal fasciculi are situated on either side of the median raphe of the brain stem, close to the floor of the fourth ventricle. The lateral vestibular nucleus also gives origin to the *vestibulospinal tract* which courses caudally in the reticular formation of the medulla, just dorsal to the inferior olivary nucleus (Fig. 84) and enters the ventral funiculus of the spinal cord (Fig. 86). All of the vestibulospinal fibers eventually terminate through synapses upon neurons in the ventral gray columns of the spinal cord. Through these connections the musculature of the neck, trunk, and extremities is reflexly affected by vestibular impulses arising in the internal ear. The effects of the vestibular mechanism

ular nerve unilaterally gives rise to similar but more pronounced and more lasting postural asymmetry than destruction of the vestibular nucleus. The close functional relationship of the vestibular and cerebellar mechanisms is indicated by the fact that stimulation or destruction of the medial cerebellar nucleus (*tectal* or *fastigal*), unilaterally, produces postural effects exactly like those resulting from stimulation or destruction of the lateral vestibular nucleus (Chambers and Sprague, 1955).

Direct vestibulocerebellar connections (from the vestibular ganglion to the cerebellum) have been mentioned. These fibers are joined by others from the vestibular nuclei which also reach the cerebellum by way of the restiform body

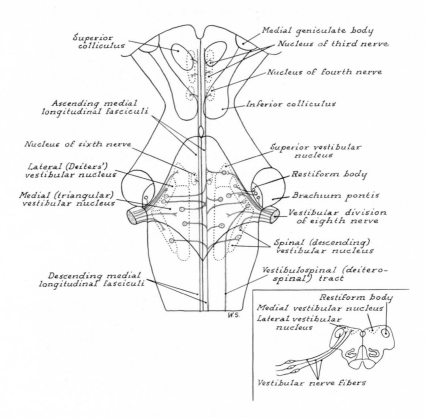

FIG. 85.   Diagram of the central connections of the vestibular nerve superimposed upon a dorsal view of the brain stem. Inset shows the manner of entry of vestibular fibers into the brain stem.

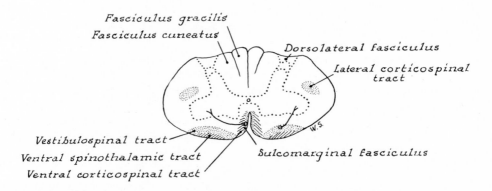

FIG. 86.   Section through cervical spinal cord showing the locations of the sulcomarginal and vestibulospinal tracts in the ventral funiculi.

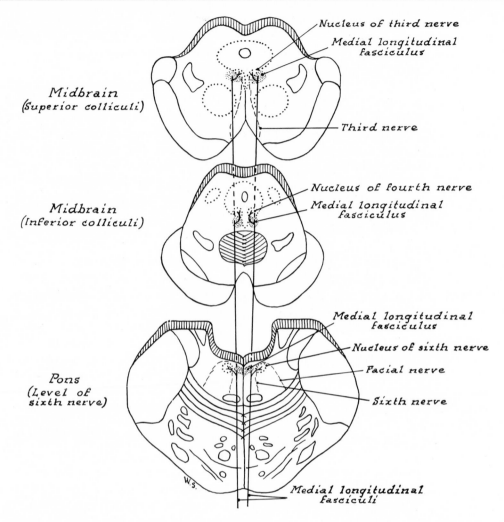

FIG. 87.   Diagram to show the close relationships of the medial longitudinal fasciculi to the motor ocular nuclei in the pons and midbrain and the connections with the nuclei.

(Fig. 85). Thus connections are made between the semicircular canals and the cerebellum in two ways—one of which involves a single neuron with its cell body in the vestibular ganglion and the other of which is a two-neuron pathway with the cell body of the second neuron in one of the vestibular nuclei. The cerebellar influence upon postural reflexes is mediated by fastigiobulbar fibers (from fastigial or tectal nucleus of cerebellum to the brain stem) which traverse the restiform body and end in vestibular nuclei and in the reticular formation of the medulla and pons. The significance of the vestibulocerebellar connections will become more apparent when the structure and function of the cerebellum are considered (Chapters 18 and 19).

A pathway from the vestibular nuclei to the cerebral cortex has not been definitely established although it is recognized that the special sense mediated by the vestibular nerve does reach the conscious level (Kempinsky, 1951; Mickle and Ades, 1954). In the cat the vestibular area is adjacent to, and overlaps, the posterior margin of the general sensory area of the arm and face and the anterior margin of the auditory cortex. There is good evidence that axons of second order neurons in the vestibular nuclei decussate in the region of the trapezoid body and then ascend between the lateral and medial lemnisci to the levels of the medial geniculate body and posterolateral ventral thalamic nucleus, one or both of which may project to the cortical vestibular area.

Evidence that vestibular impulses are projected to the cerebrum in man includes the observation that there is an area of the cortex close to that upon which auditory impulses are known to be projected which, when stimulated electrically, gives rise to a feeling of vertigo in the conscious subject. The observations of Fitzgerald and Hallpike (1942) also indicate the presence of a cortical vestibular center; in ten human subjects with lesions of one temporal lobe they found directional preponderance of caloric nystagmus (elicited by douching the external ear with warm or cold water) toward the side of the lesion. Ten cases with cerebral lesions not involving the temporal lobe exhibited normal caloric nystagmus.

Other axons from cells in the vestibular nuclei course rostrally in the *medial longitudinal fasciculi* and terminate upon motor neurons in the *abducens, trochlear,* and *oculomotor nuclei* (Figs. 86 and 87). In the mesencephalon the medial longitudinal fasciculi are ventrolateral to the central gray matter surrounding the cerebral aqueduct and are therefore in close relationship to the trochlear and oculomotor nuclei (Fig. 87). *Vestibulo-ocular reflex arcs* are responsible for movements of the eyes in response to changes in the position of the head. They also appear to be concerned in the maintenance of balanced tonicity in the eye muscles. If the semicircular canals, eighth nerve, or vestibular nuclei are injured the eyes are usually deviated to one or the other side; horizontal, vertical or rotary nystagmus also appears in most cases of injury to the vestibular system.

Nystagmus is a term applied to a more or less rhythmic oscillation of the eyes. One phase of the oscillation is more prolonged than the other and is referred to as the slow component. The shorter phase is spoken of as the quick component. Clinically, nystagmus is usually described as being in the direction of its quick component.

Tumor of the eighth nerve (acoustic neurinoma) occurs not uncommonly; it gives rise to the so-called *cerebellopontile angle syndrome*. The *cerebellopontile angle* is located on the lateral aspect of the brain stem at the junction of the pons and medulla; it is bounded superiorly by the biventral lobule of the cerebellum. The eighth, ninth, tenth, seventh, sixth, and fifth cranial nerves are closely related to one another and to the cerebellopontile angle (Fig. 49). A tumor of the eighth nerve is responsible, during its early stages, for deafness in the corresponding ear and symptoms of vestibular dysfunction (nystagmus, etc.). As it increases in size it presses upon the other nerves in the region and interferes with their function. Thus, the symptoms of such a tumor, in addition to eighth nerve symptoms, may include partial or complete ipsilateral paralysis of the soft palate (tenth nerve), paralysis of the face on the side of the lesion (seventh nerve), diminished sensibility (hypesthesia) over the distribution of the ipsilateral fifth nerve, double vision due to internal strabismus in the ipsilateral eye (sixth nerve) and ipsilateral loss of the sense of taste (ninth, tenth, and seventh nerves).

Vision is a special somatic afferent sense. The visual pathways are more

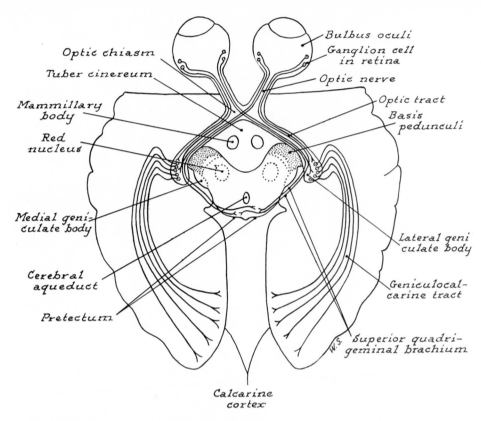

FIG. 88.   Diagram of the visual pathway. Reflex connections between the retinæ and the
pretectum are also indicated.

complex than most others for the reason that impulses arising in the temporal half of the retina are conducted to the cerebral cortex of the same side while those from the nasal half are projected upon the visual cortex of the contralateral hemisphere. The crossing of the fibers from the nasal halves of the two retinae occurs in the optic chiasm (Fig. 88).

The **optic vesicle** appears as a spherical evagination from the prosencephalon in embryos 3 to 4 millimeters in length. The outer or distal half of the vesicle invaginates into the inner half to form the *optic cup* which develops into the retina. As the optic cup migrates forward it maintains its attachment to the brain through the *optic stalk* which becomes the optic nerve when it is invaded by the axons of the ganglion cells in the developing retina. The *optic nerves,* since they develop as outgrowths from the brain, are not strictly peripheral in type; they are nevertheless commonly included in that category. That they are processes of the brain is manifested by the presence in them of all three types of glia cells (astrocytes, oligodendrocytes and microgliacytes). *Glioma,* a tumor that develops from glia cells, not infrequently occurs in the optic nerve. It will be recalled that true peripheral nerve fibers have neurilemmal sheaths; these are not present in the optic nerves which fail to regenerate when severed.

The **retina** contains three layers of cells: An outer layer of *rod and cone cells,* a middle layer of *bipolar cells,* and

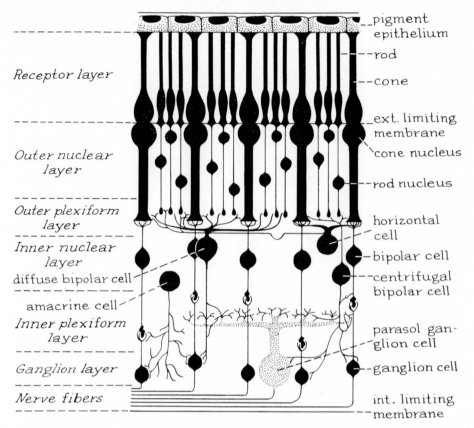

Receptor layer

Outer nuclear layer

Outer plexiform layer

Inner nuclear layer

diffuse bipolar cell

amacrine cell

Inner plexiform layer

Ganglion layer

Nerve fibers

pigment epithelium

rod

cone

ext. limiting membrane

cone nucleus

rod nucleus

horizontal cell

bipolar cell

centrifugal bipolar cell

parasol ganglion cell

ganglion cell

int. limiting membrane

FIG. 89.   Diagram to show the histologic layers of the retina and its interneuronal connections. (Modified from Walls, 1963.)

an inner layer of *ganglion cells* (Fig. 89). The rods and cones are the peripheral processes of the rod and cone cells; they extend outward through the external limiting membrane and constitute the receptor organs for vision. In adequate light, cones are much more discriminating receptors, but in dim light, rods are much more efficient. The cones alone are found in the fovea centralis where vision and sensibility to color are at their maximum. The term, *fovea centralis,* applies to a depression in the macula lutea of the retina.

The **macula lutea** is located directly posterior to the pupil or in the visual axis of the eye; in this position it is approximately 3 mm. temporal to the optic

disc where the optic nerve fibers are leaving the eye (Fig. 90). As regards the absence of rods in the fovea, it is of interest that sailors are trained, when on watch at night, to direct their eyes upward or downward in relation to their visual objectives; thus, these objectives are focused upon those areas of the retina where rods are present; if they looked directly at the object it would be focused upon the fovea and might not be seen at all.

The axons of the rod and cone cells synapse upon the dendrites of the bipolar cells (Fig. 89). The area at which these synapses occur has been termed the *outer plexiform layer*. The axons of the bipolar cells, in turn, synapse upon the dendrites of the ganglion cells; these synapses occur in the *inner plexiform layer*. The axons of the ganglion cells converge upon the region of the optic disc and emerge from the eye as the components of the optic nerve.

The **optic nerve** enters the cranial cavity through the optic foramen. Those fibers which originate in the temporal half of the retina continue past the optic chiasm into the optic tract of the same side; those from the nasal half decussate through the chiasm and enter the contralateral tract (Fig. 88).

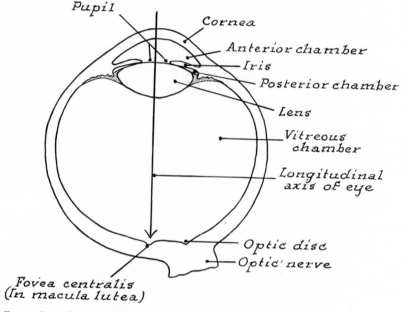

FIG. 90.   Coronal section of the bulbus oculi showing the relation of the macula lutea to the optic disc and to the longitudinal axis of the eye.

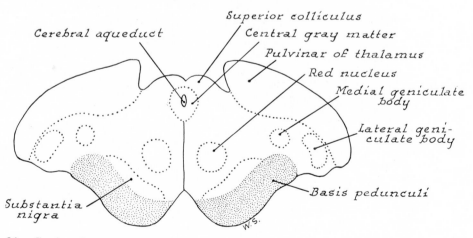

FIG. 91.   Section through the brain stem at the level of transition between mesencephalon and diencephalon.

Peduncle of sup. colliculus

Pulvinar

Medial geniculate nucl.

Lateral genicu-
late nucl.

Dentatorubro-
thalamic tract

Optic tract

Fasciculus
retroflexus

Substantia
nigra

Amygdala

Superior colliculus

Commissure of sup. colliculus

Dorsal longitudinal fasciculus

Medial longitudi-
nal fasciculus

Medial lemniscus

Central tegmental
tract

Cerebral peduncle

Oculomotor nucl.

Red nucleus

Mammillothalamic
tract

Ant. column of fornix

Tuber cinereum

Uncus

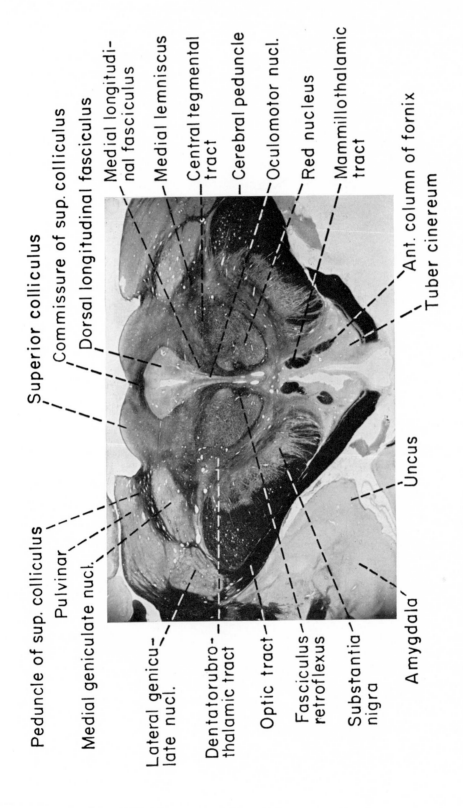

Fig. 92. Photomicrograph of transverse section through the rostral part of the superior collicular level of the midbrain which passes through the posterior thalamic nuclei. Weil stain.

The **optic tract** courses posteriorly around the cerebral peduncle and ends at the lateral geniculate body. Most of its fibers terminate by synapsing upon cells in that body but some continue past it and form the *brachium of the superior colliculus* (superior quadrigeminal brachium) which connects the lateral geniculate body with the superior col-

is, therefore, frequently referred to as the *geniculocalcarine tract* (Fig. 88). The fibers from the part of the lateral geniculate which receives impulses from the superior retinal quadrants course directly posteriorly to the superior lip of the calcarine fissure. Those from the part of the lateral geniculate related to the inferior retinal quadrants loop for-

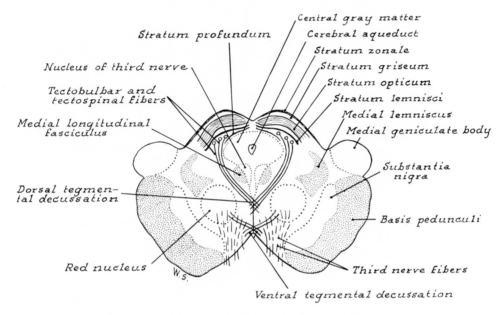

Fig. 93. Section through the mesencephalon at the level of the superior colliculi.

licular region. The latter fibers synapse upon cells in the superior colliculus and in the area just rostral to the colliculus, or pretectum (Fig. 88).

The **lateral geniculate body,** like the medial one, is a posterior thalamic nucleus. It is located just lateral to the medial geniculate body, under cover of the pulvinar of the thalamus (Figs. 91, 92 and 94). Axons of its cells traverse the sublenticular and, in part, the retrolenticular portions of the internal capsule (Crosby *et al.,* 1962). All terminate in the visual area of the cerebral cortex which is located in and around the calcarine fissure and this group of fibers

ward into the rostral temporal region before coursing posteriorly to the inferior lip of the calcarine fissure (Fig. 95).

The **superior colliculi** are laminated structures whose layers, from superficially inward, are designated as: stratum zonale, stratum griseum, stratum opticum, stratum lemnisci and stratum profundum (Fig. 93). The colliculi function as reflex centers and are particularly concerned with *visual reflexes.* The optic nerve fibers that reach the superior colliculus by way of its brachium (Figs. 88 and 94) enter the stratum opticum; they terminate chiefly in relation to cells in the stratum griseum. These, in turn,

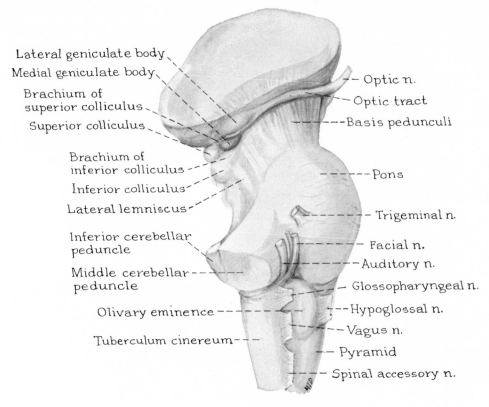

Lateral geniculate body
Medial geniculate body
Brachium of
superior colliculus
Superior colliculus

Brachium of
inferior colliculus
Inferior colliculus
Lateral lemniscus

Inferior cerebellar
peduncle

Middle cerebellar
peduncle

Olivary eminence

Tuberculum cinereum

Optic n.
Optic tract
Basis pedunculi

Pons

Trigeminal n.

Facial n.
Auditory n.
Glossopharyngeal n.
Hypoglossal n.
Vagus n.
Pyramid
Spinal accessory n.

Fig. 94.   Drawing of the brain stem, lateral view.

connect with large cells in the superior colliculus that give origin to many of the fibers of the *tectobulbar* and *tectospinal tracts* (Fig. 93) whose termination (directly or indirectly) in relation to motor neurons in the nuclei of cranial nerves and in the ventral gray columns of the cervical segments of the spinal cord has been described (Fig. 82). *Reflex reactions* to *visual stimuli* are facilitated by these connections. Through direct or indirect connections of tectobulbar fibers with cells in the nucleus of the facial nerve the eyes are closed when there is danger of flying objects entering them. Through synapses of tectospinal fibers upon anterior gray column cells in the lower cervical segments the arms and hands are raised to further protect the eyes.

Those fibers in the brachium of the superior colliculus that terminate in the *pretectum* (Fig. 88) synapse upon cells whose axons enter the *Edinger-Westphal nuclei* (Chapter 22). Visceral efferent fibers from these nuclei leave the mesencephalon and enter the orbits as components of the oculomotor nerves; there they end in the *ciliary ganglia*. Axons of cells in the ciliary ganglia supply the *constrictor pupillae muscles* (Fig. 188). This reflex arc, beginning in the retina and ending in the constrictor muscles, is responsible for constriction of the pupils in response to strong light. The pathway involved in the *light reflex* has been carefully traced by Magoun and Ranson (1935). Loss of the light reflex without loss of vision often indicates some type of pathologic process in the rostro-

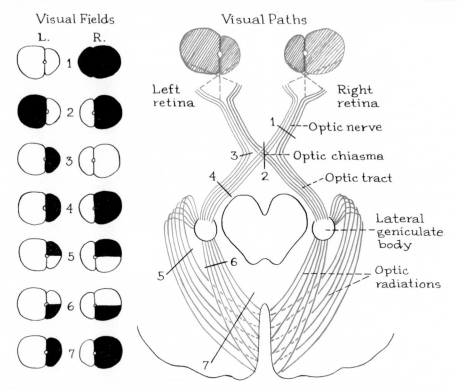

FIG. 95.   Diagram to show the central visual pathways and the effects of various lesions of the visual pathway. The black areas of the inserts indicate the visual field defects resulting from the lesions indicated by the corresponding numbers on the figure at the right. (1) complete blindness of right eye; (2) bitemporal hemianopia; (3) left nasal hemianopia; (4) right homonymous hemianopia; (5) right upper quadrant hemianopia; (6) right lower quadrant hemianopia; (7) right homonymous hemianopia. (In part after Homans.)

dorsal area of the mesencephalon (pretectum). A more detailed description of the light reflex and its pathway is presented in Chapter 22.

It is readily apparent that destruction of one optic nerve will produce total blindness in the eye on that side (Fig. 95, 1). Destruction of the optic chiasm, such as may occur in association with pituitary tumor, results in blindness that is limited to those parts of the fields of vision that are projected upon the nasal halves of both retinae. This is designated as *bitemporal hemianopia* since the patient fails to see objects in either temporal field (Fig. 95, 2). Destruction of the fibers from the temporal hemiretina

produces a unilateral nasal hemianopia (Fig. 95, 3). This may result from enlargement of the internal carotid artery at the site where it lies in the angle formed by the optic nerve and optic tract. Blindness is routinely described with reference to the fields of vision rather than with reference to the part of the retina involved. Since light rays enter the eye only through the pupil and since they travel in straight lines, it is obvious that the nasal half of the retina functions in the perception of objects in the temporal field of vision while the temporal half is responsible for the nasal field.

Any lesion which destroys the optic tract on one side will result in blindness in the contralateral fields of vision (the nasal field of the ipsilateral eye and the temporal field of the contralateral one). This type of visual defect is referred to as right or left *homonymous hemianopia* (Fig. 95, 4). The same type of blindness results from complete unilateral destruction of the geniculocalcarine tract or of the visual cortex (Fig. 95, 7). Destruction of the upper lip of the calcarine cortex on one side produces a visual loss in the lower quadrant of the contralateral visual field (contralateral inferior quadrantic anopia). A contralateral superior quadrantic anopia would result from destroying the lower lip of the calcarine cortex. The geniculocalcarine fibers, as they approach the visual cortex, are so arranged that lesions in the upper or lower parts of the tract would result in quadrantic field defects comparable to those described for destruction of the respective calcarine lips (Fig. 95, 5 and 6 respectively). It is important to note that the quadrantopia frequently found in individuals with tumors in the temporal lobe of the cerebrum most commonly involves the upper fields of vision. This may be explained by the concept of separate courses for the geniculocalcarine fibers, at their origin from the lateral geniculate body, which are activated respectively by visual stimuli in the upper and lower quadrants of the visual fields (Purves-Stewart and Worster-Drought, 1952). According to this concept, those fibers representing the upper visual fields course forward and then laterally along the outer boundary of the posterior horn of the lateral ventricle (Meyer's loop) while those of the lower visual fields course directly backward beneath the floor of the ventricle (Fig. 95). Thus the fibers in the more exposed position (Meyer's loop) would be interrupted without injury to the more direct (medioinferior) fibers.

Commissural fibers, other than visual,

are associated with the optic chiasm and are designated as *dorsal* (of *Ganser*) and *ventral* (of *Gudden and Meynert*) *supra optic decussations*. The physiologic significance of the supraoptic decussations remains conjectural although the distribution of component fibers has been extensively studied. Bucher and Bürgi (1953) found fibers to the dorsal supraoptic decussation ascending through the midbrain in the medial longitudinal fasciculus; after traversing the medial area of the subthalamus (which provides continuity between midbrain tegmentum and diencephalon) and decussating above and behind the optic chiasm, these fibers passed laterally above the optic tract, pierced the internal capsule and terminated in the reticular nucleus of the thalamus (located at the surface of the thalamus which is in contact with the internal capsule). Finer fibers from the decussation were traced to the pretectum and superior colliculus of the same and opposite sides. The finely myelinated fibers of the ventral supraoptic decussation ascended toward it in the lateral tegmental areas of the midbrain; after swinging across the cerebral peduncle, passing forward on the inner aspect of the optic tract and decussating within and behind the optic chiasm, these fibers ended in the region ventral to the medial geniculate body and, via the superior quadrigeminal brachium, in the superior colliculus. A possible functional connection of the dorsal supraoptic decussation with the vestibular system was suggested on the basis of the presence of fibers ascending to the decussation in the medial longitudinal fasciculus. The distribution of fibers of the dorsal supraoptic decussation to the reticular nucleus of the thalamus may implicate it in cortical facilitatory systems (extralemniscal system, Chapters 5 and 20).

The **special visceral sense of smell** is mediated by the olfactory cells found in

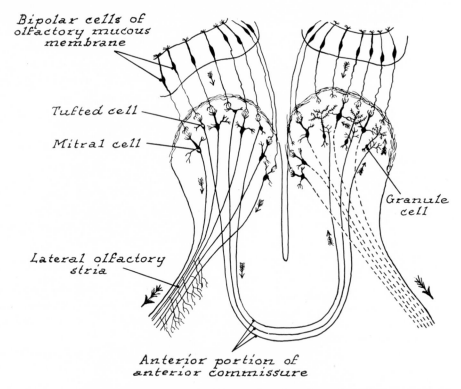

FIG. 96.   Diagram showing the course of olfactory impulses from the olfactory mucous membrane to the olfactory bulbs and from the bulbs to the olfactory cortex (after Cajal).

the olfactory mucous membrane. The peripheral processes or *dendrites* of the *olfactory cells* reach the surface of the mucous membrane by traversing the spaces between the supporting cells. The central processes or *axons* form the unmyelinated *olfactory nerves* which enter the cranial cavity through the openings in the cribriform plates of the ethmoid. Within the anterior cranial fossa they end in the olfactory bulbs which rest upon the cribriform plates (Fig. 96).

The **olfactory bulb** is a laminated structure whose superficial layer consists of unmyelinated nerve fibers from the olfactory nerves. Under this superficial layer there are several layers of gray matter and, finally, a layer of myelinated nerve fibers passing to and from the olfactory tract. A central core of neuroglia replaces the cavity which is present in some of the lower animals (Fig. 97).

Three types of cells—mitral, granule, and tufted—are found in the gray matter of the olfactory bulb. The dendrites of the *mitral* and *tufted cells* receive olfactory impulses from the olfactory nerves (Fig. 96); their axons enter the layer of myelinated fibers and are thus directed into the *olfactory tract*; the tract connects the bulb with the ventral aspect of the cerebrum (Fig. 98). The thicker axons of the mitral cells mainly enter the olfactory areas of the brain by way of the *lateral olfactory stria*; the finer axons of the tufted cells pass through the *anterior commissure* to the opposite olfactory bulb (Fig. 96). The *granule cells* probably function as internuncial neurons.

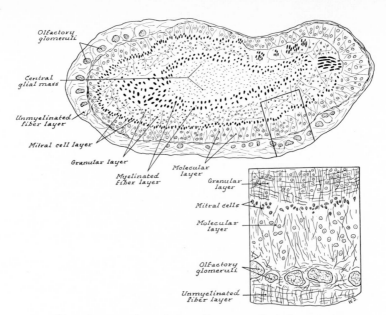

Olfactory
glomeruli

Central
glial mass

Unmyelinated
fiber layer

Mitral cell layer

Granular layer

Myelinated
fiber layer

Molecular
layer

Granular
layer

Mitral cells

Molecular
layer

Olfactory
glomeruli

Unmyelinated
fiber layer

FIG. 97.   Cross-section of the olfactory bulb (after Koelliker).

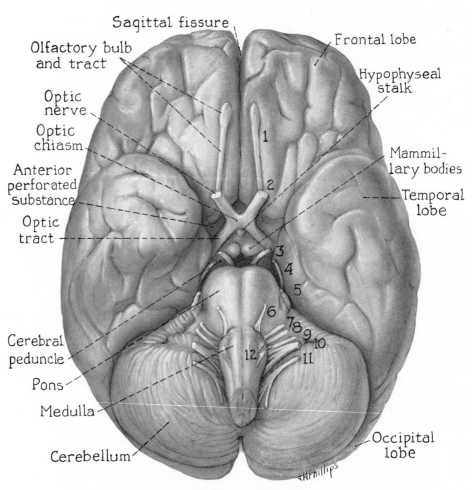

Saqittal fissure

Frontal lobe

Olfactory bulb
and tract

Hypophyseal
stalk

Optic
nerve

Optic
chiasm

Mammil-
lary bodies

Anterior
perforated
substance

Temporal
lobe

Optic
tract

Cerebral
peduncle

Pons

Medulla

Cerebellum

Occipital
lobe

1
2
3
4
5
6
7 8 9
10
11
12

FIG. 98.   Drawing of the brain showing the ventral surface.

(120)

The **secondary olfactory fibers,** by way of the olfactory tract and its two main divisions—the *lateral* and *medial olfactory striae*—terminate in the olfactory cortex. It thus appears that the olfactory pathway may include only two neurons —the first in the olfactory mucous membrane and the second in the olfactory bulb. At least one more neuron must be involved when the impulse is shunted to the opposite olfactory bulb through the anterior commissure and then relayed to the cortex from there (Fig. 96).

The **nervus terminalis** is closely associated with the olfactory nerve but whether it is olfactory in function has not been determined. According to Pearson (1941) and others the peripheral fibers of the nerve originate from ganglion cells in the *ganglion terminalis* and are distributed chiefly to the nasal septum and its epithelium. The ganglion, in the human embryo, consists of groups of cells along the medial border of the olfactory bulb. The central processes of the sensory cells in the ganglion have been traced into the forebrains of embryos. Multipolar cells, associated with the unipolar and bipolar sensory cells in the ganglion terminalis, are thought to have an autonomic function.

The smell brain, or *rhinencephalon,* has lost much of its importance as such in man and, for that reason, it will not be considered in all its manifold and complex details. In some of the lower animals the rhinencephalon is extremely important—so important that the very existence of the animal may depend upon it. Perhaps the greatest significance of the rhinencephalon in man is in the regulation of visceral functions and its involvement in emotional expression. The major aspects of its anatomy are described in Chapter 23.

BIBLIOGRAPHY

AREY, L. B., 1946: *Developmental Anatomy,* 5th Ed., W. B. Saunders Co., Philadelphia.

ALLEN, W. F., 1923a: Origin and distribution of the tractus solitarius in the guinea pig. J. Comp. Neurol., *35,* 171-204.

———— 1923b: Origin and destination of the secondary visceral fibers in the guinea pig. J. Comp. Neurol., *35,* 275-311.

BAGSHAW, M. H. and PRIBRAM, K. N., 1953: Cortical organization in gustation (Macaca mulatta). J. Neurophysiol., *16,* 499-508.

BARNES, W. T., MAGOUN, H. W. and RANSON, S. W., 1943: The ascending auditory pathway in the brain stem of the monkey. J. Comp. Neurol., *79,* 129-152.

BÉKÉSEY, G. and ROSENBLITH, W. A., 1951: *Handbook of Experimental Psychology,* S. S. STEVENS, ed., John Wiley & Sons, New York, Chap. 27.

BÖRNSTEIN, W. S., 1940-1941: Cortical representation of taste in man and monkey. II. The localization of the cortical taste area in man and a method of measuring impairment of taste in man. Yale J. Biol. Med., *13,* 133-156.

BUCHER, V. M. and BÜRGI, S. M., 1953: Some observations on the fiber connections of the di- and mesencephalon in the cat. Part III. The supraoptic decussations. J. Comp. Neurol., *98,* 355-379.

CHAMBERS, W. W. and SPRAGUE, J. M., 1955: Functional localization in the cerebellum. I. Organization in longitudinal corticonuclear zones and their contribution to the control of posture, both extrapyramidal and pyramidal. J. Comp. Neurol., *103,* 105-129.

CROSBY, E. C., HUMPHREY, T. and LAUER, E. W., 1962: *Correlative Anatomy of the Nervous System.* The Macmillan Co., New York.

EYSTER, J. A. E., BAST, T. H. and KRASNO, M. R., 1935: Studies on the electrical response of the cochlea. Am. J. Physiol., *113,* 40.

FITZGERALD, G. and HALLPIKE, C. S., 1942: Studies in human vestibular function: I. Observations on the directional preponderance "Nystagmusbereitschaft") of caloric nystagmus resulting from cerebral lesions. Brain, *65,* 115-137.

KEMPINSKY, W. H., 1951: Cortical projection of vestibular and facial nerves in cat. J. Neurophysiol., *14,* 203-210.

LEWY, F. H. and KOBRAK, H., 1936: The neural projection of the cochlear spirals on the primary acoustic centers. A.M.A. Arch. Neurol., Psychiat., *35*, 839-852.

MAGOUN, H. W. and RANSON, S. W., 1935: The central path of the light reflex. A.M.A. Arch. Ophthal., *13*, 791-811.

MICKLE, W. A. and ADES, H. W., 1954: Rostral projection pathway of the vestibular system. Am. J. Physiol., *176*, 243-246.

PATTON, H. D., RUCH, T. C. and WALKER, A. E., 1944: Experimental hypogeusia from Horsley-Clarke lesions of the thalamus in *Macaca mulatta*. J. Neurophysiol., *7*, 171-184.

PATTON, H. D. and RUCH, T. C., 1946: The relation of the foot of the pre- and postcentral gyrus to taste in the monkey and chimpanzee. Fed. Proc., *5*, 79.

PEARCE, G. W. and GLEES, P., 1953: Experimental studies on the descending tectal pathways of the cat. J. Anat., *87*, 443.

PEARSON, A. A., 1941: The development of the nervus terminalis in man. J. Comp. Neurol., *75*, 39-66.

PENFIELD, W. and RASMUSSEN, T., 1950: *The Cerebral Cortex of Man*, The Macmillan Co., New York.

PURVES-STEWART, J. and WORSTER-DROUGHT, C., 1952: *The Diagnosis of Nervous Diseases*, 10th Ed., Edward Arnold Co., London.

ROSE, J. E., GALAMBOS, R. and HUGHES, J. R., 1957: Tonotopic organization of frequency sensitive units in the cochlear nuclei of the cat. Anat. Rec., *127*, 358.

STEVENS, S. S., DAVIS, H. and LURIE, M. H., 1935: The localization of pitch perception on the basilar membrane. J. Gen. Psychol., *13*, 297-315.

STOTLER, W. A., 1953: An experimental study of the cells and connections of the superior olivary complex of the cat. J. Comp. Neurol., *98*, 401-431.

WALLS, G. L., 1942: *The Vertebrate Eye and Its Adaptive Radiation*. Hafner Publishing Co., New York.

Chapter 9

The Internal Capsule

ALL the pathways to the cerebral cortex, with the single exception of that for smell, have been seen to have relay stations in the thalamus; in the case of each pathway it has been indicated that the axon of the final neuron reaches the cortex by way of the internal capsule.

tively the retrolenticular and the sublentiform parts of the internal capsule.

The **internal capsule, in horizontal sections of the brain** which pass through the thalamus and lentiform nucleus, is seen to have the conformation of a widely opened "V" (Fig. 100). The point at

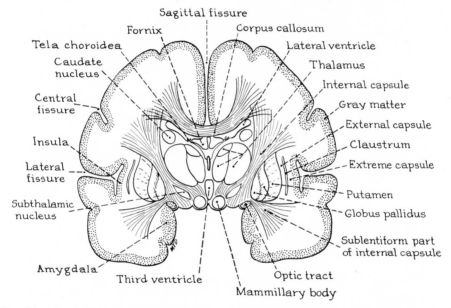

FIG. 99. Diagram of a frontal section through the brain at the diencephalic level.

The position of the internal capsule in frontal sections of the brain at the thalamic level has been noted. It will be remembered that its posterior limb is placed between the thalamus and the lentiform nucleus and that some of its fibers course laterally beneath the lentiform nucleus (Fig. 99). Visual fibers from the lateral geniculate body and auditory fibers from the medial geniculate body, to the cortex, traverse respec-

which the anterior and posterior limbs of the capsule meet is termed the *genu.* The *posterior limb,* because of its position between the thalamus and lentiform nucleus is often called the *thalamolentiform* or *lenticulothalamic* portion while the *anterior limb,* which lies between the lentiform and caudate nuclei, is designated as *lenticulocaudate.* The V-shape of the internal capsule is due to the conformation of the lentiform nucleus and

(123)

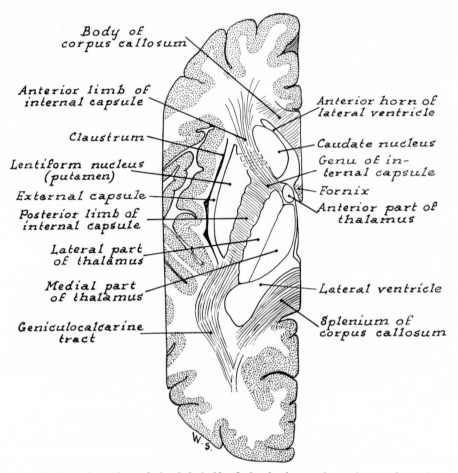

Body of
corpus callosum

Anterior limb of
internal capsule

Claustrum

Lentiform nucleus
(putamen)

External capsule

Posterior limb of
internal capsule

Lateral part
of thalamus

Medial part
of thalamus

Geniculocalcarine
tract

Anterior horn of
lateral ventricle

Caudate nucleus

Genu of in-
ternal capsule

Fornix

Anterior part of
thalamus

Lateral ventricle

Splenium of
corpus callosum

W. S.

FIG. 100.   Horizontal section of the left half of the brain to show the configuration of the
internal capsule (modified from Toldt).

to the positions of the thalamus and caudate nucleus.

The **lentiform and caudate nuclei,** together with the **amygdaloid nucleus** and **claustrum,** constitute the **basal ganglia** whose structure (and function, so far as it has been established) will be discussed later (Chapter 16). The caudate nucleus is continuous with the lower part of the rostral end of the lentiform nucleus (Fig. 101). From this origin it arches dorsally around the thalamus and finally terminates in relation to the amygdaloid nucleus in the roof of the temporal horn of the lateral ventricle. The claustrum is a narrow strip of gray matter lateral to the lentiform nucleus from which it is separated by the external capsule (Figs. 99 and 100).

The **anterior limb of the internal capsule** courses forward, upward and laterally through the space developed between the lentiform and caudate nuclei (Figs. 100 and 101). Numerous strands of gray matter connect the two nuclei and pass through the internal capsule (Fig. 100). They are responsible for the striated appearance of this part of the internal capsule and for the name—*corpus striatum* —which has been applied to the area composed of the two nuclei and the intervening limb of the internal capsule.

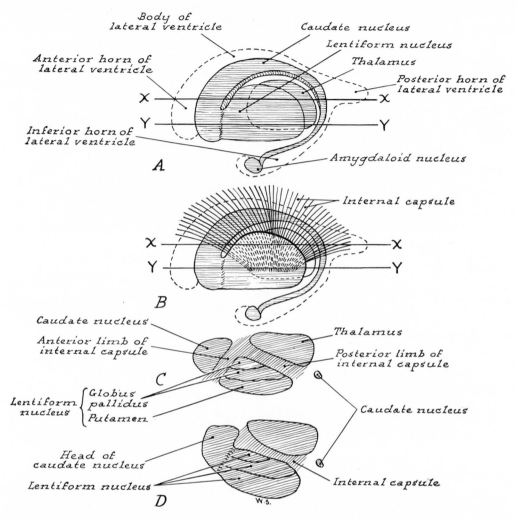

FIG. 101. *A*, Diagram of basal ganglia (not including the claustrum) as seen from the lateral side. The relationship of the lateral ventricle to the nuclei is indicated. *B*, Diagram of the basal ganglia to show the relationship of the internal capsule to its component nuclei. *C*, Horizontal section through the basal ganglia and thalamus at the level designated as "X" in *A* and *B*. *D*, Horizontal section at level "Y" in *A* and *B*. (Modified from Jackson-Morris.)

The internal capsule, as previously stated, contains *corticipetal* and *corticifugal* fibers; the former are processes of neurons in the thalamus, while the latter are the processes of cortical neurons.

Corticobulbar fibers course downward through the genu of the internal capsule (Fig. 102). Component fibers of the anterior limb (Fig. 102) include the *frontopontine* (of cortical origin), *ante-rior thalamic radiations* (thalamocortical), and *corticothalamic fibers*. The posterior limb (Fig. 102) contains *thalamocortical, corticospinal, corticothalamic and corticorubral fibers*. Other fibers in the posterior limb which are not indicated in the diagram are *corticotectal, corticonigral and corticotegmental fibers*. Thalamocortical fibers include those which branch off the posterior limb to course through the sub- and retrolentiform parts of the capsule (auditory and visual radiations).

The **Corticobulbar fibers** originate mainly in the motor and premotor areas of the cerebral cortex and terminate in relation to cells in the motor nuclei of cranial nerves. **Corticopontile fibers** arise in the frontal, temporal, parietal and oc-

Thalamocortical fibers in the anterior limb of the internal capsule arise from nuclei in all three parts of the thalamus and are concerned with visceral and somatic reflexes. Those concerned with visceral reflexes terminate in the more anterior areas of the frontal lobe where frontal corticothalamic fibers have their origin. Those having to do with somatic

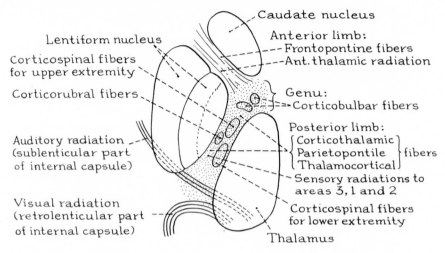

FIG. 102. Diagram to illustrate the parts of the internal capsule and the various fiber systems in the respective parts as seen in horizontal section.

cipital areas of the cerebral cortex and terminate by synapsing upon neurons whose cell bodies are in the pontile nuclei in the basilar part of the pons (Fig. 54). The corticobulbar fibers are concerned with the voluntary activity of muscles in the head region while the corticopontile fibers function in the coordination of voluntary muscles of the head, neck, trunk and extremities.

Corticothalamic fibers in the anterior limb of the internal capsule originate in the frontal lobe cortex and terminate principally in the medial and anterior parts of the thalamus. Those in the posterior limb originate from parietal, temporal and occipital cortices and end in the lateral part of the thalamus and in the geniculate bodies.

reflexes connect the lateral part of the thalamus with those cortical areas in the posterior part of the frontal lobe from which large numbers of corticopontile fibers originate. The relation of the latter to cerebellar reflex arcs will be considered at some length in Chapter 18.

The **posterior half of the posterior limb of the internal capsule** contains those *thalamocortical fibers* which reach the *general sensory* or *somatesthetic area* of the cortex. They therefore arise from the *posterolateral* and *posteromedial ventral nuclei* in the lateral part of the thalamus (Fig. 103). *General sensory impulses* from the head, neck, trunk and extremities reach the cortex by way of these fibers. Such impulses have previously been traced from the receptors to the

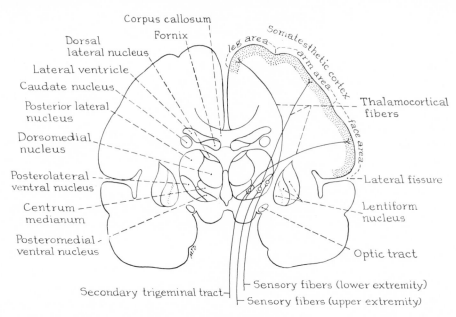

FIG. 103. Diagram showing the termination of sensory tracts in the nuclei of the lateral part of the thalamus and the projection of these nuclei upon the somatesthetic cortex by way of the internal capsule (modified from Ranson).

thalamic nuclei by way of the ventral and lateral spinothalamic tracts, the fasciculi gracilis and cuneatus and medial lemniscus, and the ventral trigeminal lemniscus.

A **nonspecific thalamocortical projection system** originates in the reticular nucleus of the thalamus which, as previously noted, is immediately adjacent to the internal capsule (Hanbery *et al.,* 1954). The multisynaptic extralemniscal cortical arousal system terminates directly or indirectly, through relays in centrum medianum (Fig. 103) and other intralaminar nuclei of the thalamus, in the reticular nucleus (Chapters 5 and 20). The most posterior part of the reticular nucleus projects to the visual cortex; in order from posterior to anterior, pro-

jections from the nucleus reach posterior parietal, anterior parietal (or general sensory), motor, anterior cingulate (Fig. 107) and extreme frontal areas of the cerebral cortex through both posterior and anterior limbs of the internal capsule. Thus the nonspecific sensory impulses necessary for alerting all areas of the cortex to "attention" may be diffusely projected to the cerebrum by way of the internal capsule in conjunction with the projection of visual, auditory and general sensory impulses to specific sensory areas.

BIBLIOGRAPHY

HANBERY, J., AJMONE-MARSAN, C. and DILWORTH, M., 1954: Pathways of nonspecific thalamo-cortical projection system. Electroencephalo. and Clin. Neurophysiol., 6, 103-118.

Chapter 10

The Cerebrum; A Descriptive Orientation

The **cerebrum** contains the highest centers of the nervous system and is the most massive portion; it occupies the greater part of the cranial cavity and covers the brain stem and cerebellum. It is divided into two lateral *hemispheres* by the *sagittal fissure* into which dips the double fold of dura mater known as the falx cerebri (Fig. 104). The *frontal* poles of the hemispheres project forward into the anterior cranial fossa and rest upon the orbital plates of the frontal bone. The *occipital poles* project posteriorly into the posterior cranial fossa where they rest upon the tentorium cerebelli (Fig. 104). The tentorium, which is also a double fold of dura mater, separates the occipital poles from the superior surface of the cerebellum. The *temporal poles* project forward and downward into the middle cranial fossa on either side of the body of the sphenoid bone; they rest upon the horizontal portions of the temporal squamae and the greater wings

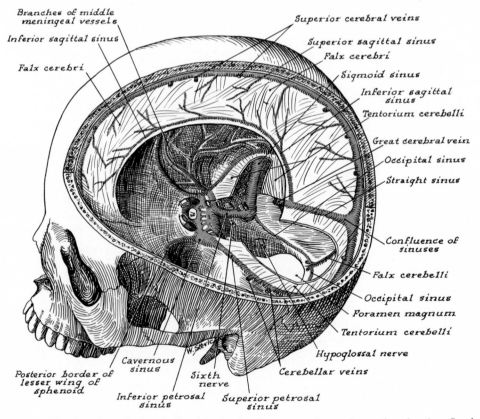

FIG. 104.   The interior of the skull with the brain removed to show the dural reflections.
(After Sobotta-McMurrich.)

of the sphenoid. Each cerebral hemisphere consists of a central core of white matter completely surrounded by gray matter. The gray masses (caudate, lentiform and amygdaloid nuclei and claustrum) which have been mentioned as constituting the basal ganglia are buried in the white matter (Fig. 105).

The **white matter** consists of *corticipetal (afferent)* and *corticifugal (effer-* those of association and commissural neurons.

Each cerebral hemisphere has three surfaces—dorsolateral, medial and inferior. The dorsolateral surface is in relation to the calvarium, the medial surface is in relation to the falx cerebri and the inferior surface rests upon the floor of the cranial cavity anteriorly and upon the tentorium cerebelli posteriorly. All

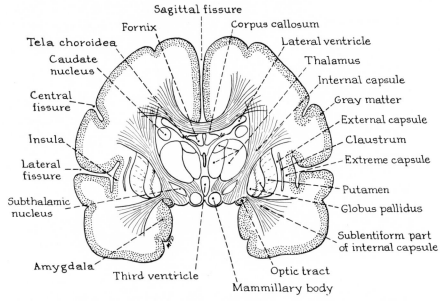

Fig. 105.   Diagram of a frontal section through the brain at the diencephalic level.

ent) projection fibers, association fibers which connect the neurons of one cortical area with those of another, and *commissural fibers* which cross from one hemisphere to the other in the massive *corpus callosum* and in the lesser *hippocampal* and *anterior commissures.* The corpus callosum is found at the inferior limit of the sagittal fissure.

The **gray matter,** or **cortex,** contains the cell bodies of neurons upon which the various sensory impulses are projected, those of neurons giving rise to corticospinal, corticobulbar, corticopontile and other fibers destined for lower levels of the central nervous system and

the surfaces are highly convoluted, thus increasing the cortical surface area. The convolutions, or gyri, are separated from one another by intervening fissures and sulci.

The **dorsolateral surface** is the most extensive and is markedly convex (Fig. 106). It presents two deep fissures and a number of sulci which divide it into numerous lobes and gyri. The *lateral,* or *Sylvian, fissure* begins on the inferior surface of the hemisphere, on a line with the optic chiasm; it courses laterally between the temporal and frontal lobes and, on reaching the dorsolateral surface, lies between these two lobes. It divides into *anterior horizontal, anterior ascending,* and *posterior rami;* the two anterior rami project forward and upward, respectively, on the frontal lobe; the posterior ramus continues posteriorly, at first between the frontal and temporal lobes, and then between the temporal and parietal lobes (Fig. 106). The *central,* or *Rolandic, fissure* begins about one centimeter pos-

trarily delimited anteriorly by a line drawn from the pre-occipital notch on the inferior border, to the parieto-occipital fissure on the dorsal border of the hemisphere. It is a triangular lobe with its apex at the occipital pole (Fig. 106). A second line drawn from the posterior limit of the posterior ramus of the lateral fissure to the midpoint of the first line

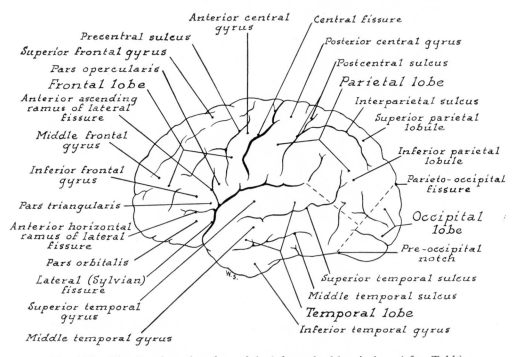

Fig. 106. The dorsolateral surface of the left cerebral hemisphere (after Toldt).

terior to the midpoint of the superior border of the hemisphere and extends downward and forward (Fig. 106). It forms an angle of about 70 degrees with the superior border and terminates at or near the posterior ramus of the lateral fissure. The central fissure separates the frontal and parietal lobes. The lateral and central fissures are constant in position, although the latter is sometimes interrupted at one or more points. Other sulci on the dorsolateral surface are subject to considerable variation.

The **occipital lobe** is more or less arbi-

completes the boundary between the parietal and temporal lobes.

The **frontal lobe** usually presents certain well-marked sulci which divide it into relatively well-demarcated gyri (Fig. 106). The *precentral sulcus* parallels the central fissure and forms the anterior boundary of the *anterior central gyrus.* The *superior* and *inferior frontal sulci,* which more or less parallel the superior border, divide the area anterior to the precentral sulcus into *superior, middle* and *inferior frontal gyri.* The inferior frontal gyrus is divided by the anterior horizontal and the anterior ascending rami of the lateral fissure into *pars orbitalis, pars triangularis* and *pars opercularis.*

The **parietal lobe** is crossed by the *postcentral sulcus* which parallels the central fissure and forms the posterior boundary of the *posterior central gyrus* (Fig. 106). The *interparietal sulcus* begins a little above the midpoint of the postcentral sulcus and extends backward

the median sagittal plane and the brain stem is then removed by cutting through the thalamus (Fig. 107). In such a preparation the remaining portion of the thalamus is partially surrounded by the *fornix* which, in turn, is partially surrounded by the *corpus callosum.* The corpus callosum, which constitutes the great commissure connecting the two hemispheres, is seen in cut section. It consists of an inferiorly placed *rostrum,* attached

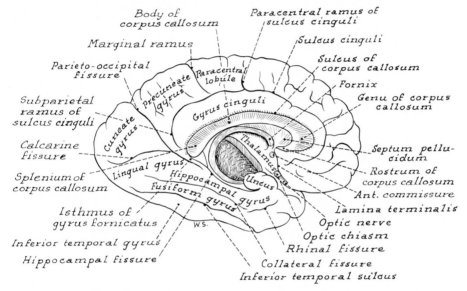

Fig. 107.—The medial surface of the left cerebral hemisphere (after Toldt).

and downward to terminate near the anterior boundary of the occipital lobe. It divides that part of the parietal lobe posterior to the postcentral sulcus into *superior* and *inferior parietal lobules.*

The **temporal lobe** is divided into *superior, middle* and *inferior temporal gyri* by the *superior, middle* and *inferior temporal sulci.* The inferior temporal sulcus is on the inferior surface of the temporal lobe (Fig. 108) but the three gyri are all visible on the lateral surface (Fig. 106).

The **medial surface of the cerebral hemisphere** can be examined in its entirety only if the brain is sectioned in

to the lamina terminalis, a *genu,* a *body* and a posterior, expanded *splenium.* Anteriorly the fornix is attached to the corpus callosum by the *septum pellucidum.* The fornix is a projection pathway from the hippocampi (within the temporal lobes) to the mammillary bodies and will not be discussed at this time. The thalamus, fornix, and corpus callosum, as they are seen in a median sagittal section of the brain (Fig. 107), are completely surrounded by the convoluted medial surface of the hemisphere.

The *sulcus of the corpus callosum* is in immediate relationship to that structure (Fig. 107) and is continuous around the splenium with the *hippocampal fissure*. The *sulcus cinguli* parallels the callosal sulcus and forms the peripheral boundary of the *gyrus cinguli*. It gives off a *paracentral ramus* which reaches the superior border a few centimeters anterior to the notch formed by the central fissure. The sulcus cinguli terminates by dividing into *marginal* and *subparietal rami*.

short distance above the occipital pole of the hemisphere. It gives origin, at about its midpoint to the *parieto-occipital fissure* which courses upward and slightly backward to end at the superior border. It will be remembered that the termination of the parieto-occipital fissure at the superior border, apparent on the dorsolateral surface, indicated the boundary between parietal and occipital lobes. On

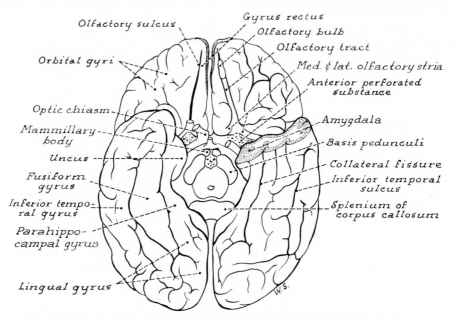

FIG. 108. The inferior surface of the cerebrum (after Toldt). The anterior part of the left temporal lobe, the brain stem caudal to the mesencephalic level, the right olfactory tract and bulb and the left half of the optic chiasm have been removed.

The quadrilateral gyrus between the paracentral and marginal rami of the sulcus cinguli is called the *paracentral lobule*. The anterior and posterior central gyri extend over the superior border into this lobule. The area peripheral to the sulcus cinguli and anterior to the paracentral sulcus is a medial extension of the superior frontal gyrus.

The *calcarine fissure* begins slightly inferior to the splenium of the corpus callosum (Fig. 107); from there it extends posteriorly and upward and then posteriorly and downward to terminate a

the medial surface the fissure itself serves to separate these two lobes.

The *precuneate gyrus* is bounded by the marginal and subparietal rami of the sulcus cinguli, the parieto-occipital fissure and the superior border. It is a medial extension of the superior parietal lobule. The triangular area between the parieto-occipital fissure and the posterior half of the calcarine fissure is designated as the *cuneate gyrus*. It and the *lingual gyrus* are continuous with the occipital lobe of the dorsolateral surface.

The *lingual gyrus* lies between the

calcarine and collateral fissures. The *collateral fissure* is on the medio-inferior surface of the temporal lobe. The lingual gyrus is continuous anteriorly with the *hippocampal gyrus* which lies between the collateral and hippocampal fissures. The hippocampal gyrus terminates anteriorly by curving around the anterior end of the hippocampal fissure. The resultant hook-shaped structure is known as the uncus (Fig. 108). It may be noted (Fig. 107) that the cingulate gyrus is connected to the hippocampal gyrus by a narrow convolution, the *isthmus of gyrus fornicatus*. The cingulate gyrus, isthmus, hippocampal gyrus and uncus comprise the *fornicate gyrus*.

The inferior surface of the temporal lobe, because of its obliquity, is not sharply delimited from its medial surface; the inferior temporal sulcus is therefore visible from the medial side (Fig. 107). The area between it and the collateral fissure is called the *fusiform gyrus*. The *rhinal fissure,* when present, continues forward the line of the collateral fissure and completes the separation of hippocampal and fusiform gyri.

The inferior surface of the frontal lobe of the cerebral hemisphere (Fig. 108) presents the *olfactory sulcus* about one centimeter lateral to its medial border; the olfactory tract lies in this sulcus. It may be noted that the olfactory tract divides into medial and lateral olfactory stria as it approaches the anterior perforated substance. The area medial to the sulcus is known as the *gyrus rectus*. Lateral to the sulcus the surface is irregularly convoluted and the convolutions are termed the *orbital gyri*.

Chapter 11

The Sensory and Associative Mechanisms of the Cerebral Cortex

THE **posterior central gyrus,** in the anterior part of the parietal lobe, is the *general sensory* or *somatesthetic area* of the cortex (Fig. 106). Sensory impulses from the contralateral half of the face, oral cavity, pharynx and abdomen reach the lower part of the posterior central gyrus; as has been observed, those from the face and oral cavity are brought to this area from the posteromedial ventral thalamic nucleus by way of the posterior limb of the internal capsule. The area for reception of impulses from the upper extremity is immediately superior to that for the eye and above it the head, neck, trunk and lower extremity are represented in that order from below upward. The foot and the genitalia are represented in that part of the posterior central gyrus that extends into the paracentral lobule on the medial surface of the hemisphere (Fig. 109). General sensory impulses from the areas caudal to the head reach the somatesthetic area from the postero-lateral ventral thalamic nucleus by way of the posterior limb of the internal capsule (Fig. 103). The posterior ventral nucleus of the thalamus (including posterolateral and posteromedial nuclei) may, according to Clark and Powell (1953), be assumed to be composed of a number of vertical laminae arranged serially in a lateromedial direction with each lamina receiving afferent impulses related to all modalities of general sensation from a specific region of the body. Those impulses from the lower limbs and perineal region are received in the most

laterally situated laminae and those from the head region in the most medially situated lamina with intervening laminae concerned with impulses from intermediate regions in a regular serial order. Mountcastle and Henneman (1952) described a similar arrangement of these nuclei.

In addition to being represented contralaterally there is considerable evidence to indicate that pain sense is, to a limited degree, conducted from receptors to the *ipsilateral* thalamus. At necropsy after hemispherectomy Austin and Grant (1955) found complete degeneration of the posterolateral ventral nucleus of the human thalamus. Yet, while these patients lived, retention of pain sense was observed. These authors postulated ipsilateral thalamic representation. Fulton (1949), in discussing the contralateral residual sensibility in hemispherectomized men and hemidecorticate monkeys, stated that the remaining crude sensation is due to both ipsilateral thalamic representation and residual thalamic function on the operated side. In the totally hemispherectomized monkey, as reported by White *et al.* (1959), the ipsilateral thalamus was completely extirpated and there was retention of pain sensibility. These preparations would seem to answer the problem in favor of ipsilateral sensory representation in the thalamus. Localization of pain remains poor in the totally hemispherectomized animals except in the face. The retention of painful reception and localization over the tri-

(134)

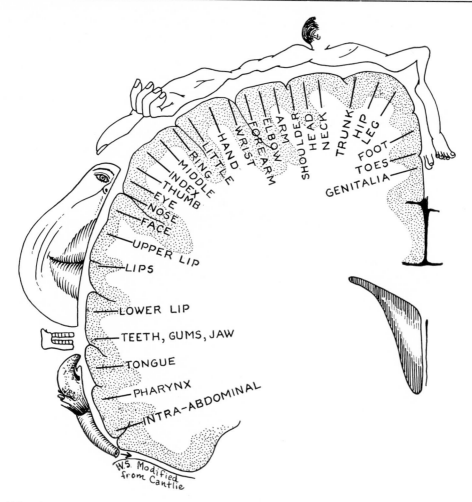

Fig. 109. Sensory homunculus showing representation in the sensory cortex (after Penfield and Rasmussen, *Cerebral Cortex of Man,* The MacMillan Co.).

geminal area has been documented in man after hemispherectomy. Little difference was found in the degree of contralateral hypesthesia between hemidecorticate and totally hemispherectomized monkeys. Light touch, vibratory sensation, position sense and placing reactions were measurably absent in both. This is in general agreement with the findings of Mettler (1943) and of Walker and Fulton (1938).

Perception of a given sensory stimulus probably involves considerably more than a simple synaptic termination of thalamocortical fibers upon a group of neurons in the sensory cortex. Chang (1950) has determined, electroencephalographically, that afferent impulses resulting from stimulation of peripheral receptors give rise, in the cortex, to periodically recurring cortical waves which he interpreted as the repetitive discharges of reverberating circuits between thalamic nuclei and the sensory cortex. A description of reverberating circuits as they probably exist within the brain appears on page 144; in addition to cortico-subcortical there are intracortical and subcortical circuits. The repetitive discharges described by Chang were abolished by interruption of corticothalamic connections, indicating their dependence upon a cortico-subcortical reverberating circuit.

Parietal lesions which involve the somatesthetic area result in the patient's failure to perceive weak stimuli, inability

the pain threshold does not result from a cortical lesion. When he had occasion to observe an increased threshold for pain or complete anesthesia in the presence of a cortical lesion he attributed these findings to shock or damage to subcortical structures.

It has been shown that lesions of the posterior ventral thalamic nuclei in cats

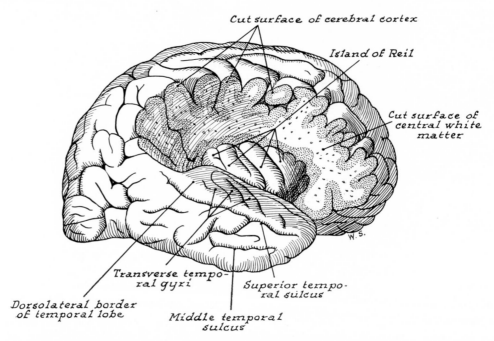

FIG. 110. Dorsolateral view of the right cerebral hemisphere with the lower parts of the parietal and frontal areas removed to expose the superior surface of the temporal lobe and the insula in the depth of the lateral fissure (in part after Sobotta-McMurrich).

to localize the point at which a perceptible stimulus is applied and loss of ability to differentiate between one- and two-point stimulation. Stereognostic sense and the sense of position are also impaired. The probability that pain stimuli are perceived at the thalamic level has been noted (Chapter 5). That this is true is indicated by the fact that pain sensibility is altered to a lesser extent by lesions of the somatesthetic area than are tactile and proprioceptive senses. Head (1918) stated that an increase in

account for supersensitivity of the sensory cortex (Spiegel and Szekely, 1954). Such supersensitivity may play a role in the spontaneous pain and hyperpathia *(thalamic* or *Dejerine-Roussy syndrome)* seen in man following lesions of these nuclei. The symptoms were thought to be due to the supersensitivity of the sensory cortex to afferent impulses reaching it via extrathalamic pathways, particularly those which may involve a relay in the hypothalamus. That this is not the only factor involved is indicated by the fact that ablation of the sensory cortex does not abolish thalamic pain (Spiegel, *et al.*, 1954). Thus the hypothalamus and its reverberating circuits through cortical areas other than the postcentral gyrus assume increasing importance in the normal and abnormal reactions of the individual to painful stimuli.

Electrical stimulation of the posterior central gyrus evokes accurately localized sensory impressions in the conscious human subject (Penfield and Rasmussen, 1950; Penfield and Jasper, 1954). A number of workers have also reported that it is possible to elicit discrete and complex movements by stimulation of the area with strong currents. Such movements may be mainly facilitated by association neurons whose axons connect the soma-testhetic area with the motor and premotor areas of the cortex.

The **auditory area** of the cortex is buried in the posterior ramus of the lateral fissure. The posterior half of the superior surface of the superior temporal gyrus, forming the lower boundary of the lateral fissure, presents two or three transverse gyri (Fig. 110). The most anterior of these gyri is usually more prominent than the others; it is referred to as the *convolution of Heschl* and it constitutes the cortical center for hearing. Auditory impulses reach the area from the medial geniculate body by way of the sublentiform part of the internal capsule (Fig. 99). Both ears are represented in the auditory area of either side.

Tumors in either temporal lobe which impinge upon the transverse gyri account for auditory symptoms; these include tinnitus and diminution of auditory acuity which are almost always manifested bilaterally, and auditory hallucinations. Such tumors are also likely to produce visual and olfactory symptoms. The visual symptoms are due to pressure upon the geniculocalcarine fibers (Fig. 95) and the olfactory disturbances re-sult from involvement of the olfactory cortex on the medial side of the temporal lobe (uncus and hippocampal gyrus).

Unilateral destruction of the auditory area does not cause deafness but may, when done on the left side in right-handed individuals, result in inability to associate the usual meaning with the sounds heard; this condition is referred to as *sensory aphasia* or, more specifically, as *auditory verbal agnosia* (Schuell, 1953). Aphasia of sensory type occurred in sixteen of a series of sixty-two individuals with temporal lobe tumors reported by Strobos (1953); fourteen of these were right-handed with left-sided tumors while two definitely left-handed patients had tumors on the right side. The tendency toward concentration of certain functions in the left hemisphere of right-handed individuals or *left cerebral dominance* is a distinguishing characteristic of the human brain. *Motor aphasia,* manifested by loss of the faculty of vocal expression, is due to destruction of the *motor speech area* which is in the inferior frontal gyrus of the left hemisphere in right-handed subjects; it is also an indication of left cerebral dominance.

Stimulation of the auditory area, as previously noted, gives rise to roaring and buzzing sensations. Stimulation of the cortex adjacent to the auditory area gives rise to vertigo and thus indicates that vestibular impulses are also projected upon temporal areas. Spiegel (1934) described the **vestibular area** as lying just medial to the auditory gyrus and, as previously mentioned, Mickle and Ades (1954) found it to be adjacent to, and actually overlapping, the auditory area in the cat. Massopust and Daigle (1960) described an area anterior to the auditory area of the cat, to which impulses, predominantly crossed, were projected from the medial and spinal vestibular nuclei. Vertigo was a symptom in eleven of the sixty-two cases of temporal lobe tumor reported by Strobos (1953); nystagmus appeared in only four.

The **visual area** of the cortex is located on both sides of the posterior half of the *calcarine fissure* and on the ventral side of its anterior half (Fig. 107). It may extend around the occipital pole on to the dorsolateral surface of the hemisphere. Visual impulses reach the calcarine area from the *lateral geniculate body* by way of the *geniculocalcarine tract* (Fig. 95). *Macular* or *central vision* is projected upon the posterior limit of the calcarine area. Concentric zones, progressing anteriorly from this point, represent successively more peripheral areas of the retina and the peripheral limits of the retina are therefore represented at the anterior limit of the calcarine fissure. Visual impulses originating in the upper quadrants of the retina are projected upon the upper portion of the visual cortex and those originating in the lower quadrants are projected upon the lower portion. Accordingly, the right upper quadrants of both retinae send impulses to the upper half of the right visual area and the right lower quadrants send them to its lower half. The former respond to visual stimuli from the left lower quadrants of the visual fields and the latter to those from the left upper quadrants.

Destruction of the calcarine cortex of one hemisphere results in contralateral homonymous hemianopia which may differ from that due to a complete lesion of one optic tract (Fig. 95, 7) in that macular or central vision is not lost. No satisfactory explanation has been advanced for the persistence of central vision in such cortical lesions. Bilateral representation of the macula has most frequently been presumed to be responsible for the phenomenon but anatomical evidence of such representation is lacking. Some workers have asserted that the sparing of macular vision in cortical le-

sions is a misconception that has arisen because lesions interpreted as completely destroying the calcarine cortex have not actually been that extensive. Foerster (1929) and Halstead *et al.* (1940) have reported cases of complete unilateral occipital lobectomy in which there was no macular sparing.

Brodmann and others have charted the various areas of the cerebral cortex on the basis of cyto-architecture and have designated each area by number. The somatesthetic area, in Brodmann's chart (Fig. 111), comprises numbered Areas 3, 1 and 2; the auditory area is numbered 41 and the visual cortex occupies Area 17. Perception of specific modalities has been demonstrated to be the function of these cortical areas; integration and association of similar and dissimilar sensory impulses are functions of association areas. General sensory impulses are integrated in the parietal cortex posterior to the posterior central gyrus with the result that the individual is enabled to differentiate between areas stimulated, between degrees of stimulation and even between types of tactile, pain, or proprioceptive stimuli applied; particularly concerned with this discriminatory function are Areas 5 and 7 (Fig. 111).

Auditory association areas include those designated as 42 and 22; on the dominant side these areas relate sounds (or words) heard at a given time with those heard at other times during the life of the individual and thus facilitate the interpretation of these sounds as they apply to the environment which obtains at any given moment in his existence. Nielsen (1953) has reported the case of a woman with thrombosis of branches of the left middle cerebral artery (which supply the superior temporal gyrus) who failed, during the acute and early chronic stages of the vascular occlusion, to comprehend the spoken word; eventually she recovered the ability to understand

and to verbalize intelligently. Two years after her first episode she suffered a thrombosis of the right middle cerebral artery and became permanently aphasic; the obvious interpretation, supported by autopsy findings, was that Areas 42 and 22 on the right side of the brain were able, after their destruction on the domi-nant side, to take over to some extent the gnostic functions which were affected by the original left-sided thrombosis.

Electrical *stimulation of the visual cortex* (Area 17) in the conscious subject gives rise to impressions of pin-points of light in corresponding loci in the fields of vision; *stimulation of the peristriate*

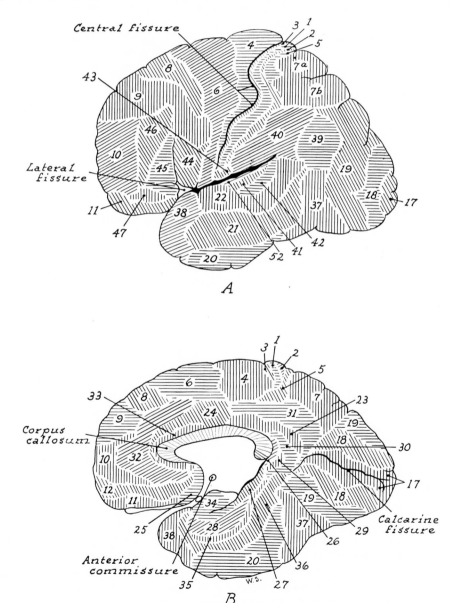

Fig. 111.   Structurally distinctive areas of the human cerebral cortex (modified from Brodmann). *A*, Dorsolateral surface. *B*, Medial surface.

area (Area 18, Fig. 111) produces integration to the extent of organization of the more primitive impressions elicited from Area 17 into geometric figures; *stimulation of Area 19* (Fig. 111) introduces color and definitive form of familiar objects.

Retention within the brain of isolated sensory impressions, such that they can be recalled at some later time and compared with current impressions, may be facilitated by *reverberating circuits* within the cortex and subjacent white matter. In such a circuit the first neuron would be fired by a sensory impulse and would, in turn, fire the second neuron which would then fire the third and so on until the original neuron was again fired by the last neuron in the circuit (Northrop, 1948). Assuming that the time required for the nervous impulse to traverse the circuit is sufficient to permit each neuron to restore its energy through normal metabolic processes, the sensory impulse which originally fired the circuit may continue to exist within it unless and until the ability of one or all the neurons involved to restore energy between firings is interfered with by injury, vascular degeneration or some toxic factor within the brain. The association of many sensory impressions of the same or different types (visual, tactile, pain, thermal, etc.) may probably be accounted for by the participation of a single neuron in more than one reverberating circuit. Purposeful activities, governed by the integration of many sensory impressions and facilitated by the recall to the current conscious level of such impressions, are possible through connections of neurons within the numerous reverberating circuits with appropriate motor neurons.

Memory for past experiences, involving the simultaneous perception and integration of all types of environmental stimuli, appears to be concentrated in an area near the posterior limit of the temporal lobe. Electrical stimulation of this part of the dorsolateral surface of the cerebrum, which is essentially encircled by visual, general sensory and auditory association areas, gives rise to integrated recall of previous experience or previous thinking. Penfield (1952) said: "The demonstration of the existence of cortical patterns that preserve the detail of current experience, as though in a library of many volumes, is one of the first steps toward a physiology of the mind. The nature of the pattern, the mechanism of its formation, the mechanism of its subsequent utilization and the integrative processes that form the substratum of consciousness will one day be translated into physiological formulas." Recent studies suggest that for lesions of the temporal lobe to cause impairment of memory they must involve the hippocampal formation (Scoville and Milner, 1957). Furthermore, the reports of Penfield and Milner (1958) indicate that temporal lobe lesions cause loss of memory only when they are bilateral and involve both the hippocampal formation and parahippocampal gyrus. A further discussion of the hippocampus and related areas is given in Chapter 23.

Cobb (1952) has emphasized the similarities between memory and the electronic computing machines and has supported the generally accepted concept that a neuron circuit can be set in action by an incoming single impulse and that the circuit may then go on reverberating as long as metabolism supports it or until it is modified by other incoming impulses.

Arnot (1952) has advanced a reasonable theory of *frontal lobe function* which replaces the older theory that memory is dependent upon the integrity of frontal cortex and its connections with other cortical and subcortical centers. Arnot's concept is that the frontal lobes, which are without primary function such as mediation of sight or hearing, act secondarily through their connections to maintain or sustain emotional states, trends of association (judgment) and motor actions or the inhibition of such actions. The functions sustained by the frontal lobes are those which can be brought under voluntary control but may operate without the help of the frontal lobe. After frontal lobotomy, states of worry, fear, depression, tension and negativism are relieved and may be replaced by states characterized by excessive intake of food, outspokenness and lack of initiative.

The **cingulate gyrus,** on the medial aspect of the cerebral hemisphere (Fig. 111, Areas 23, 24, 33) is an important link in the system of cortico-subcortical reverberating circuits responsible for "emotional expression" (Nielsen, 1951). Bilateral lesions of the cingulate gyri account for apathy, akinesia, mutism, urinary incontinence, indifference to pain and, in the terminal stages, stupor and coma (Nielsen, 1951; Barris and Schuman, 1953). Frontal lobotomies and leukotomies (section of white matter of frontal lobe) only minimally affect the afferent and efferent connections between the cingulate gyrus and the thalamo-hypothalamic nuclei; therefore, depressive states, apparently due to overactivity of more anteriorly and laterally located circuits, may be relieved by such procedures with relative integrity of those circuits responsible for active emotional expression.

BIBLIOGRAPHY

ARNOT, R., 1952: A theory of frontal lobe function. A.M.A. Arch Neurol. Psychiat., 67, 487-495.

AUSTIN, G. M. and GRANT, F. C., 1955: Physiologic observations following total hemispherectomy in man. Surgery, 38, 239-258.

BARRIS, R. W. and SCHUMAN, H. R., 1953: Bilateral anterior cingulate gyrus lesions, syndrome of the anterior cingulate gyri. Neurology, 3, 44-52.

CHANG, H. T., 1950: The repetitive discharges of corticothalamic reverberating circuit. J. Neurophysiol., 13, 235-257.

CLARK, W. E. L. and POWELL, T. P. S., 1953: On the thalamo-cortical connexions of the general sensory cortex of Macaca. Proc. Roy. Soc., Lond., B, 141, 467-487.

COBB, S., 1952: On the nature and locus of mind. A.M.A. Arch Neurol. Psychiat., 67, 172-177.

FOERSTER, O., 1929: Beiträge zur Pathophysiologie der Sehbahn und der Sehsphäre. J. Psychol. u. Neurol., 39, 463-485.

FULTON, J. F., 1949: Physiology of Nervous System. 3rd Ed., Oxford University Press, New York.

HALSTEAD, W. C., WALKER, A. E. and BUCY, P. C., 1940: Sparing and nonsparing of "macular" vision associated with occipital lobectomy in man. A.M.A. Arch. Ophthal. 24, 948-966.

HEAD, H., 1918: Sensation and the cerebral cortex. Brain, Part II, 41, 57-253.

MASSOPUST, L. C., JR. and DAIGLE, H. J., 1960: Cortical projection of the medial and spinal vestibular nuclei in the cat. Exptl. Neurol., 2, 179-185.

METTLER, F. A., 1943: Extensive unilateral cerebral removals in primate: physiologic effects and resultant degeneration. J. Comp. Neurol., 79, 185-245.

MICKLE, W. A. and ADES, H. W., 1954: Rostral projection pathway of the vestibular system. Am. J. Physiol., 176, 243-246.

MOUNTCASTLE, V. B. and HENNEMAN, E., 1952: The representation of tactile sensibility in the thalamus of the monkey. J. Comp. Neurol., 97, 409-439.

NIELSEN, J. M., 1951: Anterior cingulate gyrus and corpus callosum. Bull. Los Angeles Neurol. Soc., 16, 235-243.

———— 1953: Spontaneous recovery from aphasia: autopsy. Bull. Los Angeles Neurol. Soc., 18, 147-148.

NORTHROP, F. S. C., 1948: The neurological and behavioristic psychological basis of the ordering of society by means of ideas. Science, 107, 411-417.

PENFIELD, W., 1952: Memory mechanisms. A.M.A. Arch. Neurol. Psychiat., 67, 178-198.

PENFIELD, W. and RASMUSSEN, T., 1950: *The Cerebral Cortex of Man. A Clinical Study of Localization of Function.* The Macmillan Co., New York.

PENFIELD, W. and JASPER, H. H., 1954: *Epilepsy and the Functional Anatomy of the Human Brain.* Little, Brown & Company, Boston.

PENFIELD, W. and MILNER, B., 1958: Memory deficit produced by bilateral lesions in the hippocampal zone. A.M.A. Arch. Neurol. Psychiat., *79*, 475-497.

SCHUELL, H., 1953: Aphasic difficulties understanding spoken language. Neurology, *3*, 176-184.

SCOVILLE, W. B. and MILNER, B., 1957: Loss of recent memory after bilateral hippocampal lesions. J. Neurol., Neurosurg. Psychiat., *20*, 11-21.

SPIEGEL, E. A., 1934: Labyrinth and cortex: the electroencephalogram of the cortex in stimulation of the labyrinth. A.M.A. Arch. Neurol. Psychiat., *31*, 469-482.

SPIEGEL, E. A. and SZEKELY, E. G., 1954: Cortical supersensitivity after lesions of the ventral thalamic nuclei. Fed. Proc., *13*, 143-144.

SPIEGEL, E. A., KLETZKIN, M. S., SZEKELY, E. G. and WYCIS, H. T., 1954: Role of hypothalamic mechanisms in thalamic pain. Neurology, *4*, 739-751.

STROBOS, R. R. J., 1953: Tumors of the temporal lobe. Neurology, *3*, 752-760.

WALKER, A. E. and FULTON, J. F., 1938: Hemidecortication in chimpanzee, baboon, macaque, potto, cat and coati. A study in encephalization. J. Nervous Mental Disease, *87*, 677-700.

WHITE, R. J., SCHREINER, L. H., HUGHES, R. A., MacCARTY, C. S. and GRINDLAY, J. H., 1959: Physiologic consequences of total hemispherectomy in the monkey. Neurology, *9*, 149-159.

Chapter 12

The Cyto-Architecture of the Parietal, Temporal and Occipital Lobes

THE perceptive, integrative and motor capabilities of the cerebral cortex are facilitated by surprisingly constant and logical laminar interrelationships among the several types of neurons located therein.

The cortices of the parietal, temporal and occipital lobes of the cerebrum are similar enough in cyto-architecture that they may be discussed as a unit. Lorente de Nó (1943) described seven cell layers (Fig. 112) in these cortical areas, as follows:

I. Plexiform layer
II. Layer of small pyramids
III. Layer of medium-sized pyramids
IVa. Layer of star pyramids
IVb. Layer of star cells
V. Layer of large deep pyramids
VI. Layer of spindles

The cyto-architecture of the sensory cortex, as described by Lorente de Nó, was based on Golgi stains of the brains of mice but he stated that changes in the proportions of his drawings would make them valid for the corresponding cortical regions of any other mammal, including man.

The **plexiform layer** contains horizontal cells (Fig. 112, *C*), a few cells with short axons (Type II of Golgi) and the terminal ends of dendrites from cells of deeper layers.

The **layer of small pyramids** contains small pyramidal cells and their dendrites (Fig. 112, *H*). The dendrites of cells in the deeper strata pass through this layer and some of the dendrites of Layer III terminate in it.

The medium-sized pyramidal cells in Layer III (Fig. 112, *D*) are similar to the small pyramids in the preceding layer and their dendrites give off branches in that layer. The chief difference between Layers II and III is that some of the afferent fibers from the thalamic nuclei (Fig. 112, *T.A.*) terminate in relation to the dendrites of the medium-sized pyramids in the latter layer.

The **dendrites of the star pyramids in Layer IVa** (Fig. 112, *A*) reach the plexiform layer and also give off collaterals within Layer IV. The **dendrites of the star cells in Layer IVb** (Fig. 112, *I*) are distributed entirely within Layer IV. **Both divisions of Layer IV** are characterized by dense fibrillar plexuses formed, in the parietal area, by afferent fibers from the thalamus and, in the temporal and occipital areas, by afferents from the medial and lateral geniculate bodies (Fig. 112, *T.A.*). Because the numerous star cells which occur in these plexuses have also been called granule cells, the whole of Layer IV is also known as a granular layer.

Layer V contains large, medium and short pyramidal cells (Fig. 112, *G, J, K*). The long dendrites of the large pyramids reach the plexiform layer while collaterals and basilar dendrites are distributed within Layer V exclusively. The dendrites of the medium pyramids end in Layer IV and therefore have numerous synapses with the thalamic and genicular afferents. The dendrites of the short pyramids end within Layer V.

Spindle cells of three types—long, medium and short—are found in **Layer VI** (Fig. 112, *M, F, L*). The long spindles have dendrites which give off collaterals in Layer VI and then ascend undivided and without further collaterals to reach the plexiform layer. The dendrites of the medium spindles end in Layer IV in relation to the thalamic afferents and those of the short spindles end in Layer V.

Afferent fibers from the thalamus, as

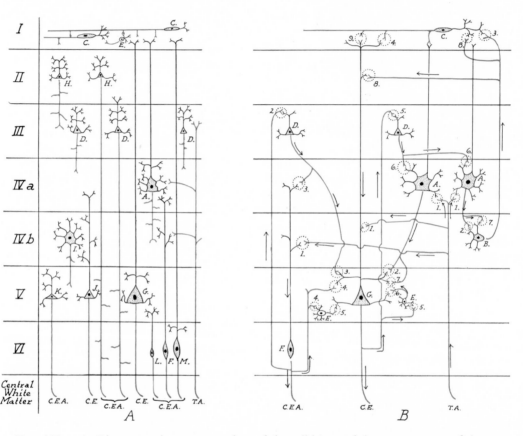

FIG. 112. *A,* Diagrammatic representation of the cell layers of the sensory areas of the cerebral cortex showing the distribution of the dendrites and axons of each type of neuron. Axons are colored red. *B,* Diagram to show some of the possibilities for neuron chains of varying lengths to bombard the large pyramidal cells with a given nervous impulse which enters the cortex over a thalamic afferent fiber (*T.A.*). Axons are colored red and, in order to avoid the confusion that would result from the use of several cells of a given type, the same cell has been utilized in two or more of the nine circuits depicted. A single impulse entering the cortex over the thalamic afferent fiber may be traced to one of the dendritic processes of the large pyramidal cell (*G*) through a single synapse (*1*) or through neuron chains containing 2 to 9 synapses.

Letters in both *A* and *B* indicate cell types as follows: *A,* star pyramidal cell; *B,* Golgi Type I cell; *C,* horizontal cell; *D,* medium pyramidal cell of Layer III; *E,* Golgi Type II cell; *F,* medium spindle cell; *G,* large pyramidal cell; *H,* small pyramidal cell; *I,* star cell; *J.,* medium pyramidal cell of Layer V; *K,* short pyramidal cell; *L,* short spindle cell; *M,* long spindle cell.

Axons in the central white matter are indicated as follows: *C.E.,* cortical efferent (projection); *C.E.A.,* cortical efferent (association); *T.A.,* thalamic afferent.

Synapses in *B* are numbered *1, 2, 3,* etc., according to their position in a given neuron chain. The direction of nervous impulses is indicated by arrows placed alongside the axon or dendrite concerned.

has been noted, chiefly terminate in relation to the star pyramids and star cells in Layer IV. *Association fibers* from other cortical areas, including commissural fibers from the opposite hemisphere, give off collaterals in the deep layers but their main areas of distribution are in Layers I to IV; the majority end in Layers II and III.

The axons of the pyramidal and star cells of Layers I to IV ramify chiefly within the gray matter but some of the axons of the former reach the underlying white matter and become association and commissural fibers (Fig. 112, *H, D*). The pyramidal axons also give off numerous collaterals, particularly in Layers V and VI. Axons of the large pyramids in Layer V become projection or association fibers. Those of the short pyramids are largely commissural and pass through the corpus callosum. Axons of spindle

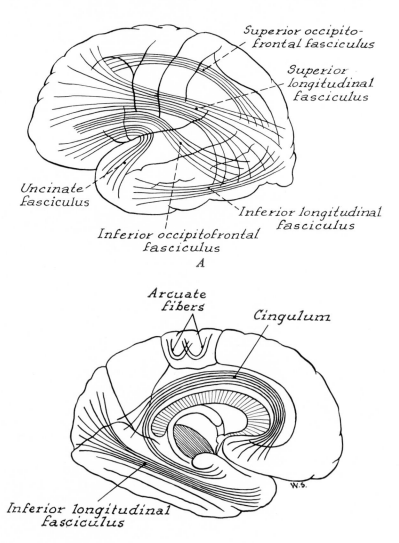

A

B

FIG. 113. Long and short association pathways within the cerebrum superimposed upon a dorsolateral view of the left hemisphere in *A* and upon a medial view in *B*. (*B* after Sobotta-McMurrich.)

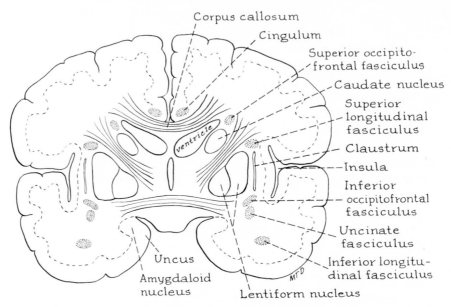

FIG. 114. Coronal section of the brain to illustrate the long association pathways in relation to other structures.

cells in Layer VI are distributed to other areas of the cortex as association fibers.

An older and perhaps more commonly used scheme with respect to the cell layers of the cerebral cortex is that of Brodmann (1909) who recognized two fundamental cortical types, *homogenetic* and *heterogenetic*. According to Brodmann, the homogenetic type shows at some stage during its development six characteristic layers, whereas the heterogenetic type never shows six layers and is more primitive or phylogenetically older (see Chapter 23). The six layers, according to the scheme of Brodmann (Fig. 115), are from the surface inward:

    I. Molecular
   II. External granular
  III. External pyramidal
  IV. Internal granular
   V. Internal pyramidal or ganglionic
  VI. Multiform or fusiform layer.

There are no fundamental differences in this scheme from that of Lorente de Nó given above.

Association fibers may be short or long (Fig. 113). The short association fibers connect adjacent gyri and, because of their course around and deep to the intervening fissure or sulcus, are often referred to as *U-fibers* or *arcuate fibers*. The long association fibers are arranged in rather definite bundles and connect more widely separated areas of the cortex. The six such bundles which are more commonly recognized include the *cingulum*, the *uncinate fasciculus*, the *superior* and *inferior longitudinal fasciculi*, and the *superior* and *inferior occipitofrontal fasciculi* (Figs. 113 and 114). The *cingulum* courses above the corpus callosum within the cingulate gyrus. It interconnects the orbitofrontal region with cortical areas throughout the extent of the fornicate gyrus. The *uncinate fasciculus* passes deep to the lateral fissure and interconnects the temporal pole region with the basal frontal cortex. The *superior longitudinal fasciculus* courses from the frontal area over the region of the insula and lentiform nucleus into the

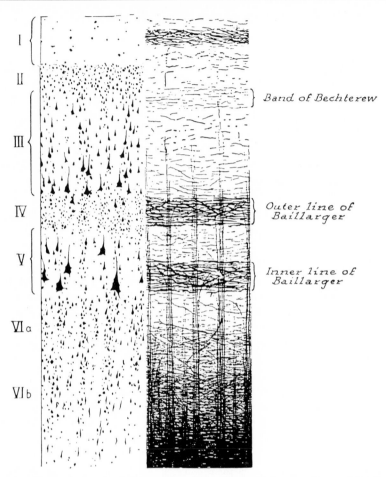

I

II

III

IV

V

VIa

VIb

Band of Bechterew

Outer line of Baillarger

Inner line of Baillarger

FIG. 115. Diagram to show the relations of the inner and outer lines of Baillarger and the band of Bechterew to the cellular layers of the cortex (Brodmann). In this figure (Brodmann) cell layer VI rather than IV is shown as being subdivided. The main layers, however, are identical to those described by Lorento de Nó and explained in the text.

temporal, parietal and occipital cortex. It contains many short fibers interconnecting these adjacent cortical regions. It is separated from the more medial and deeper coursing *superior occipitofrontal fasciculus* by fibers of the internal capsule as they continue into the corona radiata. The main bundle of fibers in the superior occipitofrontal fasciculus courses below the lateral border of the corpus callosum medial to the area at which callosal and internal capsule fibers interdigitate. This fasciculus interconnects frontal and occipital regions with temporal and insular cortex. The *inferior occipitofrontal fasciculus* lies above and adjacent to the uncinate fasciculus and courses below the lentiform nucleus and extreme capsule interconnecting occipital and frontal areas of the cortex.

The *inferior longitudinal fasciculus* extends from the temporal to occipital regions. Posteriorly, it is in relation to the more medially located system of visual radiations and considered to be a part thereof by some authors.

The **complex pattern of intracortical connections** is diagrammatically illustrated in the second part of Figure 112. A thalamic afferent fiber (*T.A.*) is shown entering the cortex from the subjacent white matter. Collaterals from this fiber synapse upon the ascending dendrite of a large deep pyramidal cell (*G*) and upon that of a medium spindle cell (*F*) within Layer IVb; its terminal divisions synapse upon the dendrites of star pyramids in Layer IVa. Numerous other possible connections with star cells and with Golgi Type I and II cells have been omitted for the sake of simplicity. The axons of the large, deep pyramidal and medium spindle cells, respectively, enter the white matter as projection (*C.E.*) and association (*C.E.A.*) fibers; collaterals from them ascend through the cortex to synapse upon the dendrites of Golgi Type II (*E*) and medium pyramidal (*D*) cells and upon those of large, deep pyramidal cells (*G*). Through the medium of the various cells and synapses depicted in the diagram a nervous impulse entering the cortex over a single thalamic afferent fiber may reach the dendrites of a given large, deep pyramidal cell through neuron chains which include from one to nine synapses. Two or more circuits have been directed through some of the cells in order to avoid the confusion which would result from the inclusion in the diagram of several more of each type of cell. Actually, many more cells (spindle, medium pyramidal, horizontal, star, and Golgi Type I and II) would probably function in the several neuron chains shown converging upon the large, deep pyramidal cell.

On the average, each synapse accounts for a conduction delay of 0.6 millisecond; therefore, the same impulse may be delivered to the pyramidal cell several times and at fairly regular intervals, depending upon the number of synapses crossed enroute. According to the ideas of Lorente de Nó (1943) and others "many of the impulses arriving at the synapse of a cell (by way of specific thalamic and other afferents) fail to cross the synapse because they do not reach threshold; but there is no evidence to prevent the assumption that any synapse is passable, provided that the conditions necessary for summation are fulfilled." Summation is accomplished through the neuron chains whose arrangement is such that each afferent impulse "causes the cortical cells to be bombarded by a succession of impulses, thus creating in them a constant state of facilitation, and eventually stimulating them to discharge into their axons."

It must be kept in mind that, in addition to the impulses from the thalamus to a given cortical area, there are also impulses arriving from all other areas of the cerebral cortex by way of association and commissural fibers. As has been mentioned, these fibers largely terminate in the second and third layers of the cortex but they may send collaterals to cells in any of the deeper layers that they traverse. Thus the afferent impulses from other cortical areas also reach the dendrites of the large pyramidal cells either directly or through neuron chains of varying lengths.

Feed-back, as applied to the nervous system means that the activity of the reverberating circuits is modified by the return of some of the out-put of the system as in-put (Cobb, 1952). When the hand is extended toward an object a series of signals flow back through visual, tactile and proprioceptive mechanisms to inform the central mechanism how far the hand is overshooting or undershooting. The amounts of error determine the return input until the error becomes zero. "A goal is aspired to and may be reached by means of a feed-back into a reverberating circuit. . . . Choice is acting on the basis of stored past experience (the 'memory' of the closed circuit) to cause a volitional act."

When stained with iron-hematoxylin the laminated character of the cortex is due to layers of myelinated fibers (Fig. 115). The concentrations of myelinated fibers have been given special designations. The *outer line of Baillarger* forms the outer part of Layer IV; the *inner line of Baillarger* is in the inner half of Layer V. The less prominent *band of Bechterew* is at the outer margin of Layer III. Baillarger's inner line is absent in the calcarine cortex but the outer line is especially well marked. The prominent outer line in this area is called the *stria of Genarri* and, because of this promi-nent stria, the calcarine cortex is often referred to as the *striate area*.

BIBLIOGRAPHY

BRODMANN, K., 1909: *Vergleichende Lokalisationslehre der Grosshirnrinde in ihren Prinzipien dargestelt auf Grund des Zellenbaues.* Leipzig, Barth.

COBB, S., 1952: On the nature and locus of mind. A.M.A. Arch. Neurol. Psychiat., *67*, 172-177.

LORENTE DE NÓ, R, 1943: Cerebral cortex: architecture, intracortical connections, motor projections. *In* Fulton's *Physiology of the Nervous System*, Chapter 15, 2nd ed., Oxford University Press, New York, pp. 274-301.

Chapter 13

The Motor Cortex and its Projections

THE **motor area of the cortex,** also designated as **Area 4,** occupies the posterior half of the anterior central gyrus (Fig. 111). It is broader superiorly than inferiorly and, like the posterior central gyrus, extends into the paracentral lobule on the medial surface of the hemisphere. Representation is similar to that in the somatesthetic area; accordingly, the area having to do with the motor innervation of the lower limb is superiorly placed and extends on to the medial surface while the head region is represented in the lowermost part (Fig. 116).

The **motor cortex** differs, structurally, from the parieto-temporo-occipital sen-

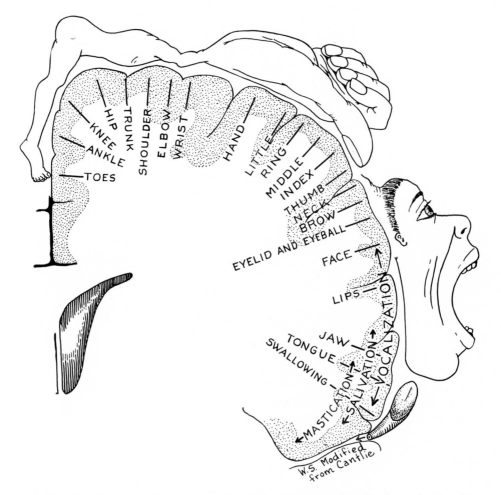

FIG. 116. Motor homunculus illustrating motor representation in Area 4 (anterior central gyrus). (After Penfield and Rasmussen, *Cerebral Cortex of Man,* The Macmillan Co.).

sory areas in that pyramidal cells are found in all layers except the outer or plexiform layer. In the posterior lip of the anterior central gyrus, layer V contains the *giant pyramidal cells of Betz* (Fig. 117). The axons of these cells along with those from other cortical pyramidal cells are distributed to motor neurons in the brain stem and spinal cord as *corticobulbar* and *corticospinal fibers* (Fig. 117). Corticobulbar fibers originate from the lateral and inferior portions of the motor cortex while corticospinal fibers originate mainly from the more superior parts. The Betz and other cortical pyramidal cells constitute the *upper motor neurons*. The *lower motor neurons,* upon which they synapse—either directly or through the medium of internuncial cells—are found in the motor nuclei of cranial nerves and in the ventral gray columns of the spinal cord.

When the motor centers in the brain evoke movement in muscle, descending nerve impulses may reach the muscles by either of two routes. The first courses directly, or through intercalated neurons, to large (alpha) ventral gray column cells and so to the muscles. The second, or indirect route, is responsible for excitation of the "small nerve" or *gamma-efferents* (Granit *et al.,* 1955). The latter route causes contraction of *intrafusal muscle fibers* (within the neuromuscular spindles), causing negligible tension as measured externally but sufficing to stretch the primary sensory endings in the muscle spindles and, through the stretch reflex arc (Fig. 39), to activate the main muscle fibers. This circuitous initiation of contraction introduces delay but has the advantage that, during shortening, the muscles are under the influence of the servo-properties of the stretch reflex. A constant rate of discharge over the *alpha route* sets up tension which is independent of length. The *gamma-efferent system,* however, is be-

lieved to operate a servo-mechanism which makes the main muscle follow length changes in the spindle. At a constant rate of gamma discharge the muscle will tend to maintain a fixed length independent of tension. The circumstances under which one or the other of these routes or various mixtures of the two are called into play are not known although it is probable that posture would mainly employ the gamma route and that rapid movements with minimum reaction time traverse the alpha route.

Experiments indicate that the relation of upper to lower motor neurons concerned with alpha-motor innervation of facial muscles and the distal muscles of the limbs is a monosynaptic one and that more than one synapse is involved in the alpha-motor pathway to proximal limb muscles (Bernhard and Bohm, 1954).

The **corticobulbar fibers,** as has been observed, traverse the genu of the internal capsule and the **corticospinal fibers** pass through its posterior limb (Fig. 118). From the internal capsule both sets of fibers enter the basis pedunculi of the mesencephalon where, except for a small medial bundle of corticobulbar fibers, they occupy its middle three-fifths (Fig. 119). Corticospinal, together with some corticobulbar, fibers are arranged in longitudinal bundles in the basilar part of the pons (Fig. 120). The bundles are intermingled with the pontile fibers and nuclei; collaterals from corticospinal fibers terminate in the pontile nuclei and thus provide for reverberating circuits through the cerebellum which return impulses to the motor cortex (Chapter 18).

Corticospinal fibers, after traversing the basis pontis, enter the pyramids of the medulla (Fig. 121). It should be noted that, throughout their course to this point, they have remained on the side of their origin. At the caudal limits of the pyramids 80 to 90 per cent of of them cross to the opposite side through

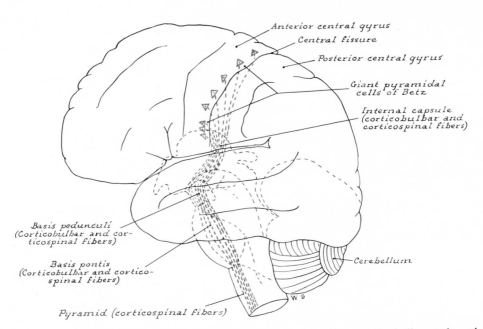

FIG. 117. Diagram to show the origin and course of some of the corticobulbar and cortico-spinal fibers. The descending fibers are superimposed upon a lateral view of the brain in which the positions of the brain stem and cerebellum are indicated by dotted lines. Corticobulbar fibers are colored blue—corticospinal fibers red.

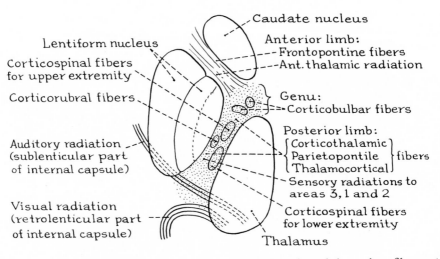

FIG. 118. Diagram to illustrate the parts of the internal capsule and the various fiber systems in the respective parts as seen in horizontal section.

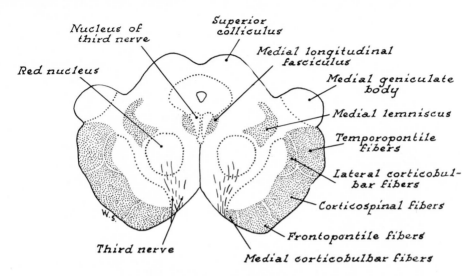

Fig. 119. Section through the mesencephalon showing the locations of the various types of fibers in the basis pedunculi.

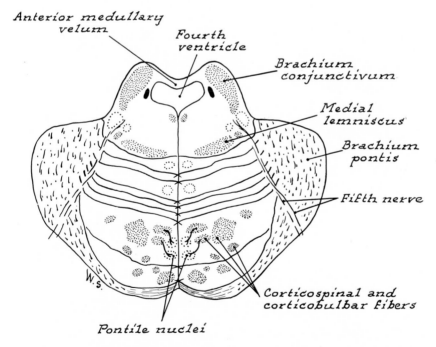

Fig. 120. Section through the rostral part of the pons showing the pyramidal fibers arranged as irregular bundles in its basilar part.

the *motor* or *pyramidal decussation* and enter the *lateral corticospinal tracts* in the lateral funiculi of the spinal cord (Figs. 35, 122 and 124). The lateral corticospinal tracts, like the sensory tracts, are specifically laminated; the most laterally placed fibers have the longest intramedullary course and end in the most caudal segments of the spinal cord.

Uncrossed corticospinal fibers (10 to 20 per cent) enter the ventral funiculi of the spinal cord where they form the *ventral corticospinal tracts* (Figs. 123 and 124). They also terminate in relation to ventral gray column cells but may cross to the opposite side through the ventral white commissure just before doing so. The ventral corticospinal tracts do not extend below the thoracic levels of the cord.

The **corticospinal tracts** are often referred to as the *pyramidal tracts* because they pass through the medullary pyramids. The pyramidal tracts are, in fact,

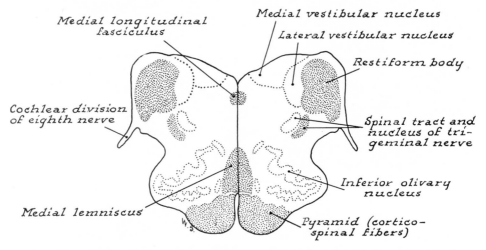

FIG. 121.　Section through the medulla showing the location of the corticospinal fibers in the pyramids.

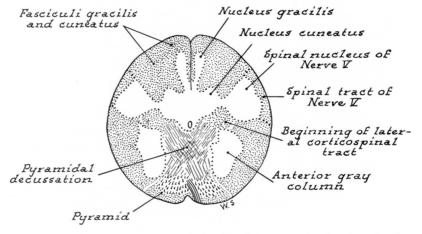

FIG. 122.　Section through the lower end of the medulla showing the decussation of corticospinal fibers.

by definition those fibers which arise in the cortex and pass through the medullary pyramids to the spinal cord. It is to be emphasized that these fibers do not arise solely from the giant cells of Betz, nor do they arise exclusively from area 4. Lassek (1940) has shown that there are approximately 34,000 Betz cells in each cerebral hemisphere and that each pyramid contains about 1 million axons. About 30,000 of these fibers are of large local anaesthesia (Chambers *et al.*, 1948).

Evidence for fibers within the pyramidal tracts which subserve functions other than motor has been provided by a number of recent anatomical and physiological studies. These studies indicate that the pyramidal tracts contain many fibers of cortical origin which serve to modulate sensory input at subcortical levels. In cats and primates, direct corti-

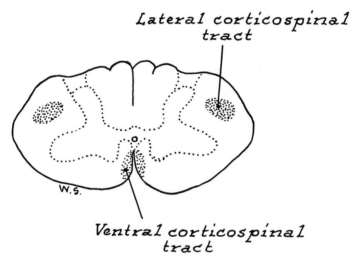

FIG. 123.   Section through cervical spinal cord to show the positions of the lateral and ventral corticospinal tracts.

diameter, 9 to 22 μ, which compares favorably to the number of Betz cells (Lassek, 1942).

From the various estimates that have been made, it appears that about one-third of the pyramidal tract fibers originate in area 4 and that approximately 20 per cent arise from cells in the post-central gyrus (Levin and Bradford, 1938; Levin, 1949). Area 6 has also been reported to contribute pyramidal fibers (Minckler, 1944) and studies in the monkey indicate an origin from areas 4, 6, 8, 3, 1, 2, 5 and 7 (Woolsey and Chang, 1947). Threshold movements have been elicited from stimulating area 4 and areas 6 and 5 of the monkey under cal fibers coursing via the pyramidal tracts have been traced to the dorsal column nuclei and to the spinal trigeminal nucleus (Chambers and Liu, 1957; Walberg, 1957; Kuypers, 1958a, b, c). Significantly, these fibers have been shown to modify the excitability of the posterior column nuclei (Towe and Jabbur, 1961; Jabbur and Towe, 1961a; Towe and Zimmerman, 1962). Peripherally evoked activity of neurons in these sensory nuclei can be either facilitated or depressed by stimulating the sensorimotor cortex in cats having complete brain stem transections except for the pyramidal tracts (Jabbur and Towe, 1961b).

The **corticobulbar fibers,** in gradually decreasing numbers, accompany the corticospinal fibers through the mesencephalon and pons (Fig. 124).

The fibers which accompany the corticospinals to the levels of the respective motor nuclei are considered as direct corticobulbars. Others which leave the corticospinal fibers at levels above the motor nuclei subserved and course caudally, generally in the medial lemniscus

to their termination, are designated *aberrant corticobulbars* (Dejerine, 1914). The corticobulbar fibers are functionally like the corticospinals and most decussate (note exception below) at or near the level of the motor nucleus in which they terminate.

Three main bundles of aberrant corticobulbar fibers are recognized; *aberrant fibers of the peduncle, aberrant fibers of the pons,* and *bulbopontile aberrant fibers*

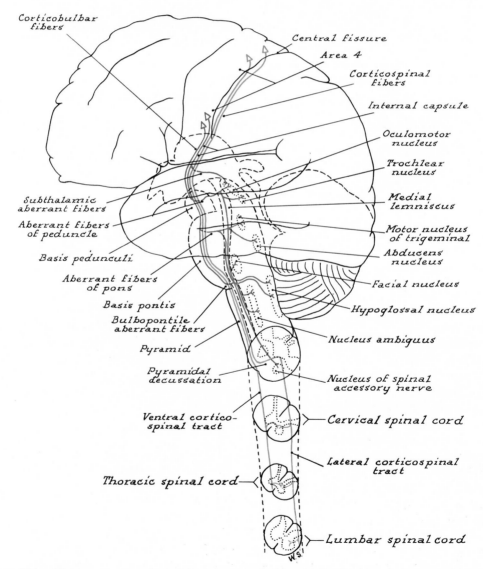

FIG. 124. Diagram to show the origin, course and ultimate distribution of the pyramidal and corticobulbar fibers. Corticobulbar fibers are blue—corticospinal fibers red.

(Fig. 124). A fourth and smaller bundle of corticobulbar fibers, given off in the subthalamic region, was designated as *subthalamic aberrant.*

The **aberrant fibers of the peduncle** leave the dorsal aspect of the basis pedunculi in the rostral part of the mesencephalon; they are distributed, by way of the medial lemniscus, to the nuclei of the contralateral third, fourth and sixth nerves and to the cells of origin of the spinal portion of the spinal accessory nerve.

The **aberrant fibers of the pons** separate from the pyramidal system in the rostral part of the basis pontis and enter the medial lemniscus; they are mainly distributed to the motor nucleus of the contralateral fifth nerve, to the nucleus ambiguus and to the hypoglossal nucleus. The *nucleus ambiguus* extends through-

out the length of the medulla and gives origin to special visceral efferent fibers of the ninth, tenth and eleventh nerves.

The **bulbopontile aberrant fibers** separate from the main mass of pyramidal fibers at the level of the junction of pons and medulla; they are distributed to the nuclei of the facial and hypoglossal nerves and to the nucleus ambiguus. The part of the facial nucleus which innervates the upper part of the face receives fibers from the motor areas of both hemispheres while that part from which the peripheral fibers to the lower muscles of the face originate, receives upper motor neuron fibers only from the contralateral motor cortex (Fig. 125). This is indicated by the observation that unilateral destruction of the lower part of the motor cortex or of the genu of the internal capsule results in paralysis of only the lower part

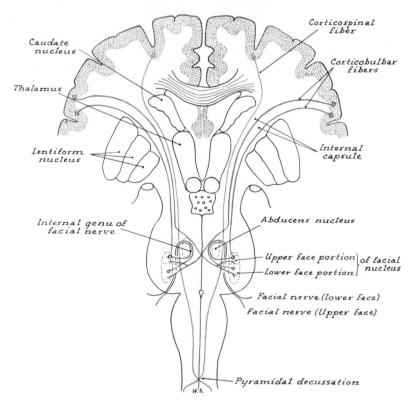

FIG. 125. Diagram to show the probable distribution of corticobulbar fibers to the facial nuclei. (In part after Villiger.)

of the face on the contralateral side. The orbicularis oculi and frontalis muscles still function bilaterally. Upper motor neuron paralysis of the facial muscles can thus be readily differentiated from lower motor neuron paralysis such as might result from destruction of the facial nerve in its canal; the latter type of paralysis involves all the facial muscles on the side of the lesion.

The **subthalamic aberrant fibers** are distributed to the rostral part of the oculomotor nucleus (Fig. 124).

BIBLIOGRAPHY

BERNHARD, C. G. and BOHM, E., 1954: Cortical representation and functional significance of the corticomotoneuronal system. A.M.A. Arch. Neurol. Psychiat., *72*, 473-502.

CHAMBERS, W. W., EVERETT, N. B. and WINDLE, W. F., 1948: Electrical stimulation of the cerebral cortex of the monkey under local anesthesia. Anat. Rec., *100*, 148.

CHAMBERS, W. W. and LIU, C. N., 1957: Cortico-spinal tract of the cat. An attempt to correlate the pattern of degeneration with deficits in reflex activity following neocortical lesions. J. Comp. Neurol., *108*, 23-55.

DEJERINE, J., 1914: *Semiologie des Affections du Systeme Nerveux*. Masson et Cie, Paris.

GRANIT, R., HOLMGREN, B. and MERTON, P. A., 1955: The two routes for excitation of muscle and their subservience to the cerebellum. J. Physiol., *130*, 213-224.

JABBUR, S. J. and TOWE, A. L., 1961a: The influence of the cerebral cortex on the dorsal column nuclei. Nervous Inhibitions —Proceedings of an Intern. Symposium. Pergamon Press, London, New York, pp. 419-423.

———— 1961b: Cortical excitation of neurons in dorsal column nuclei of cat,

including an analysis of pathways. J. Neurophysiol., *24*, 499-509.

KUYPERS, H. G. J. M., 1958a: An anatomical analysis of cortico-bulbar connexions to the pons and lower brain stem in the cat. J. Anat., *92*, 198-218.

———— 1958b: Corticobulbar connexions to the pons and lower brain-stem in man. An anatomical study. Brain, *81*, 364-388.

———— 1958c: Some projections from the peri-central cortex to the pons and lower brain stem in monkey and chimpanzee. J. Comp. Neurol., *110*, 221-251.

LASSEK, A. M., 1940: The human pyramidal tract. II. A numerical investigation of the Betz cells of the motor area. A.M.A. Arch. Neurol. Psychiat., *44*, 718-724.

———— 1942: The pyramidal tract. The effect of pre- and postcentral cortical lesions on the fiber components of the pyramids in monkey. J. Nerv. Ment. Dis., *95*, 721-729.

LEVIN, P. M., 1949: Efferent fibers. *In The Precentral Motor Cortex*, P. C. BUCY, ed., University of Illinois Press, Urbana, Chap. 5, pp. 135-148.

LEVIN, P. M. and BRADFORD, F. K., 1938: The exact origin of the cortico-spinal tract in the monkey. J. Comp. Neurol., *68*, 411-422.

MINCKLER, J., 1944: The course of efferent fibers from the human premotor cortex. J. Comp. Neurol., *81*, 259-277.

TOWE, A. L. and JABBUR, S. J., 1961: Cortical inhibition of neurons in dorsal column nuclei of cat, J. Neurophysiol., *24*, 488-498.

TOWE, A. L. and ZIMMERMAN, I. D., 1962: Peripherally evoked cortical reflex in the cuneate nucleus. Nature, *194*, 1250-1251.

WALBERG, F., 1957: Corticofugal fibers to the nuclei of the dorsal columns. An experimental study in the cat. Brain, *80*, 273-287.

WOOLSEY, C. W. and CHANG, H. T., 1947: Activation of the cerebral cortex by antidromic volleys in the pyramidal tract. Assoc. Res. Nerv. Ment. Dis., *27*, 146-161.

Chapter 14

The Lower Motor Neurons

LOWER motor neurons, in relation to which corticobulbar and corticospinal fibers terminate, were briefly referred to in the preceding chapter. They are found in the motor nuclei of cranial nerves and in the ventral gray columns of the spinal cord.

The **oculomotor nuclei** are located in the central gray matter of the mesencephalon, ventral to the cerebral aqueduct, and at the level of the superior colliculi (Figs. 126 and 63). Each nucleus gives origin to *somatic efferent fibers* which course ventrally through the red nucleus and emerge from the mesencephalon through the oculomotor sulcus on the medial side of the basis pedunculi (Fig. 126). The fibers of the oculomotor nerve, like those of the trochlear and abducens nerves, to be discussed subsequently, are classified as *somatic efferent* because they supply muscles which are derived from mesenchymal condensations homologous with head somites (Patten, 1953). *In its extramedullary course* the oculomotor nerve passes through the cavernous sinus and superior orbital fissure; within the orbit it is distributed to all the extrinsic muscles of the eye except the superior oblique and lateral rectus. Warwick (1953) studied the retrograde degeneration in the oculomotor nuclei which followed removal of one or more eye muscles. He found a marked degree of segregation of the neurons innervating individual muscles. Of particular significance was the finding that the unpaired caudal central area is concerned with the innervation of the levators palpebrarum.

The **trochlear nuclei** are found directly caudal to the oculomotor nuclei, at the level of the inferior colliculi (Fig. 127 and 61). The *somatic efferent fibers* from the trochlear nucleus course dorsally and somewhat caudally around the central gray matter and decussate to the opposite side through the anterior medullary velum. The *anterior medullary velum* stretches between the superior borders of the brachia conjunctiva and forms the roof of the rostral part of the fourth ventricle (Fig. 120). The trochlear nerve, after its decussation, emerges from the lateral margin of the velum and encircles the mesencephalon to reach the cavernous sinus. It courses through the sinus and the superior orbital fissure and ends in the superior oblique muscle of the eye. It is probable that the corticobulbar fibers to the trochlear nucleus are uncrossed; if not, the superior oblique muscle receives its cortical innervation from the ipsilateral hemisphere.

The **motor nucleus of the trigeminal nerve** is in the pons, just medial to the main sensory nucleus (Figs. 128 and 57). The fibers originating from it are classified as *special visceral efferent* since they innervate striated muscles derived from the mesoderm of the visceral (branchial) arches. Together with the proprioceptive fibers from the mesencephalic nucleus, they form the *portio minor* of the trigeminal nerve which, after emerging from the pons just rostral to the portio major, crosses the superior border of the petrosa, passes posterior to the semilunar ganglion, and emerges from the cranial cavity through the foramen ovale. The motor and proprioceptive

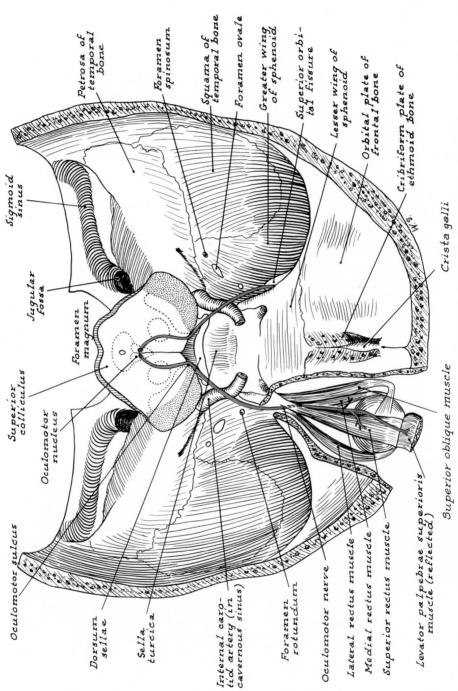

Petrosa of temporal bone

Foramen spinosum

Squama of temporal bone

Foramen ovale

Greater wing of sphenoid

Superior orbital fissure

Lesser wing of sphenoid

Orbital plate of frontal bone

Cribriform plate of ethmoid bone

Sigmoid sinus

Jugular fossa

Foramen magnum

Superior colliculus

Oculomotor nucleus

Crista galli

Superior oblique muscle

Oculomotor sulcus

Dorsum sellae

Sella turcica

Internal carotid artery (in cavernous sinus)

Foramen rotundum

Oculomotor nerve

Lateral rectus muscle

Medial rectus muscle

Superior rectus muscle

Levator palpebrae superioris muscle (reflected)

FIG. 126. Diagram of a part of the floor of the cranial cavity with a section of the mesencephalon *in situ* to show the origin and course of the oculomotor nerve. The orbital cavity and superior orbital fissure have been opened on the left by removal of portions of the orbital plate of the frontal bone and the lesser wing of the sphenoid. The distribution of the oculomotor nerve to the inferior rectus and inferior oblique muscles is not shown.

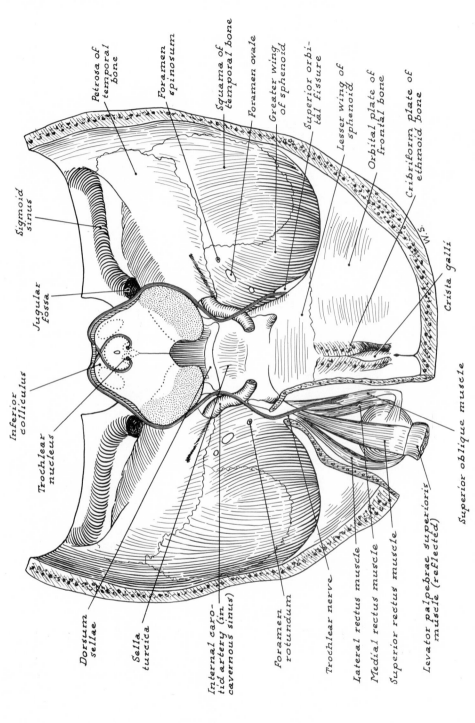

Fig. 127. Diagram of a part of the floor of the cranial cavity with a section of the mesencephalon *in situ* to show the origin, course and distribution of the trochlear nerve.

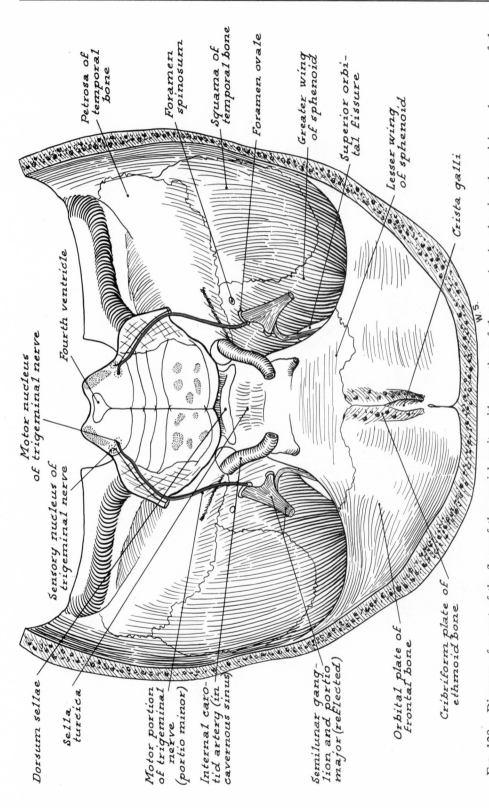

Petrosa of temporal bone

Foramen spinosum

Squama of temporal bone

Foramen ovale

Greater wing of sphenoid

Superior orbital fissure

Lesser wing of sphenoid

Crista galli

Motor nucleus of trigeminal nerve

Fourth ventricle

Sensory nucleus of trigeminal nerve

Dorsum sellae

Sella turcica

Motor portion of trigeminal nerve (portio minor)

Internal carotid artery (in cavernous sinus)

Semilunar ganglion, and portio major (reflected)

Orbital plate of frontal bone

Cribriform plate of ethmoid bone

W. S.

FIG. 128. Diagram of a part of the floor of the cranial cavity with a section of the pons *in situ* showing the origin and course of the motor fibers of the trigeminal nerve. The semilunar ganglion has been reflected forward to show the exit of the portio minor from the cranial cavity through the foramen ovale.

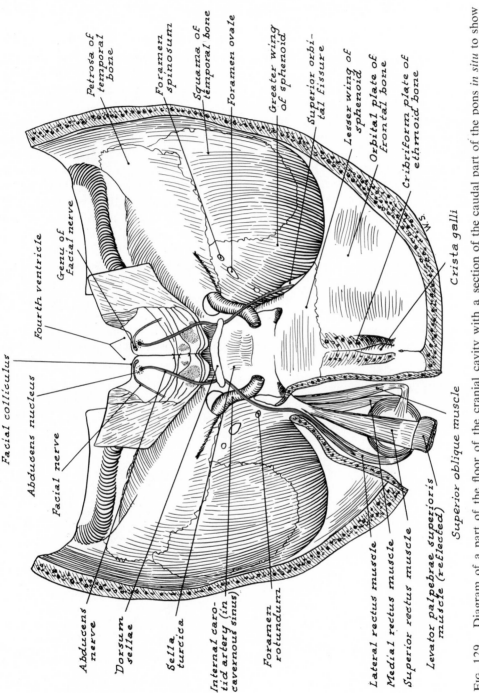

Facial colliculus

Abducens nucleus

Facial nerve

Fourth ventricle

Genu of facial nerve

Petrosa of temporal bone

Foramen spinosum

Squama of temporal bone

Foramen ovale

Greater wing of sphenoid

Superior orbital fissure

Lesser wing of sphenoid

Orbital plate of frontal bone

Cribriform plate of ethmoid bone

Crista galli

Superior oblique muscle

Levator palpebrae superioris muscle (reflected)

Superior rectus muscle

Medial rectus muscle

Lateral rectus muscle

Foramen rotundum

Internal carotid artery (in cavernous sinus)

Sella turcica

Dorsum sellae

Abducens nerve

FIG. 129. Diagram of a part of the floor of the cranial cavity with a section of the caudal part of the pons *in situ* to show the origin and course of the abducens nerve.

fibers are distributed to the muscles of mastication, to the mylohyoid muscle and anterior belly of the digastric, and to the tensors palati and tympani; those to the last two muscles reach them by way of the otic ganglion.

The **nucleus of the abducens nerve** is situated in the caudal third of the pons, beneath the floor of the fourth ventricle; it is more or less separated from the floor of the ventricle by the genu of the facial nerve (Figs. 129 and 55). The nucleus and the genu are responsible for an elevation in the floor of the ventricle known either as the *facial colliculus* or the *abducens eminence*. The *somatic efferent* fibers of the abducens nerve course ventrally and caudally through the tegmentum and basis pontis and emerge from the brain stem through the sulcus formed at the junction of the medulla and pons (Fig. 49). At its point of emergence the nerve is just lateral to the rostral limit of the

pyramid of the medulla. Its course from this point is forward through a notch formed at the junction of the temporal petrosa and the dorsum sellae and then through the cavernous sinus; it enters the orbit by way of the superior orbital fissure and innervates the lateral rectus muscle (Fig. 129).

The proximity of the motor ocular nuclei (oculomotor, trochlear and abducens) to the medial longitudinal fasciculi (Fig. 87) has been previously noted. The vestibulo-ocular connections by way of the fasciculi and their functions in eye reflexes and in the maintenance of tone in the eye muscles have been discussed (Chapter 8).

The **nucleus of the facial nerve** is ventrolateral and caudal to that of the abducens nerve (Fig. 130). Its neurons are included in the *special visceral efferent* group. The fibers originating in the nucleus course dorsomedially through

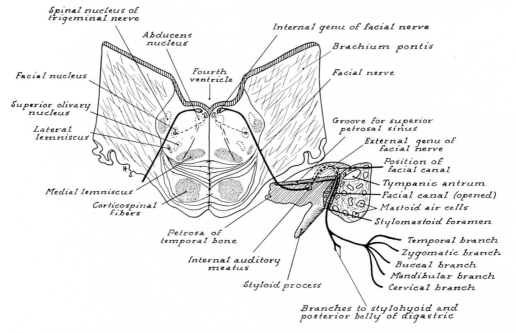

F1G. 130.   Section through the caudal part of the pons showing, diagrammatically, the origin and course within the pons of the facial nerve fibers. On the right the petromastoid portion of the temporal bone, sectioned through the descending part of the facial canal, is so oriented as to illustrate the course of the nerve from internal auditory meatus to stylomastoid foramen.

the tegmentum of the pons and around the caudal limit of the abducens nucleus. They then turn sharply forward and continue in that direction beneath the floor of the fourth ventricle and dorsomedial to the abducens nucleus for a distance of about one-half centimeter when they again change their course and pass laterally across the dorsal aspect of the abducens nucleus. After crossing the

the substance of the parotid gland, is distributed to the muscles of expression. The *external genu* of the nerve is in the facial canal at the point where the canal changes its direction from lateral to posterior (Fig. 130).

The **nucleus ambiguus,** so-called because it is not clearly defined in sections of the medulla, occupies a position dorsal to the inferior olivary nucleus (Fig. 131).

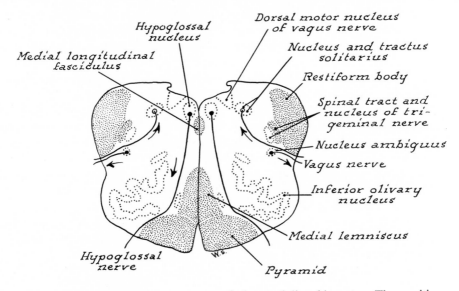

FIG. 131. Section through the open part of the medulla oblongata. The positions of the hypoglossal nucleus and nucleus ambiguus are indicated as are the routes of the efferent fibers arising from them. Sensory fibers of the vagus nerve are also shown entering the medulla and terminating in the nucleus solitarius. Direction of conduction is indicated by arrows.

nucleus they pass ventrolaterally and caudally through the tegmentum and basis pontis; they finally emerge at the sulcus between pons and medulla, some distance lateral to the point of emergence of the abducens nerve. That portion of the facial nerve in relation to the abducens nucleus is designated as its *internal genu.*

The **facial nerve,** after its emergence from the brain stem, courses through the internal auditory and facial canals; it leaves the latter canal by way of the stylomastoid foramen and, after having divided into its terminal branches within

As has been previously stated, it extends throughout the length of the medulla and gives origin to *special visceral efferent fibers* of the glossopharyngeal and vagus nerves and to some of those of the spinal accessory. The fibers unite to form a series of filaments that emerge from the medulla along the line of the dorsolateral sulcus. The ninth, tenth and eleventh nerves all emerge from the cranial cavity through the jugular foramen.

The **special visceral efferent fibers** of the *glossopharyngeal nerve* are distributed to the stylopharyngeus and superior constrictor muscles (Patten, 1953) and those of the *vagus* to muscles of the pharynx and larynx. Those of the *spinal accessory* (from the nucleus ambiguus) join the vagus and are also distributed to the pharynx and larynx. Other special visceral efferent fibers of the spinal accessory nerve arise from cells in the lateral part of the ventral gray column of the upper five or six cervical segments of the spinal cord, enter the cranial cavity through the foramen magnum, join the cranial fibers and, after passing through the jugular foramen, are distributed to the sternocleidomastoid and trapezius muscles.

The **nuclei of the hypoglossal nerves** are found in the medulla beneath the floor of the fourth ventricle, on either side of the median raphé (Figs. 131 and 45). They account for bilateral eminences in the floor of the ventricle known as the *hypoglossal trigones* (Fig. 34). The medial longitudinal fasciculi are immediately ventral to the nuclei. The fibers of the hypoglossal nerve (somatic efferent) course ventrally and somewhat laterally from their origin in the nucleus and emerge from the medulla just lateral to the pyramid (Fig. 131). The hypoglossal nerve leaves the cranial cavity through the hypoglossal canal and is distributed to the muscles of the tongue which are classified as somatic because of their derivation from occipital myotomes.

The **ventral gray column cells** in the spinal cord, with the probable exception of those which give origin to the spinal root of the spinal accessory nerve, are somatic efferent in function. Their axons emerge from the cord in the region of the ventrolateral sulcus and enter the ventral roots of the spinal nerves (Fig. 2). After traversing the ventral root and trunk of a given spinal nerve they are distributed by way of its ventral and dorsal divisions to striated muscles of mesodermal somite origin.

Somatic and special visceral efferent nerve fibers terminate in motor end plates (Fig. 17). Motor end plates are usually located near the midpoints of muscle fibers; they account for elevated areas on the fibers which are covered by sarcolemma. The neurilemmal sheaths of the nerve fibers appear to become continuous with the sarcolemma while the myelin sheaths terminate upon reaching it. Underneath the sarcolemma the nerve fibers divide into fibrils which form a network in relation to the sarcoplasm.

BIBLIOGRAPHY

PATTEN, B. M., 1953: *Human Embryology*, 2nd Ed., The Blakiston Company, Philadelphia.

WARWICK, R., 1953: Representation of the extra-ocular muscles in the oculomotor nuclei of the monkey. J. Comp. Neurol., *98*, 449-503.

Chapter 15

The Functions of the Motor Cortex and Motor Pathways

CORTICAL area 4 of Brodmann which extends mediolaterally along the precentral gyrus is known as the primary motor area (Fig. 133). As discussed in Chapter 13, this area is no longer considered to be the exclusive site of origin for the pyramidal (corticospinal) tract, nor is it the only cortical area concerned with volitional or skilled movements. Nevertheless, numerous studies, particularly those of Penfield and associates (Penfield and Rasmussen, 1950), have

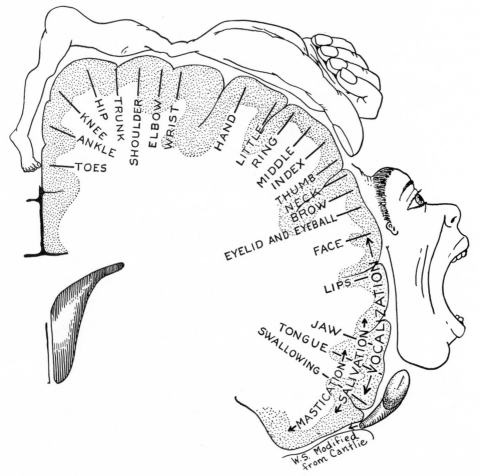

FIG. 132.   Motor homunculus illustrating motor representation in Area 4 (anterior central gyrus). (After Penfield and Rasmussen, *Cerebral Cortex of Man*, The Macmillan Co.)

shown that area 4 is most fundamentally involved in the execution of delicate movements. That electrical stimulation of the frontal lobe of man, particularly of the precentral gyrus, produced movements in the opposite limbs has been known for almost 100 years (Fritsch and Hitzig, 1870). However, the details of the representation of the body on the cortex as well as the functional implications of this somatotopic representation are still in dispute. Figure 132 shows the pattern of motor representation together with an indication of the amount of cortex concerned with various bodily parts. It may be noted that as in the case of

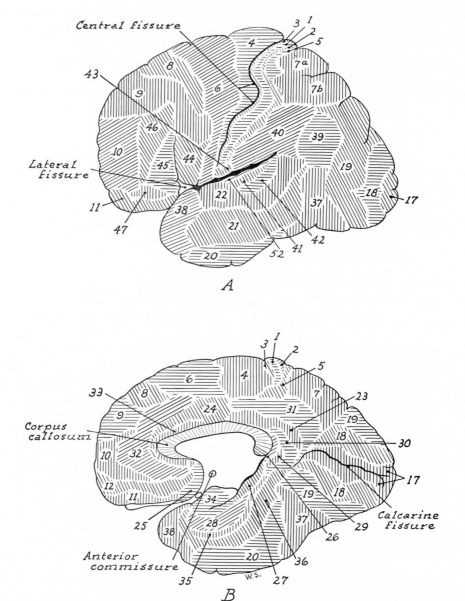

FIG. 133. Structurally distinctive areas of the human cerebral cortex (modified from Brodmann). A, Dorsolateral surface. B, Medial surface.

the somatesthetic cortex the body has an upside down representation in the motor area. The leg area is represented in large part medially within the paracentral lobule and the face area is represented inferolaterally. The arm representation is in between. The larger areas of the cortex devoted to those parts of the body with the capacity for the finer and highly controlled movements reflects the increased number of underlying cortical cells which activate or govern these movements. With respect to the often disputed question of whether functional organization in the cortex is in terms of movements or muscles, the studies of Chang *et al.* (1947) have shown that it is the latter. These investigators established that in the monkey motor cortex there is a focus of neurons surrounded by a field for each muscle and that the foci for two muscles never overlap, even though the field of one muscle may overlap the field for another. These studies supported by those of Bernhard and Bohm (1954) and the experiments of Patton and Amassian (1954 and 1960) lead to the concept that the different movements are organized through the many connections of intracortical neurons with the Betz and other pyramidal cells in the deep layers rather than through the arrangement of these cells (Ruch *et al.,* 1961).

There is general agreement amongst the various investigators relative to the mediolateral extent and pattern of somatotropic localization within the primary motor cortex. There is less agreement, however, about the extent of the area anteriorly. According to Woolsey *et al.* (1952), the axial musculature of the monkey is represented in cortical area 6; additionally, Woolsey *et al.* (1952) and Crosby *et al.* (1962) include a part of the frontal eye fields, area 8, in the primary motor area.

A small second motor area of body representation has been described which is located in the part of the precentral gyrus which extends along the upper lip of the lateral fissure (Figs. 134 and 135), Sugar *et al.* (1948), Lauer (1952), Woolsey *et al.* (1952), Penfield and Rasmussen (1950). A third somatotropic area of motor representation, the *supplementary motor area* (Figs. 134 and 135) has been described for man (Penfield and Welch, 1951) and for the monkey (Woolsey *et al.,* 1952). This area is located within the medial hemispheric portion of area 6 (Fig. 135). Little is known about the anatomical and physiological parameters of these lesser motor areas. There is recent evidence, however, that the supplementary motor area of the monkey exerts its effects through the extrapyramidal system and contributes no fibers to the pyramidal tracts (DeVito and Smith, 1959). No doubt, much of the confusion which exists relative to primary motor areas is due to the overlapping of cortical areas related respectively to the pyramidal and extrapyramidal system. (The latter is considered in Chapter 16.)

Capsular hemiplegia, due to destruction of fibers in the internal capsule, is the most common lesion in man which damages or destroys the descending system of cortical fibers. The clinical signs of capsular hemiplegia are: *paralysis* or *paresis* on the contralateral side, *exaggerated deep reflexes* (knee jerk, ankle jerk, and others which constitute responses to lengthening of muscles); *absence* of *abdominal and cremasteric reflexes*; and the appearance of the *Babinski sign*. The paralysis is at first flaccid in character and later becomes spastic. (Flaccid paralysis is characterized by lack of resistance to passive movement of an affected extremity and spastic paralysis by increased resistance. Absence of deep reflexes is ordinarily associated with flaccidity; an increased activity of

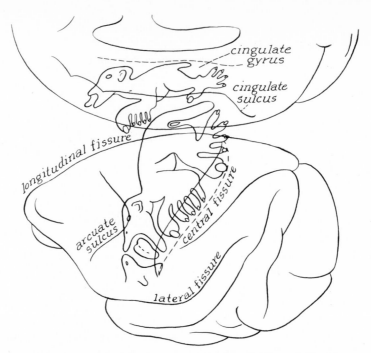

Fig. 134. Diagram to illustrate the somatotropic organization of the primary and secondary motor areas respectively in relation to the central and longitudinal fissures. The precentral and cingulate gyri have been rolled back to show the localization in the buried cortex. A dotted line represents the bottom and the solid line indicates the top of a fissure. An ipsilateral face area is shown inferiorly. Note that much of the primary simunculus and the major part of the supplementary area extend into area 6 of the premotor area (after Woolsely *et al.*, 1952).

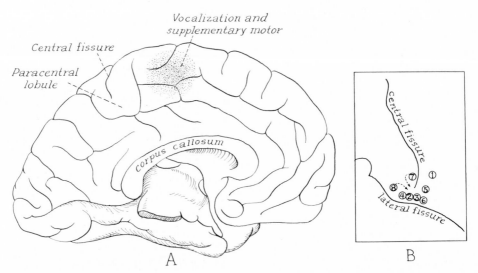

Fig. 135. Diagram illustrating the secondary motor areas in the human cerebral cortex. *A,* Vocalization and supplementary motor area on the medial surface. *B,* The secondary motor in the opercular region. Stimulation at 1 produced movement in hand of opposite side; at 2, desire to move contralateral hand; at 3, movement of contralateral hand and foot; at 4, desire to move hand on side stimulated; at 5, desire to move and paralysis of contralateral hand; at 6, desire to move and paralysis of contralateral foot; at 7, subcortical stimulation produced movement of ipsilateral toe; at 8, subcortical stimulation produced movement of contralateral hand (after Penfield and Rasmussen, 1950)

(170)

these reflexes is associated with spasticity.)

The abdominal reflex consists of ipsilateral contraction of the anterior abdominal muscles in response to scratching the abdominal skin on one side. The contraction of the muscles produces deviation of the umbilicus toward that side. Unlike the deep reflexes, the abdominal reflex is thought to have a cortical arc. The afferent impulses arising in the receptors in the skin of the anterior abdominal wall reach the parietal cortex and, according to Brock (1945), the frontal cortex as well. The efferent side of the arc is within or closely associated with the pyramidal tract and, for that reason, is interrupted by a lesion in the motor cortex or along the course of the pyramidal fibers. The reflex is either diminished or abolished, depending upon the extent of the lesion and such alterations may be limited to the lower half of the abdominal wall in pyramidal tract lesions at midthoracic levels.

The cremaster reflex is also of the superficial variety and probably depends upon a cortical arc. It consists of contraction of the cremaster muscle with consequent retraction of the testis in response to lightly scratching the skin of the inner side of the thigh.

The Babinski sign requires explanation; it is often referred to as a "positive Babinski sign," but this is a misnomer. When a blunt instrument is drawn across the lateral side of the plantar surface of the foot of a normal subject in a heel-to-toe direction, the toes are flexed (plantar flexion); the most striking degree of flexion is exhibited by the great toe. This is a normal reaction and it is correctly called the plantar reflex. When the same stimulus is applied in the case of upper motor neuron disease, there is an upward or dorsiflexion, particularly of the great toe, with or without fanning of the other toes. This is due to the contraction of physiologic flexors. This abnormal response is known as the *sign of Babinski*.

The Babinski sign in response to plantar stimulation occurs normally in infants. This may be due to the fact that the corticospinal fibers are not completely myelinated for a considerable period after birth (six to eighteen months or longer). Although absolute correlation between myelination and function of nerve tracts has not been proven, enough experimental evidence has been presented to warrant the assumption that incomplete myelination may be a factor in the dorsiflexion response in infants.

Exaggeration of the deep reflexes (hyperreflexia) has been explained in somewhat the same manner as the change in character of the plantar reflex. Deep reflexes include all stretch or myotatic ones of the phasic type. They are elicited by a sharp tap on the tendon or muscle. These function through spinal or brain stem arcs as has been previously explained. The knee jerk was described in detail (Chapter 5) and its arc is typical of the others. Although an exaggeration of these reflexes may result from inflammation or irritation at the segmental level, a persistence of the hyperactivity is usually due to damage of descending fibers which are inhibitory to the reflex. Fulton and Kennard (1934) and subsequent investigators have determined that in order for increased deep reflexes and spasticity to occur, there must be an involvement of the cortically originating extrapyramidal fibers. A discussion follows in the immediate section and in Chapter 16.

Lesions of the motor cortex or of its projections in man seldom, if ever, occur in pure form. For example, a so-called upper motor neuron lesion, of which capsular hemiplegia is the most common, involves both pyramidal and extrapyramidal fibers as these are intermixed within the posterior limb of the internal capsule (Fig. 118). (Reference to their proximity of origin and likelihood of some overlap at the cortical level was discussed above.) It follows that the only possibilities for interrupting pyramidal fibers in pure culture are at the medullary pyramids (Fig. 131) or at the cortex, *i.e.*, a lesion localized to the posterior part of the precentral gyrus (area 4). These localized interruptions of pyramidal tract fibers have been made in the monkey and chimpanzee and, in general, the results have been the same from removing area 4 or in sectioning the pyramidal tract (Fulton, 1949; Tower, 1940, 1949; Hines, 1937, 1949). The results of area 4 ablation were a deficit of voluntary isolated or fine movements with flaccidity rather than spasticity. There was no evidence of exaggerated deep reflexes. The results were confirmed by pyramidal tract sectioning. Flaccidity was apparent in both the monkey and chimpanzee although less in the latter. There was an absence of abdominal reflexes and the Babinski sign appeared in the chimpanzee. The status of the cremasteric reflex could not be assessed in the pyramidectomized chimpanzee which was a female. Since it is a superficial reflex, like the abdominal, it can reasonably be assumed to be absent following pyramidectomy.

From these experiments, it would appear that the remaining signs of capsular hemiplegia are attributable to damage of cortically originating extrapyramidal fibers. These include *spasticity, exaggerated deep reflexes* and some *paralysis* (gross movements). It is to be noted, however, that Foerster (1936) reported a return of brisk deep reflexes in the leg eight to ten days after small destructive lesions were made in cortical area 4.

Extrapyramidal pathways from the cortex to the brain stem and spinal cord

include *corticopontine, corticonigral, corticorubral, corticostriate, corticopallidal, corticotegmental, corticosubthalamic, corticohypothalamic* and *corticothalamic* fibers. Although some of these overlap in origin with the pyramidal tract fibers, they differ in that they are interrupted by one or more synapses in subcortical centers before neuronal contact is made at the segmental level. Another difference is that by definition these extrapyramidal fibers do not pass through the medullary pyramids. This system of fibers is considered in more detail in Chapter 16 along with the subcortical components of the extrapyramidal system.

The basis for the recovery of voluntary activity that follows after a lesion (*e.g.*, in the internal capsule) which supposedly interrupts all corticospinal fibers to a limb or entire side of the body has been of considerable dispute. No doubt the return of voluntary movement is in part due to recovery of function in neurons impaired only temporarily by edema or related phenomena of the pathologic process. As these tissue reactions subside, the neurons which were not permanently damaged could function normally. Additionally, since cortically originating extrapyramidal fibers support at least some complex voluntary movements, the non-damaged fibers of this system could be responsible for residual function.

Another consideration to be made relative to residual or so-called return of function is the extent of bilateral representation of muscles in the cortex.

All muscles may be represented to some extent in the ipsilateral motor cortex. Those of the eyelids, jaw and trunk, which act bilaterally, have the greatest degree of bilateral representation. The proximal muscles of the limbs receive less innervation from the ipsilateral cortex and those of the fingers and toes least of all. So far as the eyelids and jaw are concerned, their ipsilateral innervation may be accounted for on the basis of uncrossed corticobulbar fibers. In attempting to account for ipsilateral innervation of the trunk and upper extremity the first possibility that suggests itself is the uncrossed or ventral corticospinal tract although it is usually conceded that its component fibers cross through the anterior commissure, just before their termination, and end in relation to ventral gray column cells on the side opposite that of their cortical origin (Fig. 124). Lewandowsky (1907), however, found some ventral corticospinal fibers which failed to cross to the opposite side; such uncrossed fibers, terminating in relation to ipsilateral ventral gray column cells, might account for ipsilateral (cortical) innervation of the muscles of the upper limbs and trunk. The presence of some uncrossed fibers in the lateral corticospinal tracts, as reported by the same author could account for ipsilateral innervation of the lower extremities.

Bernhard and Bohm (1954) found, in monkeys, that monosynaptic relationships between upper and lower motor neurons were responsible for the individuality of movements in the distal hand muscles and that this monosynaptic system was only contralaterally represented in the motor cortex. They assumed, because stimulation studies on the human cerebral cortex by Penfield and Rasmussen (1950) indicated that only contralateral responses could be obtained by cortical stimulation, that a monosynaptic system, with contralateral representation, plays an even more important role in man than in the monkey for corticospinal activation of both distal and proximal muscles in the extremities. It seems probable that much of the ipsilateral innervation which has been attributed to Area 4 is actually a function of extrapyramidal fibers with their origins in adjacent areas of the cortex. Support for such an assumption is provided by the experiments of Bernhard and Bohm who found that the cortical field from which monosynaptic responses in a given nerve can be elicited is more restricted than those from which polysynaptic (delayed) responses can be evoked, and that the cortical field from which polysynaptic facilitation of a certain group of lower motor neurons could be evoked had a greater expansion anteriorly (presumably into Area 6) than the field from which monosynaptic responses in the same group of neurons were elicited.

The totally hemispherectomized monkey regains agility in standing, walking, and climbing but no resumption of function for finer movements has been seen. The hemispherectomized animal may actively grasp a wire screen with the contralateral fingers or toes but the contralateral extremities are never used for feeding, picking up objects or other fine motions (White et al., 1959). Nevertheless, the restoration of motor function in the monkey after total hemispherectomy gives credence to the theory of bilaterality of motor innervation. Bilateral movements from cortical stimulation have been observed by Bucy and Fulton (1933) and by Wyss (1938), in the monkey. Bates (1953) produced ipsilateral movements upon stimulation of the medial surface of the human hemisphere. It is probable that the residuals of motor function observed after human hemispherectomy, as in the monkey, may be explained, at least in part, on the basis of ipsilateral cortical innervation travelling via the direct, uncrossed pyramidal tract although it is recognized that removal of a hemisphere in the human is not as complete as that accomplished in the monkey (White et al., 1959).

BIBLIOGRAPHY

BATES, J. A. V., 1953: Stimulation of medial surface of human cerebral hemisphere after hemispherectomy. Brain, *76*, 405-447.

BERNHARD, C. G. and BOHM, E., 1954: Cortical representation and functional significance of the corticomotoneuronal system. A.M.A. Arch. Neurol. Psychiat., *72*, 473-502.

BROCK, S., 1945: *The Basis of Clinical Neurology*. 2nd Ed., Williams & Wilkins Co., Baltimore.

BUCY, P. C. and FULTON, J. F., 1933: Ipsilateral representation in motor and premotor cortex of monkeys. Brain, *56*, 318-342.

CHANG, H. T., RUCH, T. C. and WARD, A. A., JR., 1947: Topographical representation of muscles in motor cortex of monkeys. J. Neurophysiol., *10*, 39-56.

CROSBY, E. C., HUMPHREY, T. and LAUER, E. W., 1962: *Correlative Anatomy of the Nervous System*. The Macmillan Co., New York.

DEVITO, J. L. and SMITH, O. A., JR., 1959: Projections from the mesial frontal cortex (supplementary motor area) to the cerebral hemispheres and brain stem of the *Macaca mulatta*. J. Comp. Neurol., *111*, 261-277.

FOERSTER, O., 1936: The motor cortex in man in the light of Hughlings Jackson's doctrines. Brain, *59*, 135-159.

FRITSCH, G. and HITZIG, E., 1870: Über die elektrische Erregbarkiet des Grosshirns, Arch. Anat. u. Physiol., *37*, 300-332.

FULTON, J. F. and KENNARD, M. A., 1934: A study of flaccid and spastic paralyses produced by lesions of the cerebral cortex in primates. Assoc. Res. Nerv. Ment. Dis., *13*, 158-210.

FULTON, J. F., 1949: *Physiology of Nervous System*. 3rd Ed., Oxford University Press, New York.

HINES, M., 1937: The "motor" cortex. Bull. Johns Hopkins Hosp., *60*, 313-336.

———— 1949: Significance of the precentral motor cortex. *In The Precentral Motor Cortex*. 2nd Ed., P. C. BUCY, ed., University of Illinois Press, Urbana.

LAUER, E. W., 1952: Ipsilateral facial representation in motor cortex of macaque. J. Neurophysiol., *15*, 1-4.

LEWANDOWSKY, M., 1907: *Die Functionen des zentralen Nervensystems*. G. Fischer, Jena.

PATTON, H. D. and AMASSIAN, V. E., 1954: Single—and multiple—unit analysis of cortical stage of pyramidal tract activation. J. Neurophysiol., *17*, 345-363.

———— 1960: The pyramidal tract: its excitation and functions. *In Handbook of Physiology, Vol. II, Sec. 1, Neurophysiology*. JOHN FIELD, Ed.-in-Chief, Williams & Wilkins Co., Baltimore, pp. 837-862.

PENFIELD, W. and RASMUSSEN, T., 1950: *The Cerebral Cortex of Man; A Clinical Study of Localization of Function*. The Macmillan Co., New York.

PENFIELD, W. and WELCH, K., 1951: The supplementary motor area of the cerebral cortex. A clinical and experimental study. A.M.A. Arch. Neurol. Psychiat., *66*, 289-317.

RUCH, T. C., PATTON, H. D., WOODBURY, S. W. and TOWE, A. W., 1961: *Neurophysiology*. W. B. Saunders, Philadelphia.

SUGAR, O., CHUSID, J. G. and FRENCH, J. D., 1948: A second motor cortex in the monkey (*Macaca mulatta*). J. Neuropathol. Exptl. Neurol., *7*, 182-189.

TOWER, SARAH S., 1940: Pyramidal lesion in the monkey. Brain, *63*, 36-90.

———— 1949: The pyramidal tract. *In The Precentral Motor Cortex*. 2nd Ed., P. C. BUCY, ed. University of Illinois Press, Urbana.

WHITE, R. J., SCHREINER, L. H., HUGHES, R. A., MacCARTY, C. S. and GRINDLAY, J. H., 1959: Physiologic consequences of total hemispherectomy in the monkey. Neurology, *9*, 149-159.

WOOLSEY, C. N., SETTLAGE, P. H., MEYER, D. R., SENCER, W., PINTO-HAMUY, TERESA and TRAVIS, ANN M., 1952: Patterns of localization in precentral and "supplementary" motor areas and their relation to the concept of a premotor area. Assoc. Res. Nerv. Ment. Dis., *30*, 238-264.

WYSS, O. A. M., 1938: On an ipsilateral motor effect from cortical stimulation in the Macaque monkey. J. Neurophysiol., *1*, 125-126.

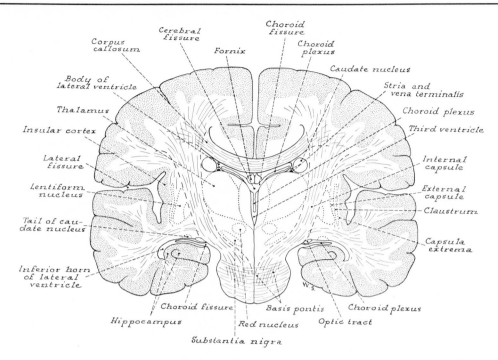

Fig. 138. Diagram of a frontal section of the brain showing the relations of the insula, basal ganglia and diencephalon.

trema. The insular part of the cerebral cortex or *island of Reil* can be readily exposed by removal of the opercular portions of the frontal, parietal, and temporal lobes of the cerebrum (Fig. 110). The insular cortex, overgrown by the adjacent neopallial areas of the cortex, is buried in the depth of the lateral fissure. The lentiform nucleus and claustrum are separated from one another by the *external capsule* and, as previously noted, the internal capsule is closely applied to the inner surface of the lentiform nucleus. The *internal capsule* fills the interval developed between the lentiform nucleus and the body of the caudate nucleus (Fig. 137).

The **lentiform nucleus** rests upon the anterior perforated substance which is lateral to the optic chiasm (Fig. 108). When sectioned, the lentiform nucleus is seen to be divided into lateral and medial portions by the *external medullary lamina*

(Figs. 137 and 139); the lateral portion is designated as the *putamen* and the medial portion as the *globus pallidus.* The globus pallidus is subdivided into external and internal parts by the *internal medullary lamina* (Figs. 137 and 139).

The **putamen** contains small triangular or polygonal cells with short axons and larger cells with long axons and multi-directional dendrites. The small neurons participate in internuclear connections between putamen, caudate nucleus and globus pallidus. The long axons of the larger neurons contribute to the efferent pathways from the lentiform nucleus.

The **globus pallidus** is the main efferent center of the basal ganglia. It contains neurons of the motor type—large, multipolar and pyramidal or spindle shaped.

The **caudate nucleus** consists of head, body and tail. The head is continuous with the anterior end of the lentiform

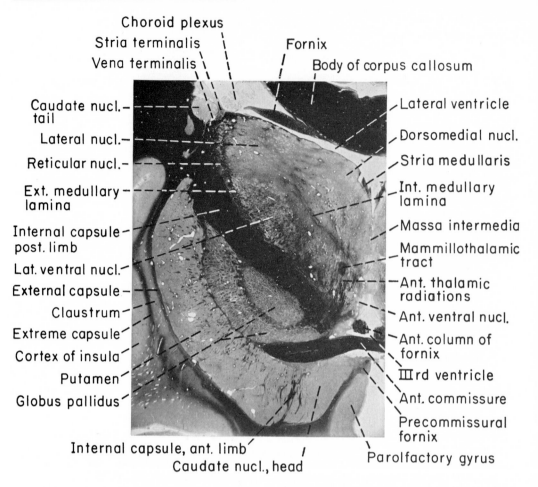

Choroid plexus
Stria terminalis
Vena terminalis
Fornix
Body of corpus callosum

Caudate nucl.-tail
Lateral nucl.-
Reticular nucl.-
Ext. medullary lamina
Internal capsule post. limb
Lat. ventral nucl.
External capsule
Claustrum
Extreme capsule
Cortex of insula
Putamen
Globus pallidus

Lateral ventricle
Dorsomedial nucl.
Stria medullaris
Int. medullary lamina
Massa intermedia
Mammillothalamic tract
Ant. thalamic radiations
Ant. ventral nucl.
Ant. column of fornix
IIIrd ventricle
Ant. commissure
Precommissural fornix

Internal capsule, ant. limb
Caudate nucl., head
Parolfactory gyrus

FIG. 139. Photomicrograph of an oblique section through the diencephalon and basal telencephalon illustrating the thalamus and basal ganglia. Weil stain.

nucleus (Fig. 137) and also rests upon the anterior perforated substance. The body begins at the level of the rostral end of the thalamus and, gradually becoming reduced in circumference, arches upward and caudally over the thalamus and internal capsule. The still more attenuated tail continues around the posterior limit of the thalamus and enters the temporal lobe of the cerebrum where it courses downward and forward in the roof of the inferior horn of the lateral ventricle; it finally ends at the amygdaloid nucleus. Small stellate cells in the caudate nucleus send their axons to the

putamen and globus pallidus of the lentiform nucleus. Axons of larger multipolar cells scattered among the stellate cells are distributed exclusively to the globus pallidus.

The **amygdaloid nucleus** is buried within the tip of the temporal lobe, above the rostral limit of the lateral ventricle (Fig. 137). Although it is included as one of the classical basal ganglia, it has no known motor functions and is related instead to the olfactory system and limbic lobe. Thus, discussion of the amygdaloid nucleus is deferred to Chapter 23 which treats the rhinencephalon.

The **claustrum,** although included as a part of the basal ganglia, is usually considered to be a detached portion of the insular cortex. Rae (1954) found the claustrum to have direct connections with areas 9 and 11, area 22 and the insular cortex and indirect connections with the olfactory bulb and the nuclei of the diffuse thalamic projection system. He suspected functional relationships with the amygdaloid complex, substantia nigra and putamen but could not throw any real light upon the significance of these claustral connections.

The **corpus striatum** is the combination of caudate nucleus and lentiform nucleus with the intervening fibers of the internal capsule. Strands of gray matter connecting the two nuclei through the anterior limb of the internal capsule are responsible for its striated appearance (Figs. 139 and 100). The *striatum* includes only the caudate nucleus and the putamen of the lentiform nucleus. The phylogenetic terms—archistriatum, paleostriatum and neostriatum—are often used and should be defined. The *archistriatum* includes only the amygdaloid nucleus; the *paleostriatum* is the globus pallidus; the term, *neostriatum,* is synonymous with *striatum* and refers to the combination of putamen and caudate nuclei which are indeed, phylogenetically newer than the other parts and are histologically similar. The globus pallidus is often referred to as *pallidum.*

It is apparent from the above that the terminology with respect to the basal ganglia is very confusing, complicated by the inclusion of the claustrum and amygdaloid nuclei which seem not to be related functionally to caudate and lentiform nuclei. Thus it is more meaningful to use a functional terminology and apply the term "basal ganglia" to the caudate and lentiform nuclei and to the related gray (*e.g.,* substantia nigra and subthalamic nucleus). Nuclei of the sub-

thalamus which are related to the striatum and pallidum and are also a part of the extrapyramidal system include the *subthalamic nucleus, zona incerta, nucleus of the field of Forel,** and the rostral extensions of the *red nucleus* and *substantia nigra* (Figs. 138-140). The **subthalamic nucleus** lies above the cerebral peduncle and medial to the internal capsule. It is surrounded by fascicles of fibers and is in relation to the rostral extent of the substantia nigra. The *zona incerta* is a small grouping of cells dorsal to the subthalamic nucleus and is separated from it by fibers of the lenticular fasciculus. The nucleus of the field of Forel (H field) consists of scattered cells which lie medial to the zona incerta and is in relation to the lenticular fasciculus and ansa lenticularis (Fig. 140). The red nucleus, prominent in the tegmentum at the superior collicular level of the midbrain extends into the caudal and medial subthalamis area (Figs. 138 and 140). The **substantia nigra,** conspicuous throughout the midbrain tegmentum, has a rostral extension into the subthalamus which lies embedded in the dorsal part of the cerebral peduncle (Figs. 140 and 63).

In addition to and surrounding the red nucleus of the midbrain tegmentum at the superior collicular level is an extensive accumulation of reticular neurons, the tegmental gray (deep tegmental nucleus) of the midbrain (Figs. 140 and 63). This nucleus extends caudally through the level of the inferior colliculus and, as indicated below, has many connections with the above-mentioned subtelencephalic and subthalamic nuclei as

*Forel, whose name is applied to certain areas of the subthalamus, used the German word *Haube* to designate the "cap" of fibers rostral to the red nucleus. As a result, the letter H is used with reference to groups of fibers in this area. The prerubral field is the H field of Forel, the thalamic fasciculus is equivalent to the H_1 field and the H_2 field designates the lenticular fasciculus.

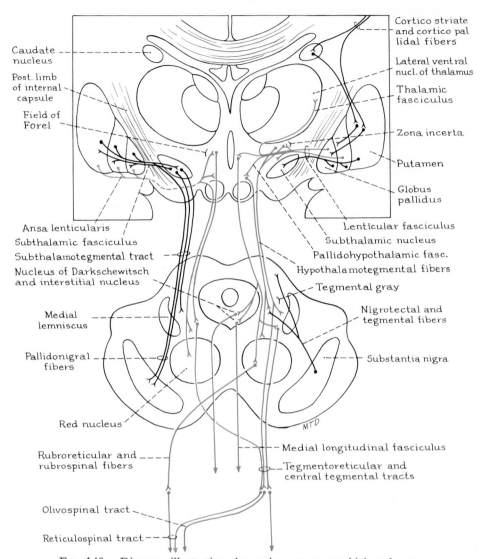

Caudate nucleus

Post. limb of internal capsule

Field of Forel

Cortico striate and cortico pal lidal fibers

Lateral ventral nucl. of thalamus

Thalamic fasciculus

Zona incerta

Putamen

Globus pallidus

Ansa lenticularis
Subthalamic fasciculus
Subthalamotegmental tract
Nucleus of Darkschewitsch
and interstitial nucleus

Medial lemniscus

Pallidonigral fibers

Red nucleus

Rubroreticular and rubrospinal fibers

Olivospinal tract

Reticulospinal tract

Lenticular fasciculus
Subthalamic nucleus
Pallidohypothalamic fasc.
Hypothalamotegmental fibers

Tegmental gray

Nigrotectal and tegmental fibers

Substantia nigra

Medial longitudinal fasciculus

Tegmentoreticular and central tegmental tracts

Fig. 140.   Diagram illustrating the major extrapyramidal pathways.

well as with extrapyramidal areas of the cortex. The conspicuous *central tegmental tract* (Figs. 140, 141 and 61) is believed to arise in large part from the deep tegmental nucleus and from the periaqueductal gray and red nucleus. It serves as a descending motor pathway to reticular neurons in more caudal brain stem levels. Many of the fibers in the central tegmental tract are short, others extend to the medulla (*e.g.,* to the inferior olivary nucleus) and some have

been traced to upper cord levels (Bebin, 1956).

Many cortically originating extrapyramidal fibers impinge upon these nuclei. Although there is no general agreement relative to the cortical areas which contribute extrapyramidal fibers to the respective basal telencephalic and brain stem nuclei, the majority of fibers arise from areas 4, 6 and 8. The cortically originating extrapyramidal pathways were listed in Chapter 15. Although some

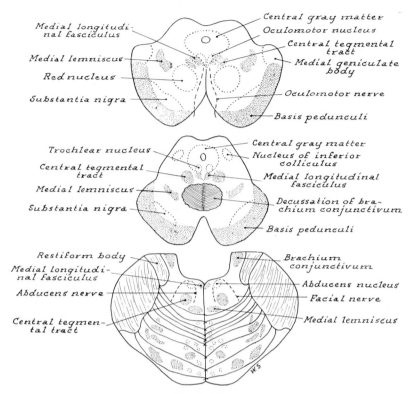

FIG. 141. Cross sections of the midbrain and pons showing the location of the central tegmental tract.

of these are treated in greater detail elsewhere, all are briefly considered here.

The **corticopontine fibers** which synapse in the basal pontine gray comprise a large system which relates the cortex to the cerebellum. This system includes frontopontocerebellar fibers which are known to arise primarily from areas 4 and 6, temporopontocerebellar, and occipitopontocerebellar fibers. This system of fibers is discussed in connection with the cerebellum, Chapter 18.

Corticonigral fibers originate in areas 4, 5 and 6 (Fig. 142), and from prefrontal areas 9, 10, 11 and 12. Those originating more rostrally synapse on the more rostral part of the substantia nigra and the others in the more caudal parts.

It seems best to consider the cortical fibers to caudate and lentiform nucleus together, *i.e.,* the **corticostriate** and **corti-copallidal.** It is generally agreed that these have a widespread origin, although anatomical support for the extent and details of origin in man is limited. There is, however, good evidence that in the monkey, fibers reach the caudate-lentiform complex from areas 4, 6 and 8 and from orbital cortex of the frontal lobe. Others arise from areas 2, 5 and 7 of the parietal lobe, from the insula, from temporal pole cortex and from the cingulate gyrus (areas 23 and 24). Although the globus pallidus is believed to receive some direct cortical fibers, the major input into this large nuclear mass (caudate-lentiform) is via the caudate and putamen (Fig. 140). The efferent fibers arise primarily in the globus pallidus.

Corticorubral fibers are believed to arise from areas 4 and 6, at least in the monkey (Fig. 142). **Corticosubthalamic**

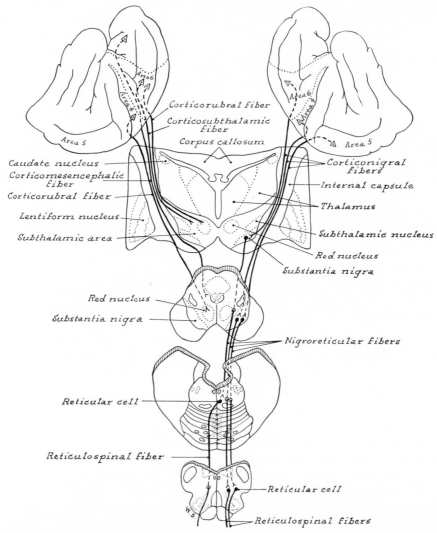

Fig. 142. Diagram to show the origin and distribution of some of the cortically originating extrapyramidal projection fibers.

fibers to the subthalamic nucleus, zona incerta, and surrounding neurons arise from cortical areas 4 and 6 (Meyer, 1949). From these same areas, 4 and 6, **corticotegmental (corticomesencephalic) fibers** reach the tegmental gray of the midbrain. It was noted above that the subthalamic area is continuous with the midbrain tegmentum and actually constitutes a rostral extension of the tegmentum into the diencephalon. Furthermore, the medial reticular area of the more

caudal brain stem is related to the tegmental area of the midbrain and, significantly, these related areas receive fibers, at least in part, from comparable cortical areas. With respect to medial reticular area of the medulla, physiologic neuronographic studies (strychnine stimulation and recording) indicate cortical input from the anterior part of the precentral gyrus (McCulloch et al., 1946).

Corticohypothalamic fibers originating in the frontal lobe and in area 7 of the parietal cortex have been described by Mettler (1935). Cajal (1911) found direct corticohypothalamic connections to be quite numerous but those that he described had their origins chiefly in the rhinencephalon. Ward and McCulloch (1947), employing physiologic neuronography, reported that cortical areas 6, 8, 10, 45, 46 and 47 projected to various parts of the hypothalamus, including the mammillary bodies. Efferent fibers from areas 6 and 8 of the frontal cortex to the hypothalamus have been described by Kurotsu *et al.* (1953) as demonstrated by the Marchi method. Interrelations of the hypothalamus and cerebral cortex are considered further in Chapter 20.

Corticothalamic fibers originate from many areas of the cortex and are considered in connection with the thalamus, Chapter 20. It is pertinent to mention, however, that corticothalamic fibers have been described originating in area 6 which project to the lateral ventral nucleus (Mettler, 1947).

In relation to the considerations here, the cortically originating extrapyramidal fibers to the thalamus seem important in that the lateral ventral nucleus has been shown to send projections to the globus pallidus (Denny-Brown, 1962). There are, in fact, many fibers from the nuclei of the dorsal thalamus to the caudate and lentiform nucleus. Notably the putamen and caudate have afferent connections with the centromedial nucleus, and globus pallidus receives fibers from the intralaminar nuclei (Jung and Hassler, 1960; Denny-Brown, 1962). Other afferent fibers of the pallidum include *nigropallidal* from the substantia nigra which have been described by several investigators (Ranson *et al.*, 1941; Fox and Schmitz, 1944 and others). They form a bundle which extends forward from the rostral limit of the substantia nigra, beneath the subthalamic nucleus; fascicles pass through the internal cap-

sule, enter the medial tip of the internal part of the globus pallidus and are distributed to both parts of this structure and possibly to the putamen (Woodburne *et al.*, 1946).

In summary, the considerations of the extrapyramidal system to this point have called attention to a number of subtelencephalic and upper brain stem nuclei which have a copious input of cortically originating fibers and, in addition, other afferent fibers to these nuclei have been mentioned. Of the great number of extrapyramidal cortical areas mentioned, those of the frontal lobe are considered the primary centers of origin for the extrapyramidal motor pathways which synapse in the basal ganglia and related nuclei before reaching the motor nuclei of the cranial and spinal nerves. It remains to consider the motor pathways from these basal nuclei to the motor cells of the cranial and spinal nerves. In addition, other efferent pathways of the subtelencephalic and related nuclear groups are to be considered. The great majority of efferent fibers of the basal ganglia have their origin in the lentiform nucleus. Only a few fibers originate in the putamen, a relatively larger number come from the external division of the globus pallidus and the greatest number originate from cells in its internal division (Fig. 140). The main efferent pathways from the lentiform nucleus are contained in or intimately related to three major fiber paths, the *lenticular fasciculus* (H$_2$ bundle of Forel), the *ansa lenticularis* and the *subthalamic fasciculus* (Fig. 140). The *pallidohypothalamic* and *thalamic fasciculi* branch off from the lenticular fasciculus. The *pallidonigral* fibers are closely associated with the subthalamic fasciculus (Woodburne *et al.*, 1946).

The **lenticular fasciculus** courses medially from its origin in the globus pallidus, pierces the internal capsule and enters the region of the zona incerta.

Some of the fibers synapse with cells in this zone. From the zona incerta, fibers course to the tegmentum of the midbrain and enter the central tegmental tract directly or after synapse in the tegmental gray (Woodburne *et al.*, 1946). The majority of fibers in the lenticular fasciculus continue medially in the H_2 field of Forel and many synapse in the nucleus of the field of Forel. With or without synapse in this nucleus, fibers pass caudally to the midbrain and end in the red nucleus, tegmental gray around the red nucleus, *nucleus of Darkschewitsch* and in the *interstitial nucleus of the medial longitudinal fasciculus* (Woodburne *et al.*, 1946). From the latter two nuclei, fibers arise which comprise the medial longitudinal fasciculi. These continue caudally to the motor nuclei of the cranial nerves. From cells in the red nucleus and tegmental gray which receive the lenticular fasciculus, fiber tracts arise which continue to the more caudal reticular areas of the brain stem and to the motor nuclei of origin for the cranial nerves. Motor neurons in the cervical spinal cord also receive an input from these fibers. The major descending fiber systems from the red nucleus and surrounding tegmental gray or nuclei include the *rubroreticular* and *rubrospinal, tegmentoreticular* and *central tegmental tracts* (Fig. 140). The reticulospinal tracts serve as the most important relays to the spinal neurons. *Olivospinal tracts* also provide a link in the caudal projection.

The **pallidohypothalamic fasciculus** (Fig. 140), which arises from the globus pallidus, separates from the lenticular fasciculus in the H_2 field and courses ventromedialward and rostrally to enter the hypothalamus where it terminates in the ventromedial nucleus (Woodburne *et al.*, 1946). This termination to the ventromedial nucleus is significant in that a relation is established for conduction

from the pallidum to hypothalamus to the tegmentum of the midbrain through hypothalamotegmental fibers.

The **thalamic fasciculus** (pallidothalamic fibers) (Fig. 140) courses medially in the dorsal part of the lenticular fasciculus to the H field where they curve sharply dorsalward and laterally in the H_1 field to the lateral ventral nucleus of the thalamus (Woodburne *et al.*, 1946).

The **ansa lenticularis** (Fig. 140) arises from all divisions of the lentiform nucleus. It may also contain fibers from the temporal and insular cortices (Laursen, 1955). These fibers accumulate below the lentiform nucleus to form the ansa. It courses medially, looping around the ventral border of the posterior limb of the internal capsule, into the region of the H field of Forel where some fibers synapse. Fascicles of the ansa, together with fibers originating in the nucleus of the field of Forel, continue to the red nucleus and to the more caudal portions of the tegmental nuclei of the midbrain (Woodburne *et al.*, 1946). Descending fibers from these midbrain centers and their relations with neurons at more caudal levels of the brain stem and upper cord were mentioned above in relation to the lenticular fasciculus.

Fascicles from the ansa have been traced into the hypothalamus (Woodburne *et al.*, 1946) and to the ventral thalamus.

The **subthalamic fasciculus** (Fig. 140) interconnects the lentiform nucleus with the subthalamic nucleus and it is generally agreed that the fasciculus contains both afferent and efferent components (Rundles and Papez, 1937). The efferent component (pallidosubthalamic) arises from both divisions of globus pallidus and a few fibers originate from the putamen. The fibers traverse the internal capsule ventral to the lenticular fasciculus and pass medially to the subthalamic nucleus. The afferent component (*subthalamostriate*) passes through the internal capsule and globus pallidus to the putamen.

From the subthalamic nucleus the **subthalamotegmental tract** descends into the midbrain, synapsing in the lateral tegmental gray (Woodburne *et al.*, 1946). From the tegmental gray, as described above, tegmentobulbar and tegmentospinal tracts descend to the caudal reticular areas and to the cranial and spinal nerve motor nuclei.

Pallidonigral fibers (Fig. 140) are closely associated with the subthalamic fasciculus; they separate from the pallidosubthalamic fibers and swing caudalward along the ventrolateral border of the subthalamic nucleus to enter the substantia nigra. The pallidonigral fibers are joined by fine fascicles that appear to originate from the subthalamic nucleus and which also appear to enter the substantia nigra (Woodburne *et al.*, 1946). Many fibers from substantia nigra project to the tegmental gray of the midbrain. Efferent fibers from the nigra to the pallidum have also been described (Ranson *et al.*, 1941).

To summarize the pattern of extrapyramidal projections from cortical levels to motor neurons of the brain stem and cord, it is important to note that, in general, the system is comprised of a multineuron chain. The cortically originating fibers feed into the basal ganglia which through one or more neuronal links project to the tegmental and/or reticular nuclei of the brain stem. An important pathway from the tegmental nuclei of the midbrain to reticular nuclei of more caudal brain stem levels is the central tegmental tract. The rubrospinal, rubroreticular and reticulospinal fibers are important final links in the spinalward projection. The *rubrospinal* and *rubroreticular tracts* originate from the red nuclei; immediately after their emergence from the nuclei the tracts decussate to the opposite side through the *ventral tegmental decussation (of Forel)*.

The **rubrospinal tract,** after its decussation, courses caudally through the tegmentum of the pons and reticular formation of the medulla. The tract is ventrally and medially placed in the pontile tegmentum and it lies immediately dorsal to the olivary nucleus in the medulla (Fig. 143). Within the spinal cord the rubrospinal fibers are found in the lateral funiculus immediately ventral to the lateral corticospinal tract. Rubrospinal fibers terminate in relation to ventral gray column cells.

Rubroreticular fibers are more numerous in the human brain than rubrospinal fibers. They synapse upon cells in the reticular formation whose axons, as reticulospinal fibers, are also distributed to ventral gray column cells (Fig. 143). The ratio of rubroreticular to rubrospinal fibers is reversed in the cat and in some other animals.

Reticulospinal fibers, according to Papez (1926), form *ventral* and *lateral reticulospinal tracts* in the spinal cord; the former is found in the ventral funiculus and the latter in the lateral funiculus (Fig. 143). Each contains crossed and uncrossed fibers (Niemer and Magoun, 1947) with crossings at both brain stem and spinal cord levels (Fig. 143).

Despite a great amount of experimental work on animals together with a vast number of clinical studies, we have no clear-cut appreciation of the functional interrelations of the extrapyramidal system with the other motor systems. This is particularly true with respect to the basal ganglia. It is to be kept in mind that the pyramidal system is present only in mammals. Furthermore, birds and lower vertebrates have very little cerebral cortex and the basal ganglia are the highest centers of motor coordination. In general, the movements supported in these lower forms are stereotyped or

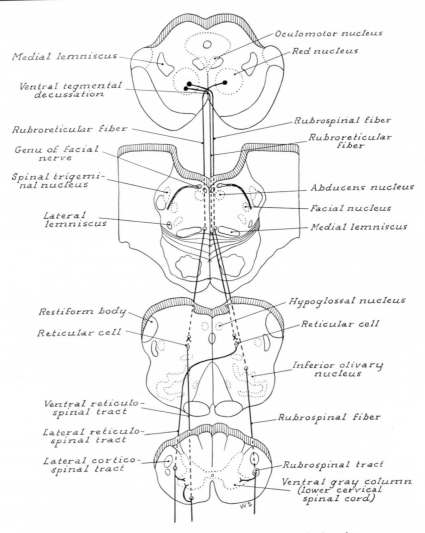

FIG. 143. The rubrospinal and rubroreticulospinal pathways.

automatic, repetitive and gross in character with an absence of precise or specific movements. This is the pattern of movements in the infant, before mature structural and functional relations are established in the pyramidal tracts and in related descending cortical fibers. It was indicated in Chapter 15 that in the case of damage or destruction of the pyramidal system there was a great amount of residual or restored motor activity. This is probably due in large part to intact components of the onto-genetically and phylogenetically primitive system (extrapyramidal).

In general, stimulation of the basal ganglia has not been very effective in producing movement nor has stimulation or the placement of lesions in the basal ganglia been very effective in clarifying their function. Nevertheless, a few clues to their function have emerged from these procedures. Forman and Ward (1957) utilized the technique of implanted electrodes to stimulate the caudate nucleus in unanesthetized cats and obtained results indicating efferent projections from the nucleus to lower centers. The reactions to stimulation were manifested contralaterally, were stereotyped and lacked the range of those elicited by stimulation of the motor cortex. They consisted of head-turning to the contralateral side and flexion of one or both contralateral extremities. The occurrence of these movements after removal of the motor cortex is "evidence against a pathway from the caudate nucleus to lower levels via the cortex being responsible for the movements obtained." A more active response to stimulation in cats with intact frontal cortices led these investigators to the conclusion that facilitation of lower motor mechanisms by the cortex, and particularly the motor cortex, plays an important part in movements elicited from stimulation of the caudate nucleus. Mettler *et al.* (1939) and others have reported that caudate and pallidal stimulation was inhibitory to cortically induced movement.

In general, experimental lesions in the basal ganglia have caused little motor dysfunction unless these were in conjunction with injury to the frontal cortex. For example, Kennard (1944) and Kennard and Fulton (1942) placed bilateral lesions in basal ganglia of monkeys and chimpanzees with no apparent effect on motor activity. However, bilateral lesions of the pallidum in animals with bilateral lesions of the motor cortex resulted in increased resistance to passive movement (rigidity), tremor and some motor weakness. Rigidity and tremor are characteristic and common symptoms of basal ganglia disease in man. A third symptom is poverty of movement or a loss of associative movements which has been reported in monkeys following bilateral destruction of the ansa lenticularis and unilateral interruption of other efferent fibers of the globus pallidus (Carey, 1957).

It is appropriate to consider the common clinical disorders attributable to damage of the basal ganglia and to discuss the resultant disturbances of posture and movement. It is to be kept in mind, however, that these disorders are usually due to rather widespread or diffuse pathologic processes and it is difficult to associate the lesions with damaged structures which underlie the motor disturbances.

Parkinson's disease, also known as **paralysis agitans** or **Parkinson's syndrome,** is characterized by a variety of symptoms, the chief ones being rigidity, alternating tremor, slowness and poverty of movement, mask-like facies and diminution of associated movements. Despite the name paralysis agitans there is no paralysis, but a disturbance of movement. The rigidity is apparent in the resistance offered in the passive movement of a limb. The rigidity is present in both flexor and extensor muscles and has the cogwheel or "lead pipe" quality. Thus, rigidity is different from spasticity which accompanies damage to the cortically originating extrapyramidal fibers.

The tremor of paralysis agitans is regular and rapid, due to alternating contractions of agonist and antagonist muscles which are often at the rate of 4 to 8 per second. It may be limited to the fingers, called "pill rolling tremor," or it may involve the entire hand or limb. It occurs at rest and disappears during sleep and when the limb is moved voluntarily.

The substantia nigra in particular and the pallidum are generally considered to be the most common or consistent sites of pathology in the Parkinson syndrome (Heath, 1947). Hassler (1956) attributes the syndrome to the destruction of substantia nigra. It is to be noted, however, that Denny-Brown (1962) presents evidence that the tremor results from the loss of corticopallidal and corticostriatal fibers and that lesions of substantia nigra appear to be associated with more restricted bulbar spasms such as yawning, respiratory and lingual compulsions.

Tremor like that of Parkinson's disease has been produced in monkeys by experimental lesions placed in the ventrolateral part of the midbrain tegmental area (Ward *et al.,* 1948; Schreiner *et al.* 1958).

Huntington's chorea, also known as **hereditary chorea,** is a degenerative disorder of middle life affecting the basal ganglia; it is characterized by jerky involuntary movements and progressive loss of mental function. In successive generations the age of onset usually decreases. The motor signs appear to be due to reduction in the number of cells in the corpus striatum, especially in the caudate nucleus, and to progressive degeneration of those which remain. The mental symptoms are explained by diminution in number of cells in the cerebral cortex, especially in the inner three layers of the frontal, parietal and temporal lobes.

Hemiballismus (hemichorea) results from unilateral lesions of the subthalamic nucleus. The jerky choreiform movements are likely to become very violent; their appearance when there is a lesion of the nucleus suggests that the pallido-subthalamo-tegmental system normally exercises a check or steadying influence on one or another of the corticospinal, corticopontocerebellar or dentato-rubro-thalamo-pallidal systems. It has been shown that hemiballismus may result from lesions in the globus pallidus or in the subthalamotegmental fibers as well as in the subthalamic nucleus itself (Papez *et al.,* 1942). Hemiballismus may be ipsilateral or contralateral to the side of the lesion, depending upon whether the location of the lesion is such as to involve pathways which subsequently cross or such as to interrupt subthalamo-tegmental fibers which have already crossed. Interruption of recurrent fibers from the subthalamic nucleus to globus pallidus appears to release the latter to abnormal activity with resultant contralateral hemiballismus of moderate degree (Martin, 1957).

Wilson's disease (hepatolenticular degeneration) is another degenerative disease associated with an error in body copper metabolism which appears in younger persons (ten to twenty-five years of age). The condition is characterized by tremor, rigidity, impairment of voluntary motion (including speech) and loss of facial expression. There may be causeless and uncontrollable laughing and crying. Softening and cavitation of the lentiform nucleus can often be seen macroscopically upon post-mortem examination of the brain from an individual having had this disease. Degeneration of nerve cells is more pronounced in the putamen than in the globus pallidus. The red nucleus, thalamus, cerebellum and cerebral cortex may show associated involvement. Cirrhosis of the liver, for some unknown reason, is usually associated with the lenticular degeneration of Wilson's disease.

Athetosis is a symptom complex found either bilaterally or unilaterally, usually of congenital origin. It may be due either to congenital maldevelopment or birth injury. The extrapyramidal system may be affected in various ways but the lesions appear to be primarily in the basal ganglia. The facial muscles move in a grimacing manner and the tongue writhes and protrudes spasmodically. There is difficulty in speaking and swallowing. The arm is adducted and internally rotated; the elbow is in semiflexion and the wrist and lesser digits are markedly flexed. The thumb is adducted and extended. The foot is turned inward and the great toe is extended. The upright position is accompanied by writhing movements. At rest, the limbs are hypotonic and movements cease during sleep.

Involvement of the basal ganglia in

brain tumors has not generally been considered responsible for extrapyramidal symptoms. Sciarra and Sprofkin (1953) have, however, reported a series of twelve cases of intracranial tumor with signs of extrapyramidal involvement; these signs included tremor, athetosis, rigidity, decrease in associated movements, slowness, mask-like facies and rhythmic alternating tremor.

In summary it has been established that the major signs of damage to the cortically originating extrapyramidal fibers are spasticity and exaggerated reflexes, whereas the signs of basal ganglia disease are tremor, rigidity and poverty of movement. Although there are no completely satisfactory explanations of the physiological mechanisms underlying these signs, it is readily apparent that a damaged or destroyed fiber tract or nucleus could not be responsible for such phenomena as tremor, spasticity and rigidity. This suggests that the components of the extrapyramidal system may be more concerned with the regulation of movement than with its initiation. This concept has, in fact, become progressively more firmly established.

Rhines and Magoun (1946) and Magoun and Rhines (1946) first demonstrated that facilitatory or inhibitory influences could be superimposed upon a wide range of motor performances, depending upon the site of stimulation within the reticular formation. The motor activities which were so affected included flexor or extensor reflexes, decerebrate rigidity and muscular responses evoked by stimulation of the motor cortex. Although there appears to be some overlap between the inhibitory area of the reticular formation and the facilitatory area, the general relationship is such that the facilitatory areas are more rostrally placed, extending forward from the medulla through pons and mesencephalon into the diencephalon (Lindsley *et al.*, 1949). Subsequent investigations, as carefully reviewed by Magoun (1958) have emphasized the more discriminative influences which can be induced by stimulation of the reticular formation and have particularly stressed the reciprocal nature of reticulospinal influences. These appear to be reciprocal in that opposite influences may be exerted upon antagonistic muscles acting at a given joint. Also, contrasting effects may be exerted upon similar muscle groups in the two halves of the body. Magoun noted the inability to evoke any inhibitory influence upon motion in the intact waking animal stimulated through implanted electrodes. He suggested that such spinal inhibition is overcome by the general excitation of the waking state or by marked activity of the spinal inhibitory mechanisms during wakefulness.

If cerebral cortical and cerebellar regions which project upon the bulbar reticular regions are ablated, a pronounced exaggeration of stretch reflexes ensues. This exaggeration of reflexes while initially marked and generalized, becomes attenuated with the passage of time and is limited to the antigravity musculature. This has been accounted for by the hypothesis that the inhibitory component of the reticulospinal mechanism depends upon excitation from cerebellar and cortical areas; in their absence the inhibitory mechanism is not intrinsically active. In the absence of inhibitory reticulospinal influences a tonic check upon postural spinal reflexes is lacking but the development of hyperreflexia would appear to involve an additional factor. Elucidation of the additional factor has been accomplished by transection of the thoracic spinal cord in animals exhibiting chronic spasticity; this was followed by loss or marked reduction of exaggerated stretch reflexes in the lower extremity, whose spinal innervation had been severed from the brain, but such reflexes in the upper extremity, whose spinal segments were still connected with the brain, maintained or increased their exaggeration. From this it appeared that the stretch hyperreflexia associated with spasticity cannot be attributed simply to loss of an inhibitory influence but is probably due to continued and unopposed presence of facilitation which proceeds downward by reticulospinal and vestibulospinal connections from the brain stem to lower motor neurons. Magoun (1958) has called attention to the fact that hyperreflexia may come to characterize the lower extremity of a chronic paraplegic man in spite of the fact that the lower part of the spinal cord has been separated from the facilitatory areas of the bulbar reticular formation and has presumed that intrinsically spinal facilitating mechanisms develop in such circumstances and are responsible for hyperreflexia.

Magoun (1958) has also reviewed the many significant investigations on *gamma-efferents* and muscle spindle regulation. He has commented that the gamma-efferent supply to the spindle, comprising as much as one-third of the ventral root outflow at some spinal levels, contributes to a recurrent loop by which the central nervous system can regulate its own proprioceptive input and, in this way, reflexly modify alpha-motor discharge responsible for both postural and phasic contractions of muscle. After discovery of the gamma-efferent innervation of the intrafusal fibers, in the muscle spindle, with the degree of tension in the muscle spindle determining the frequency of afferent firing from it, it was next determined that reticulospinal influences could markedly increase or reduce the firing of the gamma-efferent supply to muscle spindles and so alter input from them. In further analysis, it was shown that gamma control from the midbrain tegmentum is effected by two pathways,

one fast and one slow. The first activates gamma discharge upon single shock stimulation and is responsible for cooperation of gamma and spindle effects in rapid movements. The slow path requires repetitive stimulation of the brain stem and responds in a recruiting fashion. It is believed to serve in volume control of general tonic effects. The reticulospinal system, through control of the feed-back from muscle spindles by facilitation or inhibition of their gamma-efferent innervation, thus possesses an additional means of modifying motor activity over and above those effects exerted directly upon alpha-motor outflows or upon internuncial neurons influencing them. As has been indicated, the reticular formation, in turn, is influenced by extrapyramidal projections from the cerebral cortex and from the cerebellum.

This account of the inhibitory and facilitatory mechanisms provides a satisfactory framework for explaining some of the symptoms of extrapyramidal disease. Normally, it would appear that a balance exists in these two mechanisms, providing for the appropriate efferent output of stimuli to the cranial and spinal motor neurons for smooth and orderly motor activity. The mechanisms allow appropriate adjustments at various levels of the neuraxis, although there is uncertainty relative to the level at which some of the adjustments are made. Through disease or experimental lesions the balance is disturbed which would allow for overactivity of either the facilitatory or inhibitory mechanism. With respect to spasticity, discussed in relation to damage of the inhibitory cortically originating extrapyramidal fibers, there is an overacting mechanism for the extensor reflexes. The poverty of movement, one of the signs of Parkinson's disease, is attributable to interference with the descending facilitatory system (Magoun and Rhines, 1947). There is no satisfactory explanation for the rigidity of the Parkinson syndrome. Putnam and Herz (1950) have reported a decrease in rigidity following pyramidal tract section. Also Cooper and Bravo (1958) have reported a decrease or absence of rigidity and tremor after destroying the pallidum or the lateral ventral nucleus of the thalamus. The results of these surgical approaches would suggest that the pallidum is in some way responsible for or contributory to the rigidity and that the operative mechanism is through the extrapyramidal areas of the cortex.

Bucy (1949) has suggested that the tremor of basal ganglia disease is due to the continuous and oscillatory discharge through the pyramidal tracts stemming from the loss of control through the cortical-basal-ganglia-cortex circuit. According to this postulate, it is presumed that suppressor impulses from the cortex reach the substantia nigra by way of corticonigral or corticostrionigral connections, relayed to the pallidum, then to the lateral ventral nucleus of the thalamus and back by way of the thalamocortical fibers to the motor and premotor areas of the cortex where they inhibit extrapyramidal neurons. This seems unlikely since, as described above, Parkinson-like tremor has been produced in the monkey by lesions in the ventrolateral part of the midbrain tegmentum, whereas lesions within the component parts of the circuit in basal ganglia have not produced tremor. In any event it is apparent that the tremor is a release of some oscillating mechanism or center, probably caudal, to the subtelencephalic and diencephalic areas.

A number of investigators have described supressor zones in the cerebral cortex. These are not discussed since it has been conclusively shown by Marshall (1950), Marshall and Essig (1951) and others that the spreading depression which followed stimulation of the cerebral cortex (the basis upon which the zones were described) was an experimental artifact.

BIBLIOGRAPHY

BEBIN, J., 1956: The central tegmental bundle. An anatomical and experimental study in the monkey. J. Comp. Neurol., *105,* 287-332.

BUCY, P. C., 1949: Relation to abnormal involuntary movements. *In The Precentral Motor Cortex,* 2nd Ed., P. C. BUCY, ed., University of Illinois Press, Urbana, Chapt. 15, pp. 395-408.

CAJAL (RAMON Y), S., 1909-1911: *Histologie du Systeme Nerveux de l'Homme et des Vertébrés.* A. Maloine, Paris.

CAREY, J. H., 1957: Certain anatomical and functional interrelations between the tegmentum of the midbrain and the basal ganglia. J. Comp. Neurol., *108,* 57-89.

COOPER, I. S. and BRAVO, G., 1958: Chemopallidectomy and chemothalamectomy. J. Neurosurg., *15,* 244-250.

DENNY-BROWN, D., 1962: *The Basal Ganglia and Their Relation to Disorders of Movement.* Oxford University Press, New York.

FORMAN, D. and WARD, J. W., 1957: Responses to electrical stimulation of caudate nucleus in cats in chronic experiments. J. Neurophysiol., *20,* 230-244.

FOX, C. A. and SCHMITZ, J. T., 1944: The substantia nigra and the entopeduncular nucleus in the cat. J. Comp. Neurol., *80,* 323-334.

HASSLER, R., 1956: Die extrapyramidalen Rindensysteme und die zentrale Regelung der Motorik. Deut. Z. Nervenheilk., *175,* 233-258.

HEATH, J. W., 1947: Clinicopathologic aspects of Parkinsonian states. A.M.A. Arch. Neurol. Psychiat., *58,* 484-497.

JUNG, R. and HASSLER R., 1960: The extrapyramidal motor system. *In Handbook of Physiology,* Vol. II, Section 1, Neurophysiology, JOHN FIELD, ed.-in-chief, Williams & Wilkins Co., Baltimore, Chap. 35, pp. 863-927.

KENNARD, M. A., 1944: *Autonomic Function, The Precentral Motor Cortex.* The University of Illinois Press, Urbana. pp. 293-306.

KENNARD, M. A. and FULTON, J. F., 1942: Corticostriatal interrelations in monkey and chimpanzee. Assoc. Res. Nerv. Ment. Dis., *21*, 228-245.

KUROTSU, T., BAN, T. and MASAI, H., 1953: Efferent fibers from the frontal lobe to the hypothalamus. Med. J. Osaka Univ., *3*, 521-528.

LAURSEN, A. M., 1955: An experimental study of pathways from the basal ganglia. J. Comp. Neurol., *102*, 1-25.

LINDSLEY, D. B., SCHREINER, L. H. and MAGOUN, H. W., 1949: An electromyographic study of spasticity. J. Neurophysiol., *12*, 197-205.

MAGOUN, H. W., 1958: *The Waking Brain.* Charles C Thomas, Springfield.

MAGOUN, H. W. and RHINES, R., 1946: An inhibitory mechanism in the bulbar reticular formation. J. Neurophysiol., *9*, 165-171.

———— 1947: *Spasticity: The Stretch-Reflex and Extrapyramidal Systems.* Charles C Thomas, Springfield.

MARSHALL, W. H., 1950: The relation of dehydration of the brain to the spreading depression of Leão. Electroencephalo. Clin. Neurophysiol., *2*, 177-185.

MARSHALL, W. H. and ESSIG, C. F., 1951: Relation of air exposure of cortex to spreading depression of Leão. J. Neurophysiol., *14*, 265-273.

MARTIN, J. P., 1957: Hemichorea (hemiballismus) without lesions in the corpus luysii. Brain, *80*, 1-10.

McCULLOCH, W. S., GRAF, C. and MAGOUN, H.W., 1946: A cortico-bulbo-reticular pathway from area 4-S. J. Neurophysiol., *9*, 127-132.

METTLER, F. A., 1935: Corticifugal fiber connections of the cortex of *Macaca mulatta*: the frontal region. J. Comp. Neurol., *61*, 509-542.

———— 1947: Extracortical connections of the primate frontal cerebral cortex. II. Corticifugal connections. J. Comp. Neurol., *86*, 119-166.

METTLER, F. A., ADES, H. W., LIPMAN, E. and CULLER, E. A., 1939: The extrapyramidal system. A. M. A. Arch. Neurol. Psychiat., *41*, 984-995.

MEYER, MARGARET, 1949: A study of efferent connexions of the frontal lobe in the human brain after leucotomy. Brain, *72*, 265-296.

NIEMER, W. T. and MAGOUN, H. W., 1947: Reticulo-spinal tracts influencing motor activity. J. Comp. Neurol., *87*, 367-379.

PAPEZ, J. W, 1926: Reticulo-spinal tracts in the cat. Marchi method. J. Comp. Neurol., *41*, 365-399.

PAPEZ, J. W., BENNETT, A. E. and CASH, P. T., 1942: Hemichorea (hemiballismus). A.M.A. Arch. Neurol. Psychiat., *47*, 667-676.

PUTNAM, T. J. and HERZ, E., 1950. Results of spinal pyramidotomy in the treatment of the Parkinsonian syndrome. A.M.A. Arch. Neurol. Psychiat., *63*, 357-366.

RAE, A. S. L., 1954: The connections of the claustrum. Confinia Neurol., *14*, 211-219.

RANSON, S. W., RANSON, S. W., JR. and RANSON M., 1941: Fiber connections of corpus striatum as seen in Marchi preparations. A.M.A. Arch. Neurol. Psychiat., *46*, 230-249.

RHINES, R. and MAGOUN, H. W., 1946: Brain stem facilitation of cortical motor response. J. Neurophysiol., *9*, 219-229.

RUNDLES, R. W. and PAPEZ, J. W., 1937: Connections between the striatum and the substantia nigra in a human brain. A.M.A. Arch. Neurol. Psychiat., *38*, 550-563.

SCHREINER, L., MacCARTY, C. S. and GRINDLAY, J. H., 1958: Production and relief of tremor in the monkey. *In Pathogenesis and Treatment of Parkinsonism*, WILLIAM S. FIELDS, ed., Charles C Thomas, Springfield, Chap. V, pp. 118-137.

SCIARRA, D. and SPROFKIN, B. E., 1953: Symptoms and signs referable to the basal ganglia in brain tumor. A.M.A. Arch. Neurol. Psychiat., *69*, 450-461.

WARD, A. W., JR. and McCULLOCH, W. S., 1947: The projection of the frontal lobe on the hypothalamus. J. Neurophysiol., *10*, 309-314.

WARD, A. W., JR., McCULLOCH, W. S. and MAGOUN, H. W., 1948: Production of an alternating tremor at rest in monkeys. J. Neurophysiol., *11*, 317-330.

WOODBURNE, R. T., CROSBY, E. C. and McCOTTER, R. E., 1946: The mammalian midbrain and isthmus regions. Part II. The fiber connections. A. The relations of the tegmentum of the midbrain with the basal ganglia in *Macaca mulatta*. J. Comp. Neurol., *85*, 67-92.

Chapter 17

Lesions of the Motor Pathway

THE middle cerebral artery gives off internal and external striate branches near its origin from the internal carotid. These branches enter the brain through the anterior perforated substance, just lateral to the optic chiasm (Fig. 144). They supply the basal ganglia and the internal capsule. One of these, supposedly larger than the others has been referred to as the lenticulostriate artery. Charcot designated the vessel as the "artery of cerebral hemorrhage" because it was believed to be most prone to rupture, releasing blood into the brain substance. Anatomically, there is no single vessel that meets these criteria. It is true, however, that these striate branches from the middle cerebral artery are frequently the sites of cerebral hemorrhage and thrombosis. Such a hemorrhage is likely to destroy the genu and anterior part of the posterior limb of the internal capsule with resultant paralysis of the opposite side of the body. The degree of paralysis in the head region depends upon how extensively the genu is involved by the hemorrhagic process. As has been explained, the upper part of the face will be spared because the lower motor neurons which supply it receive upper motor neuron (supranuclear) fibers from the motor cortices of both sides (Fig. 125). It has also been pointed out that the contralateral trunk muscles are unlikely to be much affected by a unilateral lesion of the internal capsule since they are, in some manner, ipsilaterally innervated. Cannon *et al.* (1944) have, however, observed transient paresis of the contralateral trunk muscles following section of the basis pedunculi in monkeys.

Hemiplegia, as the term is ordinarily used, actually refers only to paralysis of the upper and lower extremities of one side; in lesions of the internal capsule it may include the facial and other muscles

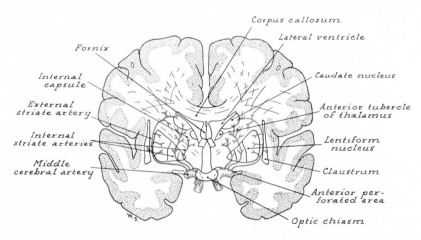

FIG. 144.   The distribution of the striate branches of the middle cerebral artery
(in part after Villiger).

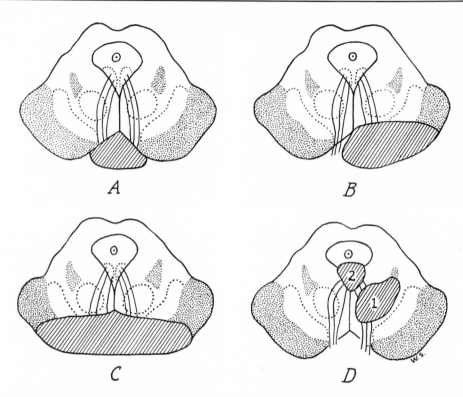

FIG. 145. Sections through the mesencephalon at the level of the superior colliculi showing the locations of lesions which interfere with voluntary motor functions. *A*, Tumor of the interpeduncular space destroying both oculomotor nerves. *B*, Unilateral expansion of a tumor of the interpeduncular space with encroachment upon the basis pedunculi. *C*, Bilateral expansion of interpeduncular tumor with partial destruction of both bases pedunculi. *D*, Lesions in the mesencephalic tegmentum (*1*) and in the central gray matter (*2*).

of the head region, but paralysis of the trunk muscles is not ordinarily implied. When hemiplegia develops as the result of unilateral hemorrhage into the internal capsule the paralyzed limbs soon become spastic and the deep reflexes are increased. The abdominal reflex is lost on the side of the paralysis and the Babinski sign usually appears on that side (Chapter 15).

Tumors developing in the interpeduncular space of the mesencephalon may destroy one or both oculomotor nerves (Fig. 145, *A*). Destruction of either nerve results in ipsilateral ptosis of the upper eyelid and outward and downward deviation of the eye. Tumors of the inter-

peduncular space, if they expand laterally, may destroy one or both bases pedunculi (Fig 145, *B* and *C*). Unilateral involvement of the basis pedunculi interrupts corticospinal fibers and eventually results in hemiplegia of the opposite side with the usual signs of an upper motor neuron lesion. Bilateral destruction of the bases pedunculi results in quadriplegia or paralysis of all four extremities.

Observations by Cannon *et al.* (1944), have indicated that unilateral interruption of the basis pedunculi in the monkey results in a syndrome that is "intermediate between spastic and hypotonic paresis." It is characterized by hypotonicity of all muscle groups except the extensors of the digits and by hyperactive deep reflexes. They explained their observations by the assumption that inhibitory pathways from the cerebral cortex do not course entirely within the basis pedunculi. (See Chapter 16 in relation to inhibitory and facilitatory mechanisms.) Those fibers whose interruption is responsible for the phenomenon of hypertonicity have, for the most part, separated from the corticospinal projection system prior to reaching the basis pedunculi while those whose interruption is responsible for hyperreflexia accompany that system through the mesencephalon.

A surprising lack of spasticity has been noted in the totally hemispherectomized monkey (White *et al.*, 1959). What spasticity is observed is limited to the affected upper extremity and is manifested by flexion. The lower extremity exhibits no evidence of resistance to passive movement and assumes a position of loose extension. Since slight hyperreflexia persists contralaterally and the affected leg is flaccid, the findings are comparable to the results of unilateral section of the basis pedunculi but would require an explanation different from that hypothesized by Cannon *et al.*, (1944). Apparently, inhibitory fibers originate both ipsi- and contralaterally with at least part of those responsible for inhibition of muscle tone coming from the ipsilateral cerebral cortex.

A lesion of the central gray matter of the mesencephalon at the superior collicular level (Fig. 145 *D2*) causes bilateral oculomotor paralysis. Such a lesion may extend caudally and also destroy the trochlear nuclei; then there will be bilateral paralysis of all the muscles of the eyes except the external recti which are supplied by the abducens nerves. Pupillary reflexes (light and accommodation) are absent in subjects with lesions of the central gray matter because of destruction of the Edinger-Westphal nuclei

and in those with peripheral oculomotor lesions because of interruption of the efferent fibers from these nuclei.

Tegmental lesions of the mesencephalon (Fig. 145 *D1*) are likely to involve the oculomotor fibers, the red nucleus and the medial lemniscus. They may extend ventrally to involve the basis pedunculi. The symptoms arising from tegmental lesions may therefore include —in addition to oculomotor paralysis— contralateral loss of tactile and proprioceptive sensibility and, due to interruption of the cerebello-rubro-spinal pathway (centered in the red nucleus), asynergia of the contralateral limbs (see Chapter 18); if the basis pedunculi is encroached upon, weakness or paralysis of the contralateral limbs will develop.

Tumors arising in either half of the basis pontis (Fig. 146, *A*) produce contralateral hemiplegia with increased deep reflexes and spasticity. The abducens fibers, as they course through the caudal part of the basis pontis, are often destroyed by such tumors; the interruption of these fibers results in internal deviation of the ipsilateral eye. Paralysis of the lower face on the side opposite the lesion is likely to be one of the symptoms arising from this type of involvement since the corticobulbar fibers to the facial nuclei are still within the main "pyramidal" system at this level; they separate from the corticospinal fibers at the level of junction of pons and medulla and course to the facial nuclei by way of the bulbopontile aberrant pyramidal bundle (Fig. 124). Some lesions of the basis pontis extend far enough laterally to involve the emerging fibers of the facial nerve (Fig. 146, *B*). In this event the entire face on the side of the lesion is paralyzed in association with contralateral hemiplegia and ipsilateral internal strabismus. The contralateral hemiplegia may include the lower half of the face as indicated above.

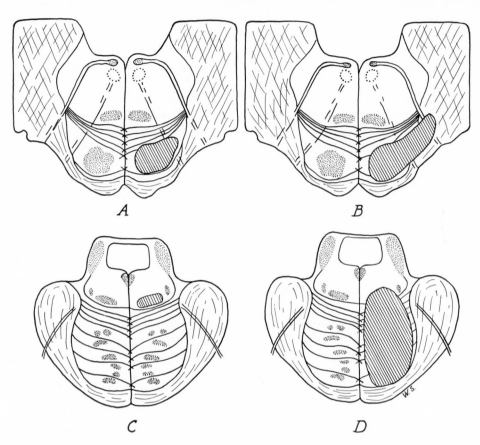

Fig. 146.—Sections through the pons showing the locations of lesions which interfere with voluntary motor functions. *A* and *B*, Unilateral lesions of the basis pontis. *C*, Tegmental lesion that interrupts corticobulbar fibers in the medial lemniscus. *D*, Combined basilar and tegmental lesions.

Upper motor neuron paralysis of the **eye muscles,** the **muscles of mastication,** the **tongue muscles** and the **muscles of the pharynx and larynx** may result from *tegmental lesions* in the pons and caudal part of the midbrain, which interrupt corticobulbar fibers. Involvement of the medial lemniscus in the pontile tegmentum (Fig. 146, *C*) destroys corticobulbar fibers destined for contralateral motor nuclei at levels caudal to the lesion (Fig. 124).

A **pontile syndrome** of particular interest results from tumor or extensive hemorrhage in the rostral part of the pons with unilateral involvement of both basilar and tegmental areas (Fig. 146, *D*). Such a lesion may damage the corticospinal and corticobulbar tracts and the medial lemniscus. The findings in this syndrome include contralateral hemiplegia, loss of tactile and proprioceptive sensibility on the contralateral side of the body, and paralysis of conjugate deviation of the eyes away from the side of the lesion. The contralateral hemiplegia includes the lower half of the face, the muscles of mastication, and the tongue. The paralysis of conjugate deviation of the eyes toward the side opposite that of the lesion is accounted for by destruction of the corticobulbar fibers, in the medial lemniscus, which terminate in the contralateral abducens nucleus (Fig. 124). The abducens nucleus of either side, through connections with the other motor ocular nuclei by way of the medial longitudinal fasciculi, is believed to serve as the pacemaker for ipsilateral conjugate deviation of the eyes. In a lesion such as has been described the abducens nucleus on the side opposite the lesion fails to receive cortical impulses and the subject is therefore unable to turn the eyes voluntarily toward that side.

hypoglossal nucleus, is of the lower motor neuron type. Lower motor neuron paralysis is flaccid in character and there is atrophy of the paralyzed musculature. Atrophy of the tongue on the ipsilateral side in the presence of unilateral lesions of the hypoglossal nerve is usually observable. The diagnosis of lingual paralysis (whether due to destruction of upper or lower motor neurons) is easily made by having the patient protrude his tongue; in the presence of unilateral paralysis the protruded tongue deviates toward the side of the paralysis.

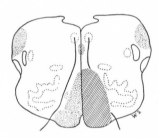

FIG. 147.   Section through the medulla showing a common type of vascular lesion due to thrombosis of one or more branches of the anterior spinal artery.

Tegmental lesions of the pons which destroy the abducens nucleus unilaterally produce conjugate deviation of the eyes toward the opposite side and paralysis of deviation toward the side of the lesion. These symptoms are due to interruption of the pacemaker mechanism. A small-celled portion of the abducens nucleus, termed "para-abducens" has sometimes been credited with the pacemaker function but this has not been clinicopathologically substantiated.

Thrombosis of branches of the anterior spinal artery may result in unilateral destruction of the pyramid, the medial lemniscus and the hypoglossal nerve (Fig. 147). The paralysis in the contralateral extremities in such cases is of the upper motor neuron type; that in the ipsilateral half of the tongue, due to destruction of the axons of cells in the

The effects of traumatic spinal cord transections are flaccid paralysis, absence of sensation and suppression of reflexes, both skeletal and visceral, below the level of the lesion. The suppression or abolition of all reflexes is known as spinal shock which is due to the functional interruption of the spinal tracts and not to the trauma of the lesion (Sherrington, 1906; Ruch, 1936). Guttmann (1952) has shown that the period of shock varies —some reflex activity may appear in three to five days, or it may not return for six weeks. The first reflexes to return are flexor movements which are followed by the appearance of the Babinski sign, indicating damage to the corticospinal tracts (see Chapter 15). Several weeks or months after transection, the flexor reflexes usually become greatly exaggerated and spasms (mass reflexes) may ap-

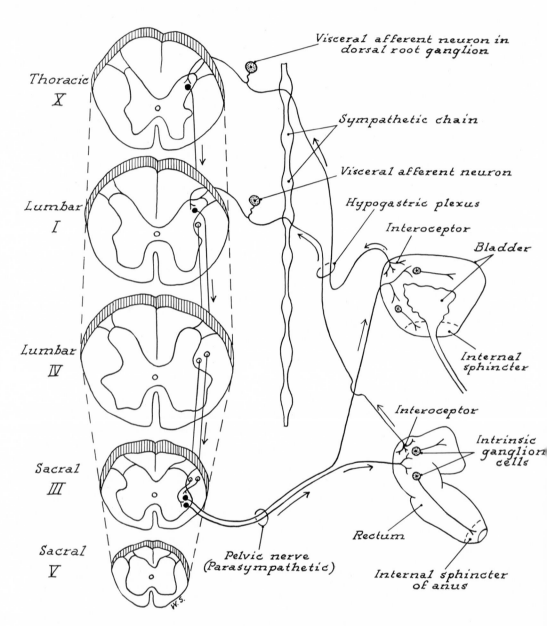

FIG. 148.   The visceral reflex arc responsible for automatic emptying of the bladder and bowel after complete transection of the spinal cord in the thoracic region.

pear. The next phase, beginning six months or more after injury, is characterized by a return of extensor reflexes (Kuhn, 1950).

It is generally agreed that spinal shock develops due to the sudden interruption of the facilitatory pathways from supraspinal levels (Hagbarth and Kerr, 1954). The recovery or return of reflexes is less readily explainable, although it has been suggested that the recovery of function is a return of spinal motoneurons from a decreased excitability state to the normal "shock state" (see Ruch *et al.*, 1961).

Complete transection of the cord in man seldom occurs except on the battlefield. More common are partial transections produced by knife or bullet wounds which may be hemisections giving rise to the classical Brown-Séquard syndrome. On the side of the hemisection, after the acute phase of the injury has passed, the pyramidal and extrapyramidal signs appear below the level of the lesion. These include the loss of voluntary movements and the sign of Babinski (damage to corticospinal tracts) and spasticity and exaggerated deep reflexes (damage to inhibitory extrapyramidal tracts). The facilitatory pathways are also interrupted but the loss of this effect is surpassed by the loss of inhibitory mechanisms which normally dampen the segmental facilitatory mechanisms. Autonomic effects may also be apparent after hemisection, *e.g.*, reduced sweating on the involved side below the level of the lesion. The sensory deficits would include the loss of positional, vibratory, proprioceptive and discriminatory tactile sensibility on the side of the lesion below the level of involvement due to severance of the posterior columns. Pain and temperature sensibility would be lost on the opposite side, beginning about two segments below the level of the lesion.

Not infrequently, intramedullary or extramedullary spinal cord tumors develop which produce various combinations of the motor signs and sensory deficits described for spinal cord transections. Although a tumor may produce a complete functional transection, the signs and symptoms are usually gradual in appearance and progressive with time. Additionally, in the early stages of growth the signs may be associated with the segmental level of development, *e.g.*, involvement of spinal roots.

Complete transverse lesions of the spinal cord account for paralysis of the external sphincters of the bladder and bowel. At first there is likely to be acute retention of bowel and bladder contents due to spasm of the internal sphincters but, after some time, so-called "cord bladder and bowel" usually develop. The cord bladder or bowel empties automatically when it is sufficiently distended. Automatic function depends upon stimulation of visceral receptors in the wall of the viscus or in the peritoneum overlying it; afferent impulses thus set up enter the spinal cord (below the level of transection) over visceral afferent fibers which make direct or indirect connections with visceral efferent neurons in the intermediolateral gray column of the sacral region (Fig. 148). The axons of the efferent neurons reach the bladder or bowel by way of the pelvic nerves and plexuses and produce relaxation of the internal sphincter together with contraction of the smooth musculature of the wall of the viscus.

Subacute combined degeneration as it occurs in pernicious anemia has been described and the resulting sensory disturbances have been enumerated. The sensory disturbances were attributed to degeneration in the dorsal funiculi. The associated degeneration in the lateral funiculi involves the lateral corticospinal tracts (Fig. 149, *A*). The patient, in addition to loss of vibratory and position sense, the sense of movement and two-

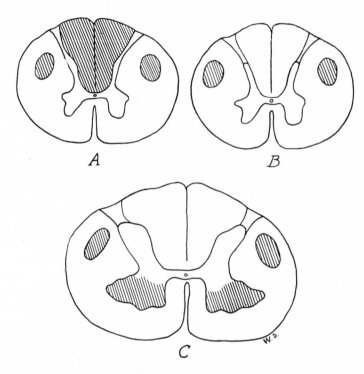

FIG. 149. *A,* Section through thoracic spinal cord showing the areas affected by subacute combined degeneration in pernicious anemia. *B,* Section through thoracic spinal cord showing the areas of degeneration in lateral sclerosis. *C,* Section through lower cervical spinal cord showing the sites of the degenerative process in amyotrophic lateral sclerosis.

point discrimination, may exhibit gradually increasing stiffness and weakness of his limbs and hyperactive deep reflexes. The motor symptoms are particularly evident in the lower extremities or may be confined to them. The abdominal reflex is usually absent or diminished and the Babinski sign is likely to be present bilaterally. The external sphincters are eventually involved unless the disease is controlled and this results in varying degrees of incontinence. A flaccid type of motor loss with decreased deep reflexes is also described as occurring in pernicious anemia (Walshe, 1947) and is attributed to peripheral neuritis.

Lateral sclerosis is a condition of unknown etiology in which the lateral corticospinal tracts are selectively and progressively involved in a degenerative process (Fig. 149, *B*). There are no sensory disturbances but the limbs, and particularly the lower limbs, are eventually paralyzed. The paralysis is typically upper motor neuron in type with increased deep reflexes and spasticity.

Anterior poliomyelitis, resulting in partial or complete destruction of ventral gray column cells, is a common cause of lower motor neuron paralysis. In this condition those muscles whose lower motor neurons have been completely destroyed are markedly atrophied. Loss of deep reflexes is associated with the atrophy. In the bulbar type of poliomyelitis the gray matter of the medulla is affected with the result that vital functions are interfered with. Although referred to as "bulbar poliomyelitis," this type of involvement might better be termed "polioencephalitis." The use of the former term arises from the fact that the bulbar syndrome is caused by the same virus that is responsible for the more common involvement of the spinal cord. Spasticity of the muscles or increased resistance to passive movement, and exaggerated deep reflexes are observed during the earlier stages of poliomyelitis. These manifestations have been attributed to irritation of the anterior gray column cells by the poliomyelitis virus or to destruction of internuncial cells within the spinal gray matter; the latter explanation has been based upon the hypothesis that the normal inhibitory effects, transmitted from reticulospinal and proprioceptive pathways to anterior gray column cells by the internuncial cells, are interrupted. Bodian (1946) demonstrated, in monkeys inoculated with poliomyelitis virus, that neither virus activity nor lesions in the spinal cord are necessary for the production of the spasticity of acute poliomyelitis; this investigator concluded, on the basis of serial sections of the brains of his monkeys, that brain lesions were responsible for the spasticity observed. Bodian suggested, since lesions were present in the reticular formation of the hind-brain, that destruction of these areas may be responsible, at least in part, for generalized spasticity because of elimination of many "inhibitor" neurons

Transection of the cauda equina accounts for lower motor neuron paralysis of the lower extremities. It is important to remember that the nerves of the cauda equina are peripheral nerves and that they will regenerate if they are sutured. Tumors arising in the lower part of the spinal canal also cause paralysis through pressure upon the cauda equina; removal of such a tumor relieves the pressure and permits regeneration and return of function of the nerves.

Jacobson (1942) sectioned the cauda equina in dogs and studied the effects of the procedure upon the bladder. He found that the bladder was "atypically" autonomous and described the autonomous bladder as one which, due to loss of normal motor innervation, functions through its intrinsic nerve plexuses and completely independently of the central nervous system. In spite of dilatation and flaccidity of its musculature, the bladder is at least partially evacuated when the intravesical tension is sufficiently increased.

Amyotrophic lateral sclerosis, of unknown etiology, affects the lateral corticospinal tracts and the ventral gray column cells (Fig. 149, C). In typical cases, signs of involvement of the lateral corticospinal tracts—spasticity, hyperactive deep reflexes and the Babinski sign—are observed in the lower extremities. In the upper extremities muscle atrophy is seen in paradoxical conjunction with hyperactive reflexes. The muscle atrophy usually appears first in the intrinsic muscles of the hands. As muscle atrophy progresses the signs of upper motor neuron disease give way to flaccidity and loss of deep reflexes; when this occurs it indicates that the lower motor neurons have been irreparably damaged and the effects of degeneration in the lateral corticospinal tracts can therefore no longer be seen in the muscles. Bulbar paralysis (soft palate, pharynx, larynx and tongue), due to involvement of lower motor neurons in the nuclei of the medulla, is a serious and constant complication of the disease and contributes significantly to its fatal termination.

BIBLIOGRAPHY

BODIAN, D., 1946: Experimental evidence on the cerebral origin of muscle spasticity in acute poliomyelitis. Proc. Soc. Exptl. Biol. Med., *61*, 170-175.

CANNON, B. W., MAGOUN, H. W. and WINDLE, W. F., 1944: Paralysis with hypotonicity and hyperreflexia subsequent to section of the basis pedunculi in monkeys. J. Neurophysiol., 7, 425-437.

GUTTMANN, L., 1952: Studies on reflex activity of the isolated cord in the spinal man. J. Nervous Mental Disease, 116, 957-972.

HAGBARTH, K. E. and KERR, D. I. B., 1954: Central influences on spinal afferent conduction. J. Neurophysiol., 17, 295-307.

JACOBSON, C. E., JR., 1942: Neurogenic vesical dysfunction: an experimental study. Proc. Staff Meet. Mayo Clinic, 17, 286-288.

KUHN, R. A., 1950: Functional capacity of the isolated human spinal cord. Brain, 75, 1-51.

RUCH, T. C., 1936: Evidence of the non-segmental character of spinal reflexes from an analysis of the cephalad effects of spinal transection (Scheff-Sherrington phenomenon). Am. J. Physiol., 114, 457-467.

RUCH, T. C., PATTON, H. D., WOODBURY, S. W. and TOWE, A. W., 1961: Neurophysiology. W. B. Saunders Co., Philadelphia.

SHERRINGTON, C. S., 1906: The Integrative Action of the Nervous System. Yale University Press, New Haven, Conn.

WALSHE, F. M. R., 1947: Diseases of the Nervous System. 5th Ed., Williams & Wilkins Co., Baltimore.

WHITE, R. J., SCHREINER, L. H., HUGHES, R. A., MACCARTY, C. S. and GRINDLAY, J. H., 1959: Physiologic consequences of total hemispherectomy in the monkey. Neurology, 9, 149-159.

Chapter 18

The Cerebellum

THE **cerebellum,** "little cerebrum," is a massive, organized accumulation of neurons located above the medulla oblongata and pons (Fig. 150) and is covered dorsally by the cerebral hemispheres (Fig. 1). It is a suprasegmental apparatus which is connected with the brain stem by three distinct bundles of nerve fibers, the *inferior, middle* and between the spinal cord and cerebral hemispheres, and having many afferent and efferent connections with these parts, it is in a favored position to serve in the control of muscle tonus and in the regulation of movement. The major subdivisions of the cerebellum are the median unpaired vermis and the paired lateral hemispheres (Fig. 151). This division

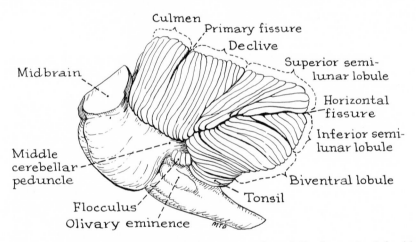

FIG. 150. Drawing of the cerebellum and the pons and medulla from the left side, inferolateral view.

superior cerebellar peduncles (Fig. 48). It will be recalled that these three peduncles are also known respectively as the restiform body, brachium pontis and brachium conjunctivum. The cerebellum plays an important role in the regulation of reflex tonus of skeletal musculature, in the control of voluntary activity and in the maintenance of equilibrium. It has, in fact, been considered as the head ganglion of the proprioceptive system. Situated above the brain stem and into median and lateral parts is more apparent on the under side. The surface of the cerebellum is comprised of numerous folia with intervening sulci and fissures which extend transversely across the hemispheres and vermis (Figs. 150 and 151). The deeper transverse depressions, fissures, have been employed for making secondary subdivisions of the vermis and hemispheres. The names given these parts by earlier investigators were based upon their shape and have no

(203)

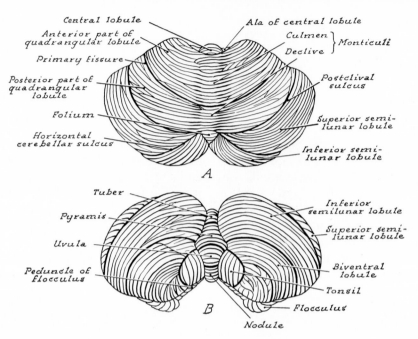

FIG. 151. *A*, Dorsal surface of the cerebellum; *B*, ventral surface of the cerebellum so oriented with relation to *A* as to indicate the continuity of folium and tuber (modified from Sobotta-McMurrich).

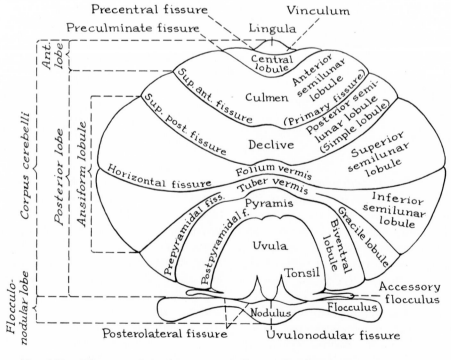

FIG. 152. Diagram of the human cerebellum (modified from Larsell, 1951).

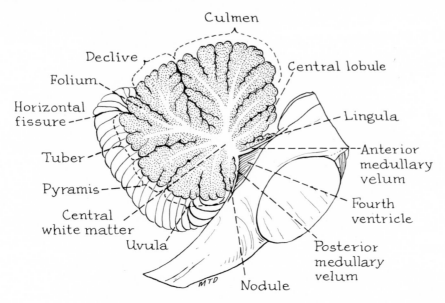

Culmen

Declive

Folium

Horizontal
fissure

Tuber

Pyramis

Central
white matter

Uvula

Central lobule

Lingula

Anterior
medullary
velum

Fourth
ventricle

Posterior
medullary
velum

Nodule

MTD

FIG. 153.   Sagittal section of the cerebellum illustrating the lobules of the vermis.

functional significance. Furthermore, there was little agreement amongst these investigators in naming the parts with the resultant confusion which exists in cerebellar terminology. One of the more common systems of terminology applied to the lobules of the cerebellum is given on the right side of Figure 152. This diagram used in conjunction with the sagittal section (Fig. 153) and with the superior and inferior views of the cerebellum (Fig. 151, *A, B*) serve to establish appropriate landmarks and boundaries of the larger gross divisions (lobes) as given by Larsell (1951) which are shown on the left side of Figure 152. To identify the various lobules and fissures it is perhaps most satisfactory to begin with the sagittal section and trace the fissures laterally. Larsell (1951) has pointed out that the post-nodular fissure and its lateral extension, the posterolateral fissure, are the first to appear in embryonic development and these separate the *flocculonodular* lobe from the remainder of the cerebellum or *corpus cerebelli*. The flocculonodular lobe which

has predominantly vestibular connections is often called *archicerebellum*, denoting its early phylogenetic appearance. The superior anterior fissure (primary fissure) divides the corpus cerebelli into anterior lobe and posterior lobe. The *anterior lobe,* and the *pyramis* and *uvula* comprise the *paleocerebellum* which primarily receives proprioceptive and exteroceptive information from the head and body. The *posterior lobe,* except for the pyramis and uvula, is considered as *neocerebellum*. The neocerebellum developed phylogenetically in conjunction with the cerebral cortex which is reflected in its extensive cortical connections through the corticopontile system. (See page 221 for a further consideration of this subdivision based upon the phylogenetic concept.)

Sections of the cerebellum show that it, like the cerebrum, consists of a cortex, a core of white matter and deeply buried nuclei (Figs. 154 and 155). The cerebellar cortex, however, has a uniform structure throughout and there are no described cytoarchitectonic subdivisions.

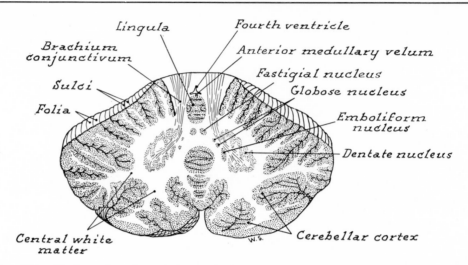

FIG. 154. Horizontal section of the cerebellum showing the arrangement of the cortical gray matter and the locations of the central nuclei within the white matter (after Sobotta-McMurrich).

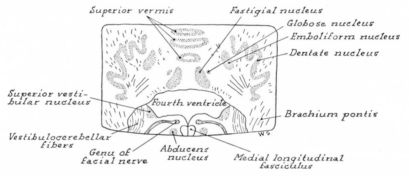

FIG. 155. Frontal section through the central white matter of the cerebellum at a level corresponding to that of the abducens nucleus in the pons, to show the positions and relations of the cerebellar nuclei (modified from Braus).

The cerebellar nuclei are buried in the core of white matter. The largest and most laterally placed nucleus, on either side, is the *dentate* (Fig. 155); it is similar in appearance to the inferior olivary nucleus. The *emboliform nucleus* is located in the medially directed hilus of the dentate nucleus and the *globose nucleus* is medial to it. The *fastigial* or *tectal nuclei* lie on either side of the midline, in the roof of the fourth ventricle. The globose and emboliform nuclei together are often called *nucleus interpositus,* particularly in lower mammals.

Histologically, the *cerebellar cortex* consists of three layers, which are from without inward the *molecular layer,* the *layer of Purkinje cells* and the *granular layer* (Fig. 156). The molecular cell layer has many processes from neurons located in the deeper cerebellar layers and is, therefore, primarily a region of synapses. There are a few scattered *stellate* cells in the upper levels of the molecular layer and more numerous deeply placed ones which are called "*basket cells.*" The axons of the basket cells course above the Purkinje cells in a plane

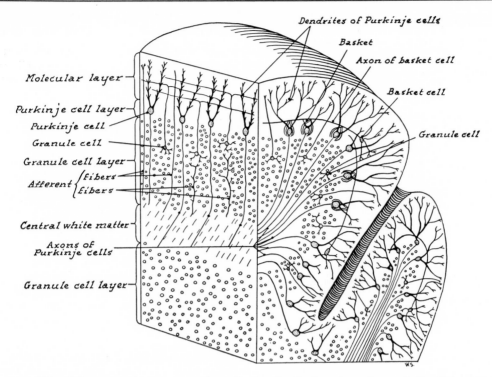

Molecular layer

Purkinje cell layer

Purkinje cell

Granule cell

Granule cell layer

Afferent { fibers
           fibers

Central white matter

Axons of Purkinje cells

Granule cell layer

Dendrites of Purkinje cells

Basket

Axon of basket cell

Basket cell

Granule cell

FIG. 156. Diagrammatic representation of a longitudinal section of a cerebellar folium (*left*) and of cross-sections of two adjacent folia (*right*) to show histologic and synaptic details (modified from Braus).

at right angles to the long axis of the *folia* and give off many collaterals. The most conspicuous are the descending collaterals which form the synaptic networks or "baskets" about the **Purkinje cells.**

The Purkinje cells are large neurons arranged in a single cell layer at the junction of the granular and molecular layers. These cells are the efferent neurons of the cerebellar cortex and their axons project to the cerebellar nuclei. Recurrent collaterals arise from the axons and some are believed to terminate on other Purkinje cells. The dendrites of the Purkinje cells extend into the molecular layer where they branch profusely and always in the transverse plane of the folium. Thus, their extent of branching is observed only in sections cut at right angles to the long axis of the folium.

The inner layer of the cerebellar cortex is called the *granular layer* because of the numerous small and closely packed cells, the granule cells (Fig. 156). A typical granule cell has 3 to 6 short slender dendrites which end in claw-like terminals. The axon is longer and extends into the molecular layer where it exhibits a T-shaped bifurcation giving rise to *parallel fibers*. These terminals course parallel with the long axis of the folium and synapse with spines on the dendritic branches of the Purkinje cells. The relations of the numerous parallel fibers with dendrites of many Purkinje cells provide the anatomical substrate for the diffusion or spread of incoming impulses as well as for convergence. Fox and Barnard 1957) have estimated that a parallel fiber, 3 mm. in length, may contact the spines of 460 Purkinje cells.

Afferent fibers to the cerebellum are usually considered to be of two types, *mossy* and *climbing fibers*. Mossy fibers synapse with the claw-like terminals of three or more granule cells (Fox and Barnard, 1957). There is considerable uncertainty relative to the origin of the climbing fibers. Dow (1942) expressed the view that all incoming cerebellar fibers except the olivocerebellar are mossy fibers, and Carrea *et al.* (1947) consider all cerebellar afferents to be of the mossy type. As the latter suggest, the climbing fibers may be intrinsic cerebellar fibers, *e.g.,* recurrent collaterals of Purkinje cells.

In addition to the granule cells, less numerous large stellate cells are present in the granule cell layer. Their dendritic terminals are in the molecular layer and their axonic terminals synapse with the claw-shaped endings of the granule cells. The **primary intrinsic circuits** of the cerebellum may be summarized as follows: Afferent mossy fibers synapse with terminals of granule cells which, through their parallel fibers, make contact with dendritic terminals of the Purkinje cells

as well as with the dendrites of basket and stellate cells. The basket cells relate many Purkinje cells in the transverse plane and the stellate cells are believed to activate other granule cells. The Purkinje cells provide the output from the cerebellar cortex through their axons to the cerebellar nuclei. This output may be modified by the recurrent collaterals of the Purkinje cells. Additionally, association fibers have been described which interconnect different regions of the cerebellar cortex (Jansen, 1933).

The **major afferent pathways** of the cerebellum from the spinal cord and brain stem include *vestibulocerebellar fibers*, the *dorsal* and *ventral spinocerebellar tracts, superficial arcuate fibers,* the *spino-olivo-cerebellar system, reticulocerebellar* and *trigeminocerebellar fibers* (Figs. 157-159). Except for the vestibulocerebellar system, these tracts in large part transmit proprioceptive impulses, although some carry, in addition, tactile and probably other sensory information as will be indicated. Other cerebellar afferents include *tectocerebellar fibers* from the tectum of the mid-

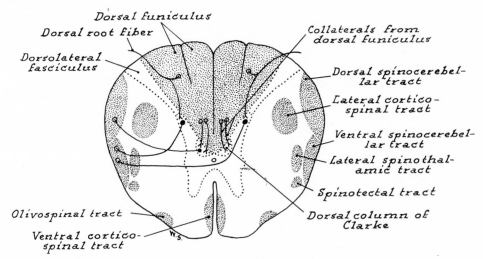

FIG. 157. Diagram of a cross-section through upper thoracic spinal cord to show the positions and relations of the spinocerebellar tracts. Collaterals from the dorsal root fibers to dorsal gray column cells and from the dorsal funiculi to Clarke's dorsal column are shown and the components of the spinocerebellar tracts are traced from their cells of origin.

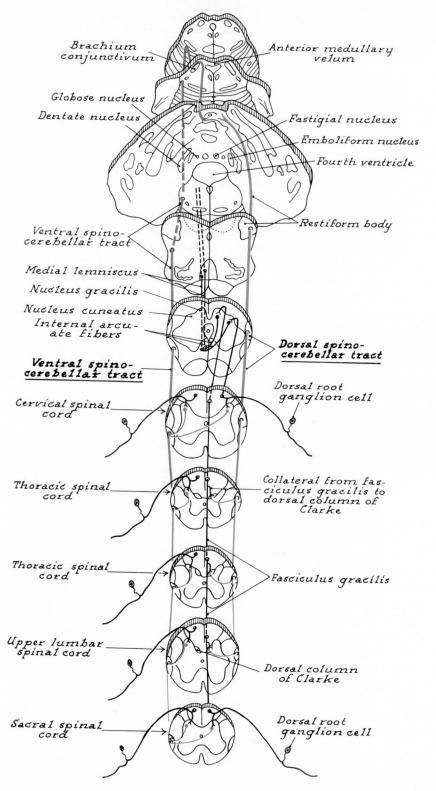

FIG. 158. Diagram to show the formation, course, and termination in the cerebellar cortex of the dorsal and ventral spinocerebellar tracts.

brain. The largest group of cerebellar afferents is the *corticopontocerebellar system* (Fig. 160).

Vestibulocerebellar fibers (Fig. 55), including both direct vestibular root fibers and secondary ones from the vestibular nuclei, end in the flocculonodular lobe and to a lesser extent in the lingula and uvula (Fig. 152). Some vestibular fibers, according to Dow (1936) and Larsell (1937) terminate directly in the fastigial nuclei. Others end in relation to granule cells (Dow, 1942; Carrea and Grundfest, 1954). The course of the vestibulocerebellar fibers to the cerebellum through the medial part of the inferior cerebellar peduncle has been described (Chapter 8).

The dorsal spinocerebellar tract (of Flechsig) is largely an uncrossed tract which is made up of the axons of neurons whose cell bodies are in the *dorsal column of Clarke* (Figs. 157 and 29). This column of nerve cells is found at the point of junction of the dorsal gray column with the dorsal gray commissure in the upper two lumbar and in all of the thoracic segments of the spinal cord. Its cells receive collaterals from the dorsal funiculi and, as stated above, send their axons into the dorsal spinocerebellar tracts. The uncrossed component of the dorsal spinocerebellar tract is greater than its crossed component (Morin and Haddad, 1953). The tract occupies a position in the lateral funiculus of the cord between the lateral corticospinal tract and the periphery. In the medulla it migrates dorsally and enters the restiform body through which it terminates in the cerebellum (Fig. 158). Proprioceptive impulses from the lower extremities and trunk reach the cerebellum by way of this tract.

The *ventral spinocerebellar tract* is composed of axons from the contra- and ipsilateral dorsal funicular gray (Fig. 158). In the lower lumbar and sacral regions a column of cells, similar in appearance and location to Clarke's column at more rostral levels, has been designated as Stilling's nucleus; it appears to contribute fibers to the ventral spinocerebellar tract. The number of crossed fibers in the ventral spinocerebellar tract is greater than the number of uncrossed fibers (Morin and Haddad, 1953). The tract is situated peripherally in the lateral funiculus immediately ventral to the dorsal spinocerebellar tract (Fig. 157). The ventral spinocerebellar tract and the spinotectal and lateral spinothalamic tracts constitute what is sometimes called *Gowers' tract*. The dorsal gray column cells whose axons contribute to the formation of the ventral spinocerebellar tract receive collaterals from the medial divisions of the dorsal roots at all levels of the spinal cord. The electrical activity in the tract, produced by stimulation of peripheral nerves, indicates representation of the four limbs (monkey and cat) as follows: contralateral hind limb maximally, ipsi- and contralateral forelimbs less and approximately equally, and ipsilateral hind limb minimally (Carrea and Grundfest, 1954).

The topographic pattern of localization in the ventral spinocerebellar tract is similar to that in the lateral spinothalamic tract with those fibers arising at sacral and lumbar levels most dorsolaterally placed, those from thoracic levels in an intermediate position and those from cervical spinal cord segments most ventromedially located (Yoss, 1953). In the caudal medulla the ventral spinocerebellar tract maintains its ventral position with relation to the dorsal spinocerebellar tract but, when the latter tract curves dorsally in the inferior cerebellar peduncle, the ventral spinocerebellar fibers continue rostrally through the medulla and the tegmentum of the pons to the level of the junction of pons and midbrain. At this point they turn dorsally around the lateral side of the superior cerebellar peduncle and enter the anterior medullary velum through which they course to the cerebellum (Fig. 158). The ventral spinocerebellar tract is often referred to as the *indirect spinocerebellar tract* because it doubles back on itself and enters the cerebellum from its rostral side. Proprioceptive impulses reach the cerebellum from the trunk as well as from all four extremities by way of the ventral spinocerebellar tracts.

Spinocerebellar fibers terminate chiefly in the vermis and paravermal portions of the anterior lobe. Most *ventral spinocerebellar fibers* end in the central lobule and culmen. Those ventral spinocerebellar fibers from the lumbar regions terminate anteriorly to those from the cervical levels of the spinal cord (Carrea and Grundfest, 1954). The *dorsal spinocerebellar tracts* distribute fibers to the *central lobule, culmen, pyramis, uvula* and *declive*. Spinocerebellar fibers end in relation to granule cells (Fig. 156). It is probable that the spinocerebellar tracts transmit exteroceptive impulses as well as proprioceptive information.

The **dorsal external arcuate fibers** (Fig. 159) are axons of cells in the *lateral cuneate nucleus* (Ferraro and Barrera, 1935). The lateral cuneate nucleus, characterized by large cells like those in the dorsal column of Clarke, lies immediately lateral to the rostral part of the main cuneate nucleus (Fig. 37). The dorsal external arcuate fibers enter the cerebellum by way of the inferior cerebellar peduncle and probably are concerned particularly with proprioceptive and exteroceptive impulses from the neck. It will be remembered that proprioceptive and tactile impulses reach the main and lateral cuneate nuclei by way of the fasciculus cuneatus and that those reaching the main nucleus are relayed upward to the thalamus through the internal arcuate fibers and the contralateral medial lemniscus. It now becomes evident that the impulses from the neck region, at least, and possibly those from the upper extremities and upper part of the trunk, are also relayed to the cerebellum from these nuclei. The ventral superficial arcuate fibers (Fig. 45) arise from the *arcuate nucleus* (Fig. 37), probably a caudal extension of the pontine gray, and from reticular cells in the lateral part of the medulla. These fibers also enter the cerebellum through the inferior cerebellar peduncle.

The **spino-olivary tract,** as classically described, originates in the spinal cord, probably from dorsal gray column cells of the opposite side. It lies in the ventral funiculus where its fibers are intermingled with olivospinal fibers (Fig. 157); the latter arise in the olivary nucleus and end in relation to ventral gray column cells. The spino-olivary tract terminates in the inferior olivary nucleus. A dorsal spino-olivary tract, which is adjacent to the dorsal spinocerebellar tract, has been demonstrated in the cat (Grundfest and Carter, 1954). The dorsal spino-olivary pathway appears to conduct mainly to the contralateral olivary nucleus with decussation high in the cervical spinal cord; although not definitely located, another relay appears to be intercalated between the spinal cord tract and the neurons which actually end in the olivary nucleus.

Olivocerebellar fibers originate in the *main* and *accessory olivary nuclei;* practically all of them cross to the opposite side through the median raphé of the medulla and enter the cerebellum by way of the interior cerebellar peduncle of that side (Fig. 159). The decussating olivocerebellar fibers are intermingled with those from the nuclei gracilis and cuneatus and are, therefore, included in the category of internal arcuate fibers. Olivocerebellar fibers are distributed to all parts of the cerebellar cortex. Affer-

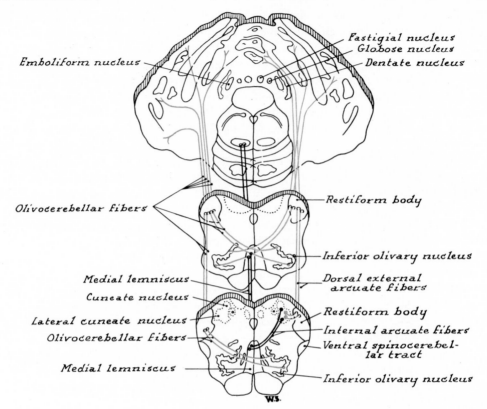

Fastigial nucleus
Globose nucleus
Dentate nucleus
Emboliform nucleus
Olivocerebellar fibers
Restiform body
Inferior olivary nucleus
Medial lemniscus
Cuneate nucleus
Dorsal external
arcuate fibers
Lateral cuneate nucleus
Restiform body
Olivocerebellar fibers
Internal arcuate fibers
Ventral spinocerebel-
lar tract
Medial lemniscus
Inferior olivary nucleus
W.S.

FIG. 159. Diagram to show the connections from the lateral cuneate and olivary nuclei to the cerebellum.

ent impulses from the spinal cord may, therefore, reach the paleo- and neocerebellum through the combined system of *spino-olivary* and *olivocerebellar fibers* (Fig. 159).

Reticulocerebellar fibers from both the medial and lateral reticular areas of the brain stem have been described. In the cat these fibers have been shown to be quite extensive (Brodal, 1953). In addition to the inclusion of the lateral reticular nucleus (Fig. 45) and the lateral tegmental area of the pons in such a system, Brodal described a "paramedian reticular nucleus" (medial to the middle-third of the olivary nucleus) which projects to the cerebellum through both uncrossed and crossed fibers with the uncrossed contingent being the more extensive. It

was shown, further, that the paramedian reticular nucleus receives afferent fibers from the spinal cord as well as descending afferents from higher brain stem centers.

Trigeminocerebellar fibers are believed to arise from the chief sensory and mesencephalic nuclei of the trigeminal nerve and enter the cerebellum with the ventral spinocerebellar fibers (Woodburne, 1936). *Tectocerebellar fibers* from the midbrain tectum have been described which course to the cerebellum along the medial aspect of the brachium conjunctivum (Woodburne, 1936; Larsell, 1951).

The **corticopontocerebellar system** of fibers is primarily related, both phylogenetically and ontogenetically, to the development of the neocortex and cere-

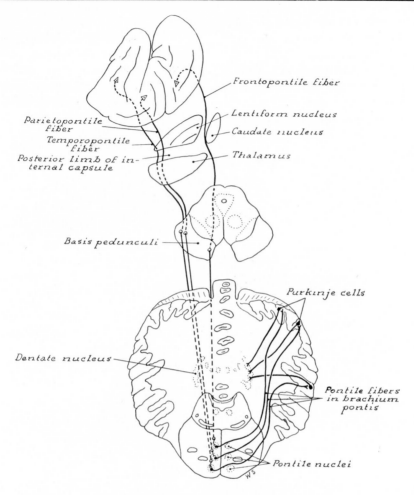

FIG. 160.   Cortico-ponto-cerebellar connections.   The origin and course of corticopontile fibers
are diagrammatically shown.

bellar hemispheres (neocerebellum). Thus, it is most highly developed in man. Corticopontine fibers arise particularly from the motor and premotor areas of the frontal lobe and lesser numbers arise from the temporal, parietal and occipital lobes (Fig. 160). *Frontopontile fibers* course caudally through the anterior limb of the internal capsule and the medial one-fifth of the basis pedunculi while the *temporo-, parieto-* and *occipitopontile fibers* traverse the posterior limb of the internal capsule and the lateral one-fifth of the basis pedunculi (Fig. 160). All the corticopontile fibers, upon reaching the basilar part of the pons, synapse upon the neurons whose cell bodies form the pontile nuclei. Pontocerebellar fibers originate in the pontile nuclei, decussate to the opposite side and enter the cerebellum by way of the middle cerebellar peduncle (Figs. 160 and 55). The great majority of these pontile fibers terminate in the neocerebellar cortex and some project to the paleocerebellum. Brodal and Jansen (1946) report that all parts of the vermis except the nodule receive pontocerebellar fibers.

It is now well established that in addition to proprioceptive stimuli the cerebellum receives projections from tactile, auditory and visual systems (Snider, 1952). These sensory-receiving areas are shown in Figures 161 and 162. It is believed that the reticulocerebellar system of fibers is involved in the relay of extero-

sponsible for a tactile projection from the face to cerebellum. Additionally, the visual and auditory systems have been shown to use brain stem nuclei for relay of stimuli to cerebellum, the superior colliculus for visual and the inferior colliculus and/or dorsal cochlear nucleus for auditory (Snider, 1950).

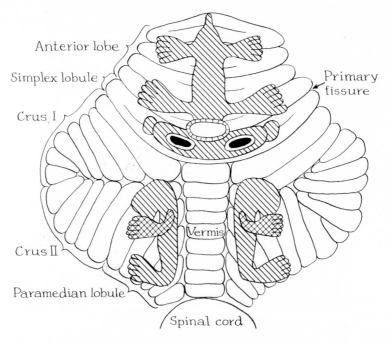

FIG. 161. Schematic drawing to illustrate the areas of projection of tactile impulses on the cerebellum of the cat (from Snider, 1952).

ceptive information as well as proprioceptive stimuli from the brain stem reticular substance to the cerebellar cortex. This seems likely since, for example, it is known that the ascending sensory systems of the cord give collaterals to the reticular nuclei of the brain stem. That the brain stem centers serve as relay stations for exteroceptive sensory information to the cerebellum is in accord with the studies of Brodal (1953) and Combs (1956) and with the observation of Snider (1943) that the fifth nerve with its brain stem nuclei is re-

Reference was made to the fact that the *Purkinje cells* are the efferent neurons of the cerebellar cortex and that these project to the cerebellar nuclei. Jansen and Brodal (1940, 1954) have shown that the pattern of projection as well as the arrangement of nuclei in relation to the cortex is such that the cerebellum can be divided into a series of *longitudinal zones, medial, intermediate,* and *lateral* (Fig. 163). It may be noted that the medial, or *vermal cortex,* projects to the *fastigial* (medial) nuclei and to the *vestibular nuclei.* The intermediate or *paravermal cortex* projects to the *interpositus nuclei (globose and emboliform),* and the lateral cortical zone projects to the *dentate (lateral nuclei).* The functional significance of these anatomical zones has been established by Chambers and Sprague (1955a, b). These authors established that in the cat the

(Fig. 163) receive projections from all divisions of the vermian cortex, areas of the paleocerebellum in which the spinocerebellar tracts end. They also receive some fibers from the vestibular nerve and nuclei. The fastigial nuclei give origin to the fastigiobulbar tracts which contain both crossed and uncrossed

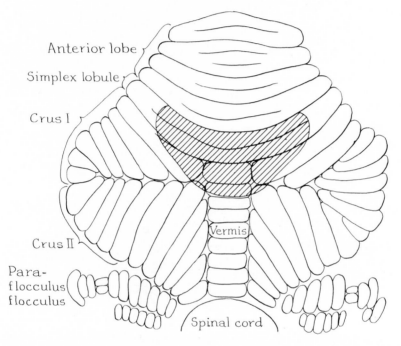

Anterior lobe

Simplex lobule

Crus I

Crus II

Para-
flocculus
flocculus

Vermis

Spinal cord

FIG. 162.   Schematic drawing to illustrate the area of projection of auditory and visual impulses on the cerebellum of the cat (from Snider, 1952).

median zone, vermal cortex and fastigial nuclei, are concerned with postural tone, equilibrium and movement of the entire body, and that the whole body is represented in each half of the vermis. The intermediate zone, paravermal cortex and nucleus interpositus, is concerned with discrete movements and postural reflexes of the ipsilateral limbs. These two cerebellar mechanisms were considered to fall into the functional classifications of motor activity known respectively as extrapyramidal and pyramidal.

It is apparent that the fastigial nuclei

fibers—chiefly the latter. The *fastigiobulbar tract* (of either side) descends in the medial part of the restiform body where its component fibers are intermingled with vestibulocerebellar fibers; it is distributed to the lateral and spinal vestibular nuclei and to cells in the reticular formation (Fig. 164). This system of fibers includes cerebello-olivary fibers to the inferior olivary nuclei. One bundle of fastigiobulbar fibers winds around the brachium conjunctivum before joining the main tract and is designated as the *uncinate fasciculus (of Russell).* Efferent

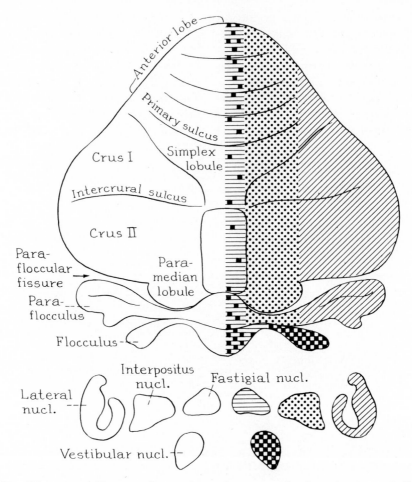

FIG. 163. Diagram to illustrate the corticonuclear zones in the primate cerebellum. The medial or vermal zone (horizontal lines) projects to the fastigial nucleus and to the vestibular nuclei; the intermediate or paravermal zone (stippled) projects to the interpositus nucleus; and the lateral zone (vertical lines) projects to the dentate nucleus (from Jansen and Brodal, 1954).

impulses, upon reaching the vestibular nuclei and reticular formation by way of the fastigiobulbar tract, may be relayed to ventral gray column cells of the spinal cord through the *vestibulospinal* and *reticulospinal tracts* or may be returned to the cerebellum by way of vestibulocerebellar or reticulocerebellar fibers and thus participate in closed (reverberating) circuits. The close functional interrelationship between the reticular formation and the anterior lobe of the cerebellum, in the cat, is indicated by the observation that stimulation of the lateral reticular formation, of the nucleus interpositus or of the lateral cortical area of the anterior lobe results in ipsilateral extension and contralateral flexion (Sprague and Chambers, 1954). Stimulation of the medial reticular formation, fastigial nucleus or medial cortical area produces a reciprocal type of reaction— ipsilateral flexion and contralateral extension.

The literature is controversial relative to the contribution of the fastigial nucleus

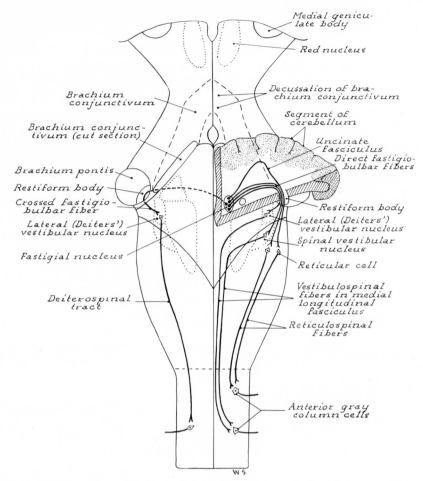

FIG. 164. Diagram of portions of the brain stem and spinal cord with a segment of cerebellum superimposed to show the fastigio-vestibulo-spinal and fastigio-reticulo-spinal connections.

to fibers in the superior cerebellar peduncle. Jansen and Jansen (1955) found that in the cat there is a fastigial component to the superior peduncle. Carpenter and Stevens (1957) concluded that in the monkey few, if any, fibers from the fastigial nuclei enter the superior cerebellar peduncle.

The **cerebellar reflex arc,** beginning with proprioceptors in muscles and contributed to by the dorsal and ventral spinocerebellar tracts, the cerebellar cortex, the fastigial nucleus and the vestibulospinal and reticulospinal tracts, aids in the maintenance of bilaterally balanced tonicity between extensor and flexor muscles of the neck, trunk, and lower extremities which is essential to the upright posture. The arc may also participate in the regulation of muscular activity by controlling the tone of the muscles antagonistic to those furnishing the positive force in a given voluntary or reflex act; over-action of the agonists and protagonists is thereby prevented and smooth movements are facilitated.

Efferent fibers from the flocculus are distributed exclusively to the superior and lateral vestibular nuclei (Dow, 1938) and those from the *nodule* and *uvula* go to the fastigial nucleus, the dorsal reticular formation of the medulla, all the vestibular nuclei and (a few only) to the medial longitudinal fasciculi. A cerebellar arc, involving these areas of cerebellar cortex is thus seen to be superimposed upon the simple vestibulospinal and vestibulo-ocular reflex arcs previously described (Chapter 8). It has been noted that unilateral destruction of

Deiters' vestibular nucleus, in the decerebrate animal, results in ipsilateral flexion and contralateral extension of the limbs similar to that following a fastigial lesion (Sprague and Chambers, 1953).

Nucleus interpositus (the combined globose and emboliform nuclei) receives Purkinje axons predominantly from the paravermian cortical zone (Fig. 163). It is apparent that this nucleus serves as the primary efferent nucleus for the paleocerebellum although it receives

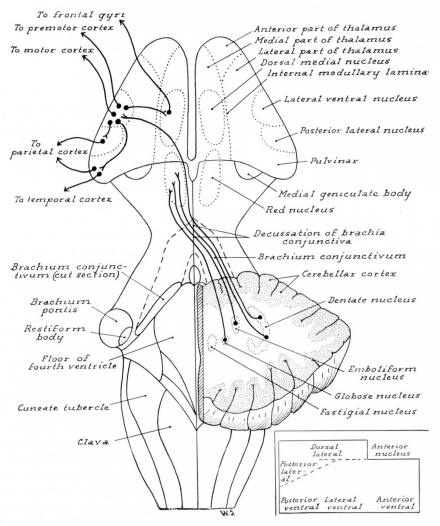

FIG. 165. Diagram to show the connections between the cerebellar nuclei and the red nucleus and those between the former nuclei and the thalamus. Inset (after Ranson) is a lateral projection of thalamic nuclei.

fibers from the medial part of the neo-cerebellum. Fibers from the interpositus and dentate nuclei enter the superior cerebellar peduncle (brachium conjunc-tivum) (Fig. 165). In the monkey, the dorsal two-thirds of the superior pedun-cle is said to contain fibers from nucleus interpositus and the dorsal part of the dentate nucleus, and the ventrolateral third contains fibers from the ventral and lateral portion of the dentate nucleus (Carpenter and Stevens, 1957). The superior cerebellar peduncle exits from the cerebellum through the isthmus re-gion of the pons, lateral to the anterior medullary velum (Figs. 165 and 59). It courses ventrally and medially into the tegmentum of the midbrain and decus-sates at the level of the inferior colliculi (Figs. 165, 141 and 61). After decus-sating, a smaller descending and a larger ascending limb are recognized. In the monkey, fibers from the descending limb are reported to arise mainly, if not ex-clusively, from the interposed and dor-sal part of the dentate nucleus (Carpenter and Stevens, 1957). These fibers were followed into the medial longitudinal fasciculus, to tegmental and reticular nuclei of the brain stem, to the inferior olivary nuclei and a few fibers to the cervical segments of the cord. The ascending limb, composed of fibers from the ventral and lateral part of the dentate nucleus and from nucleus interpositus were traced by Carpenter and Stevens (1957) to the contralateral red nucleus, lateral ventral nucleus of the thalamus and to globus pallidus.

From the **red nucleus, inferior olivary nucleus, tegmental and reticular nuclei** of the brain stem the descending path-ways for the relay of cerebellar impulses to other brain stem centers and the spinal cord include the rubrospinal, olivospinal and reticulospinal tracts. These were con-sidered in Chapter 16 in relation to the extrapyramidal system.

The lateral zone of the cerebellum in particular, and the intermediate zone to a lesser extent, can influence motor activ-ity at the level of the cerebral cortex. As indicated, these zones project to the interpositus and dentate nuclei (Fig. 163). These, in turn, provide a major input into the *lateral ventral nucleus* of the thalamus via the superior cerebellar peduncle (the major component comes from the dentate nucleus). Fibers from the red nucleus also reach the lateral ventral nucleus. The lateral ventral nu-cleus sends fibers through the internal capsule to the motor and premotor areas of the cerebral cortex (Fig. 165). Through this nucleus the neocerebellum, and the paleocerebellum to a lesser ex-tent, can influence motor activity at the level of the cortical neurons.

Cerebellar impulses, through inter-nuclear connections within the thalamus, may be conducted from the lateral ven-tral nucleus to the lateral part of the *dorsal medial nucleus* in the medial part of the thalamus, to the *dorsal lateral* and *posterior lateral nuclei* in the lateral part of the thalamus and to the *pulvinar* (Fig. 165). The lateral ventral nucleus sends fibers to the frontal gyri of the cerebrum. The dorsal and posterior lateral nuclei send fibers to the parietal lobules and the pulvinar projects upon the parietal and temporal lobes. It will be recalled that all these cortical areas give origin to extrapyramidal fibers (Chapter 16).

In the foregoing discussion of cere-bellar structure and function, brief ref-erences have been made relative to the projection of other than proprioceptive impulses to the cerebellum. During re-cent years, a number of studies have shown that tactile areas exist in the cere-bellar cortex (Dow, 1939; Snider and Stowell, 1944a, b; Adrian, 1943; Snider, 1950). In accord with these studies, Morin and Linder (1953) demonstrated conduction of tactile impulses from the

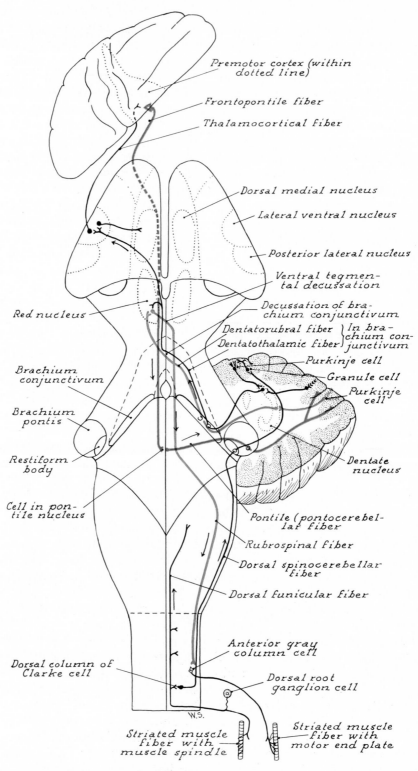

FIG. 166. Diagrammatic representation of some of the circuits involved in the coordination of complex muscular activity.

hairs around the foot pads of cats to the *paramedian lobules* of the cerebellum by way of both dorsal and ventral spinocerebellar tracts. The projection of tactile impulses is ipsilateral with a somatotropic pattern of localization (Fig. 161). The body surface is represented in the anterior lobe and bilaterally in the posterior lobe. Snider and Stowell (1944a) and Snider (1950) also demonstrated auditory and visual areas in the cerebellum (Fig. 162). These investigators have also provided evidence that motor, tactile, auditory and visual areas in the cerebrum project to these same cerebellar areas which in turn project back on the cerebral areas.

In summary, it may be said that the cerebellum receives a great variety of sensory impulses which are there monitored and/or coordinated. The cerebellum in turn projects the synthesized or appropriate impulses to the motor centers of the brain stem, spinal cord, and cerebral cortex for controlling the motoneurons (Fig. 166). The expression of control is in the maintenance of equilibrium; in the maintenance of muscle tone (*e.g.,* necessary for standing); and in the control of voluntary movements. The flocculonodular lobe is primarily concerned with vestibular mechanisms. The medial (vermal-fastigial) zone is concerned with postural mechanisms, equilibrium and movement of the entire body. The intermediate zone (paravermal-interpositus) is concerned with discrete movements and postural reflexes of the ipsilateral limbs. The lateral-dentate zone, which is most highly developed in primates, is particularly concerned with the control of discrete voluntary movements of the limbs. The signs of cerebellar disease are given in the next chapter and should serve to clarify these control mechanisms.

It is appropriate to add a few remarks relative to the more conventional division of the cerebellum into transverse zones versus the longitudinal division that has been given and which is based upon recent anatomical and physiological studies.

The transverse division separating the flocculonodular lobe (archicerebellum) from the corpus cerebelli is justified since the flocculonodular lobe is apparently concerned with vestibular phenomena only. However, for the *corpus cerebelli,* division into the three longitudinal zones is more meaningful, as has been indicated above. This is further supported by the signs and symptoms of cerebellar lesions in man. It is to be emphasized, however, that there are no sharp boundaries between these longitudinal zones. Additionally, it may be said that with respect to the phylogenetic considerations of the cerebellum, the medial zone of corpus cerebelli is roughly comparable to the parts long considered as paleocerebellum, and the intermediate and lateral zones are comparable to the neocerebellum. On the basis of fiber connections, however, these subdivisions are not distinguishable since pontocerebellar connections are distributed to paleocerebellum as well as neocerebellum (Brodal and Jansen, 1954). These investigators question the advisability of upholding the terms paleo- and neocerebellum due to the difficulty of defining them precisely.

The potential reverberating circuits involving the cerebellum and other brain and cord centers (Fig. 166) provide prime examples of neural loops that are involved in control mechanisms that may be compared with *servo-mechanisms* (Wiener, 1961). This is particularly well illustrated in the case of reciprocal cerebellocerebral connections.

BIBLIOGRAPHY

ADRIAN, E. D., 1943: Afferent areas in the cerebellum connected with the limbs. Brain *66*, 289-315.

BRODAL, A., 1953: Reticulo-cerebellar connections in the cat. An experimental study. J. Comp. Neurol., *98*, 113-153.

BRODAL, A. and JANSEN, J., 1946: The ponto-cerebellar projection in the rabbit and cat. Experimental investigations. J. Comp. Neurol., *84*, 31-118.

CARPENTER, M. B. and STEVENS, G. H., 1957: Structural and functional relationships between the deep cerebellar nuclei and the brachium conjunctivum in the rhesus monkey. J. Comp. Neurol., *107*, 109-163.

CARREA, R. M. E., REISSIG, M. and METTLER, F. A., 1947: The climbing fibers of the simian and feline cerebellum: experimental inquiry into their origin by lesions of the inferior olives and deep cerebellar nuclei. J. Comp. Neurol., *87*, 321-365.

CARREA, R. M. E. and GRUNDFEST, H., 1954: Electrophysiological studies of cerebellar inflow. I. Origin, conduction and termination of ventral spino-cerebellar tract in monkey and cat. J. Neurophysiol., *17*, 208-238.

CHAMBERS, W. W. and SPRAGUE, J. M., 1955a: Functional localization in the cerebellum. I. Organization in longitudinal cortico-nuclear zones and their contribution to the control of posture, both extrapyramidal and pyramidal. J. Comp. Neurol., *103*, 105-129.

———— 1955b: Functional localization in the cerebellum. II. Somatotopic organization in cortex and nuclei. A.M.A. Arch. Neurol. Psychiat., *74*, 653-680.

COMBS, C. M., 1956: Bulbar regions related to localized cerebellar afferent impulses. J. Neurophysiol., *19*, 285-300.

DOW, R. S., 1936: The fiber connections of the posterior parts of the cerebellum in the rat and cat. J. Comp. Neurol., *63*, 527-548.

———— 1938: Efferent connections of the flocculonodular lobe in *Macaca mulatta*. J. Comp. Neurol., *68*, 297-305.

———— 1939: Cerebellar action potentials in response to stimulation of various afferent connections. J. Neurophysiol., *2*, 543-555.

———— 1942: The evolution and anatomy of the cerebellum. Biol. Rev., *17*, 179-220.

FERRARO, A. and BARRERA, S. E., 1935: The nuclei of the posterior funiculi in *Macacus rhesus*. A.M.A. Arch. Neurol. Psychiat., *33*, 262-275.

FOX, C. A. and BARNARD, J. W., 1957: A quantitative study of the Purkinje cell dendritic branchlets and their relationship to afferent fibers. J. Anat. (Lond.), *91*, 299-313.

GRUNDFEST, H. and CARTER, W. B., 1954: Afferent relations of inferior olivary nucleus. I. Electrophysiological demonstration of dorsal spino-olivary tract in cat. J. Neurophysiol., *17*, 72-91.

JANSEN, J, 1933: Experimental studies on the intrinsic fibers of the cerebellum. I. The arcuate fibers. J. Comp. Neurol., *57*, 369-399.

JANSEN, J. and BRODAL, A., 1940: Experimentail studies on the intrinsic fibers of the cerebellum. II. The cortico-nuclear projection. J. Comp. Neurol., *73*, 267-321.

———— 1954: *Aspects of Cerebellar Anatomy*, J. JANSEN and A. BRODAL, eds., Gunderson, Oslo.

JANSEN, J. and JANSEN, J. JR., 1955: On the efferent fibers of the cerebellar nuclei in the cat. J. Comp. Neurol., *102*, 607-632.

LARSELL, O., 1937: The cerebellum. A.M.A. Arch. Neurol. Psychiat., *38*, 580-607.

———— 1951: *Anatomy of the Nervous System*. Appleton-Century-Crofts, Inc., New York.

MORIN, F. and HADDAD, B., 1953: Afferent projections to the cerebellum and the spinal pathways involved. Am. J. Physiol., *172*, 497-510.

MORIN, F. and LINDNER, D., 1953: Pathways for conduction of tactile impulses to the paramedian lobule of the cerebellum of the cat. Am. J. Physiol., *175*, 247-250.

SNIDER, R. S., 1943: A fifth cranial nerve projection to the cerebellum. Fed. Proc., *2*, 46.

———— 1950: Recent contributions to the anatomy and physiology of the cerebellum. A.M.A. Arch. Neurol. Psychiat., *64*, 196-219.

———— 1952: Interrelations of cerebellum and brain stem. Assoc. Res. Nerv. Ment. Dis., *30*, 267-281.

SNIDER, R. S. and STOWELL, A., 1944a: Receiving areas of the tactile, auditory and visual systems in the cerebellum. J. Neurophysiol., *7*, 331-357.

———— 1944b: Electroanatomical studies on a tactile system in the cerebellum of monkey (*Macaca mulatta*). Anat. Rec., *88*, 457.

SPRAGUE, J. M. and CHAMBERS, W. W., 1953: Regulation of posture in intact and decerebrate cat. I. Cerebellum, reticular formation, vestibular nuclei. J. Neurophysiol., *16*, 451-463.

———— 1954: Control of posture by reticular formation and cerebellum in the intact, anesthetized and unanesthetized and in the decerebrated cat. Am. J. Physiol., *176*, 52-64.

WIENER, N., 1961: *Cybernetics or Control and Communication in the Animal and the Machine*. The M.I.T. Press and John Wiley & Sons, New York.

WOODBURNE, R. T., 1936: A phylogenetic consideration of the primary and secondary centers and connections of the trigeminal complex in a series of vertebrates. J. Comp. Neurol., *65*, 403-501.

YOSS, R. E., 1953: Studies of the spinal cord. Part II. Topographic localization within the ventral spino-cerebellar tract in the *Macaque*. J. Comp. Neurol., *99*, 613-638.

Chapter 19

Cerebellar Dysfunction

CONCLUSIONS as to the function of the cerebellum in man are based upon the symptomatology that results from partial destruction of it by tumors or other lesions and upon the results of animal experiments. That the cerebellum is mainly a reflex center is indicated by the fact that extensive injuries to it do not cause loss of sensory perception.

The **flocculonodular lobe** is concerned with the maintenance of equilibrium or balance. Dow (1938a) demonstrated that monkeys in which this lobe was removed had gross disturbances of equilibrium without impairment in volitional movements or changes in reflexes. An animal so operated is unable to stand or walk without swaying or falling but uses his hands effectively in feeding without tremor. Tumors (medulloblastomas) of the flocculonodular lobe, which occur not uncommonly in children, cause symptoms comparable to those produced by the isolated ablations in monkeys. The patient is very unsteady on his feet, walks on a wide base, sways from side to side and he may be unable to maintain an upright position. The individual movements of the limbs are not impaired when lying in bed and there are no reflex changes. The flocculonodular lobe, therefore, appears to be exclusively concerned with the maintenance of equilibrium as might be expected in view of Dow's statements (1936 and 1938b) that most of its afferent and efferent connections are with the vestibular nerves and nuclei (Chapter 18).

The **experimental studies** of Chambers and Sprague (1955a, b) which support the anatomical studies of Jansen and Brodal (1954) have, as indicated above, contributed importantly to understanding the function of the corpus cerebelli and emphasize the importance of the concept of cerebellar organization in terms of longitudinal corticonuclear zones. These investigators, from ablation and stimulation experiments, have defined three bilaterally symmetrical zones in the cerebellum of cats. Each medial zone (vermal cortex and fastigial nucleus) regulates tone, posture, locomotion, and equilibrium of the entire body. Each intermediate zone (paravermal cortex and nucleus interpositus) is concerned with the regulation of spatially organized and skilled movements as well as the tone and posture associated with these movements of the ipsilateral limbs. Each lateral zone (cortex and dentate nucleus) is also concerned with the regulation of skilled and spatially organized movements of the ipsilateral limbs with no apparent role in the regulation of posture and tone. This analysis shows that vestibular function is not limited to the flocculonodular lobe and that the anterior lobe is not a functional unit as implied by the more conventional division of the cerebellum into lobes by the transverse fissures.

The studies of Jansen and Brodal (1954) and those of Chambers and Sprague (1955a, b) show that the paravermal and lateral zones of the cerebellum are particularly concerned with the control of volitional movements. The development of the lateral zone especially may be correlated with the development of manual dexterity in primates. Thus, in man particularly, pronounced symptoms are produced by disease processes which disturb neocerebellar mechanisms.

With lesions which involve the lateral and intermediate zones of the cerebellum or the cerebellocerebral circuit, movements tend to become *ataxic* (jerky and intermittent) and *dysmetric* (overshoot their objectives). The direction of movements is inaccurate (*pastpointing*) and rapidly alternating movements such as pronation and supination of the hands or flexion and extension of the fingers are not well performed; the latter deficiency is termed *adiadochokinesis*. *Rebound phenomena* and *decomposition of movement* are also likely to be present. In the former the patient tries to maintain flexion of the elbow against traction applied by the examiner; sudden cessation of traction results in abrupt and uncontrolled flexion of the elbow. By decomposition of movement is meant the breaking down of a complex movement, which is normally accomplished by simultaneous movements of several joints, into a succession of movements which involve only one joint at a time. (It will be recalled that the lateral and intermediate zones are essentially comparable to neocerebellum.)

Neocerebellar lesions in man may also cause *hypotonia* (diminished resistance to passive movement) and *tremor*. Cerebellar tremors increase toward the end of a given movement and are associated with dysmetria. Lesions confined to the cerebellar cortex do not result in enduring and pronounced tremors, according to Fulton (1949); when such tremors are produced by cerebellar lesions it indicates that the central nuclei have been damaged.

Nystagmus as a manifestation of damage to the internal ear, vestibular nerve, or vestibular nuclei has been discussed (Chapter 8). That the cerebellum is superimposed upon the vestibulo-ocular pathways is indicated by the fact that nystagmus is very likely to be a symptom of cerebellar lesions in man. It is probable that the cerebellum exerts its influence upon the extrinsic muscles of the eyes through the cerebello-vestibular connections described in the preceding chapter and through connections from cerebellar nuclei to the central gray matter surrounding the cerebral aqueduct in the midbrain, and to the posterior commissural nuclei (Rand, 1954) which send fibers caudally through the medial longitudinal fasciculi. The motor nuclei of the nerves to the muscles of the eye may receive impulses from either central gray matter or posterior commissural nuclei. Nystagmus may appear in patients with lesions in any part of the cerebellum except the posterior midline portions.

Asynergia, or lack of coördination, of the many muscles involved in *speech* results from cerebellar lesions. Consequently, the speech of individuals with such lesions tends to be thick and monotonous in character. *Speech coördination* has been variously localized in the lingula, lobulus simplex (declive monticuli and posterior part of the quadrangular lobule), uvula, and nodule. As suggested by Fulton (1949), "It would be more logical to believe that speech was integrated by the newer parts of the cerebellum since speech is one of the latest capacities to develop in evolutionary history." There is no evidence of dominance of one side of the cerebellum in relation to speech such as exists in the cerebral cortex.

Fulton (1949) has observed that speech is not seriously affected except by very large lesions of the cerebellum that affect the deeply placed nuclei. Variously described disturbances of speech have been noted, however, in cases of parenchymatous cortical cerebellar atrophy where the central nuclei were well preserved in the presence of marked loss of Purkinje cells and other manifestations of severe cortical degeneration (Parker and Kernohan, 1933).

The influence of the cerebellum is exerted ipsilaterally; ataxia, tremor, hypotonia, dysmetrica and other signs of cerebellar deficit localized to one or the other side of the body therefore indicate a lesion in the ipsilateral half of the cerebellum. Furthermore, the signs of cerebellar deficit are qualitatively the same whether the cerebellum itself, its afferent pathways, or its efferent pathways are damaged.

Localization of function in the cerebellum, so far as the control of specific parts of the body is concerned, is indefinite. In general, according to Brock (1945) and others (Chambers and Sprague, 1955a), the cerebellar hemispheres control the ipsilateral extremities and the vermis controls the trunk. In cases of involvement of one hemisphere the subject staggers to that side and there is likely to be irregular over-stepping and over-abduction of the ipsilateral lower extremity; there may be slight inward deviation of the foot (pes varus). The upper extremity may swing less freely than is normal when walking and the slight flexion normally present in the elbow and fingers may be lost. The trunk is often concave toward the involved side and the head may be inclined toward that side. Lesions of the anterior part of the vermis in man cause the subject to stagger forward and disease of the posterior vermis may result in a tendency to fall backward.

Tabes dorsalis, sometimes known as locomotor ataxia, has been referred to (Chapter 5). In the tabetic type of ataxia there is loss or diminution of conscious perception of all types of sensibility carried by the posterior funiculi and loss or marked diminution of deep reflexes. In cerebellar ataxia there is no interference with the conscious perception of posterior column sensibility and there is only slight diminution of the deep reflexes; in addition there may be nystagmus and postural deviations. There may be a pendular type of knee jerk in cerebellar ataxia, disturbances in equilibrium, and speech abnormalities. The sensory loss in tabes and the preservation of all types of sensory perception in cerebellar lesions are the most important considerations in differentiating the two conditions.

In the hereditary condition known as *Friedreich's ataxia* the spinocerebellar tracts in the spinal cord, the dorsal funiculi and the lateral corticospinal tracts are all more or less degenerated. The subject is ataxic in all skilled movements and there is hypotonia of the muscles of the extremities; these symptoms are due to the involvement of the spinocerebellar tracts and illustrate the fact that such involvement may give rise to the same syndrome as lesions in the cerebellum itself. Friedreich's ataxia is further characterized by defective joint and muscle sensibility, loss of vibratory sensibility and diminution in tactile discriminative ability; these symptoms are due to degeneration of the posterior funiculi. The abdominal reflexes are usually absent bilaterally and there are bilateral Babinski signs as a result of lateral corticospinal tract involvement.

Cerebellopontile angle tumors (acoustic neurinomas) have been discussed (Chapter 8) and reference was made to the fact that the biventral lobule of the cerebellum is likely to be involved by them. This results in the development of symptoms of neocerebellar deficit such as have been described, in addition to the sensory and motor loss attributed to involvement of the eighth, fifth, ninth, seventh, sixth, and tenth cranial nerves, all of which enter or emerge from the brain stem in the region of the cerebellopontile angle. Eighth nerve neurinomas were previously mentioned as the type of tumor most commonly encountered in this location. Tumors arising in the cerebellum and expanding downward into the angle may, however, produce the same combination of symptoms.

BIBLIOGRAPHY

BROCK, S., 1945: *The Basis of Clinical Neurology*, 2nd ed., Williams & Wilkins Co., Baltimore.

BRODAL, A. and JANSEN, J., 1946: The ponto-cerebellar projection in the rabbit and cat. Experimental investigations. J. Comp. Neurol., *84*, 31-118.

CHAMBERS, W. W. and SPRAGUE, J. M., 1955a: Functional localization in the cerebellum. I. Organization in longitudinal cortico-nuclear zones and their contribution to the control of posture, both extrapyramidal and pyramidal. J. Comp. Neurol., *103*, 105-129.

———— 1955b: Functional localization in the cerebellum. II. Somatotopic organization in cortex and nuclei. A.M.A. Arch. Neurol. Psychiat., *74*, 653-680.

Dow, R. S., 1936: The fiber connections of the posterior parts of the cerebellum in the rat and cat. J. Comp. Neurol., *63*, 527-548.

———— 1938a: Effect of lesions in the vestibular part of the cerebellum in primates. A.M.A. Arch. Neurol. Psychiat., *40*, 500-520.

———— 1938b: Efferent connections of the flocculonodular lobe in *Macaca mulatta*. J. Comp. Neurol., *68*, 297-305.

FULTON, J. F., 1949: *Physiology of the Nervous System*, Oxford University Press, New York.

JANSEN, J. and BRODAL, A., 1954: *Aspects of Cerebellar Anatomy*. J. JANSEN and A. BRODAL, eds., Gunderson, Oslo.

PARKER, H. L. and KERNOHAN, J. W., 1933: Parenchymatous cortical cerebellar atrophy (chronic atrophy of Purkinje's cells). Brain, *56*, 191-212.

RAND, R. W., 1954: An anatomical and experimental study of the cerebellar nuclei and their efferent pathways in the monkey. J. Comp. Neurol., *101*, 167-223.

Chapter 20

The Diencephalon

THE diencephalon (Figs. 167 and 168), or rostral portion of the brain stem is classically divided into four parts; *epithalamus; dorsal thalamus,* or thalamus proper; *hypothalamus;* and *subthalamus.* The term *interbrain* has frequently been applied to the diencephalon. The appropriateness of this term must have

tral thalamus, is functionally interrelated with the basal ganglia, and it has been adequately described.

The epithalamus is dorsally, caudally and medially placed with respect to the other divisions of the diencephalon. It is continuous caudally with the pretectum of the mesencephalon (Figs. 168

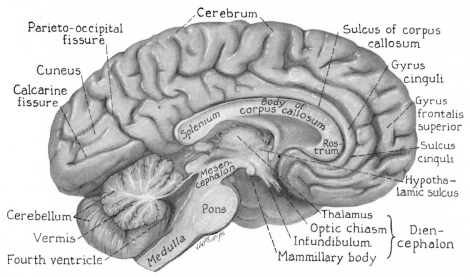

FIG. 167.   Drawing of the medial surface of adult brain illustrating the major divisions and the structures visible in a sagittal section.

become apparent to the reader who has followed the somatic and visceral sensory pathways and the extralemniscal (reticular arousal) system upward from lower levels, through the diencephalon to the cerebral cortex and who has followed the extrapyramidal system from its origin in the cerebral cortex and subcortical structures to lower motor centers. The subthalamus, often called the ven-

and 170). The structures which constitute the epithalamus include the *pineal body,* the *habenulae,* the *habenular commissure,* and the *striae medullares* (Figs. 168, 170 and 171).

The *pineal body* or epiphysis is a small projection of tissue from the dorsal diencephalic roof at the caudal margin of the habenular trigones in the region of the posterior commissure. Its dorso-

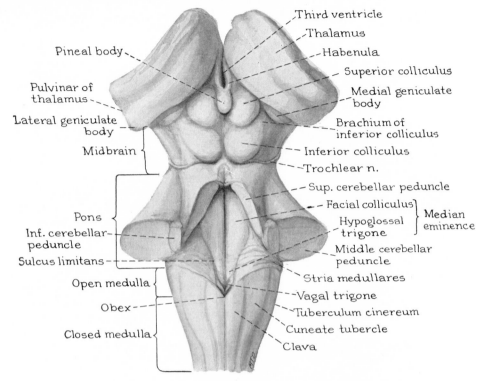

Pineal body

Pulvinar of thalamus

Lateral geniculate body

Midbrain

Pons

Inf. cerebellar-peduncle

Sulcus limitans

Open medulla

Obex

Closed medulla

Third ventricle

Thalamus

Habenula

Superior colliculus

Medial geniculate body

Brachium of inferior colliculus

Inferior colliculus

Trochlear n.

Sup. cerebellar peduncle

Facial colliculus

Hypoglossal trigone

Median eminence

Middle cerebellar peduncle

Stria medullares

Vagal trigone

Tuberculum cinereum

Cuneate tubercle

Clava

FIG. 168.   Drawing of the brain stem, dorsal view.

caudal extension is in relation to the superior colliculi. Most of the cells within the epiphysis are of glial types. In addition, there are parenchymal cells (pineocytes) which probably have a secretory role (Kelly, 1962). Photoreceptor cells which are characteristic of lower vertebrate pineal systems have not been described for birds and mammals. Little is known about the function of the epiphysis in man and other mammals. An input of fibers from the stria medullares and habenular ganglia has been described.

The habenula receives terminals from the stria medullaris and is the origin of the habenulopeduncular tract (Chapter 23).

The **dorsal thalamus** (thalamus proper) is a receiving station for sensory information from receptors throughout the body and, in fact, except for primary olfactory stimuli, serves as a relay station for all incoming sensory information which is destined for the cerebral cortex. It also serves to distribute impulses to other regions of the brain and there is good evidence that the thalamus serves to integrate much of the information received. As mentioned earlier, it would appear that pain and perhaps other sensory modalities are appreciated at thalamic level. In addition to the incoming sensory information, the thalamus receives impulses from the cerebral cortex, basal ganglia and cerebellum. Although a brief orientation to the thalamus, together with an account of certain nuclei including their afferent and efferent connections, has been given in preceding chapters, it seems desirable to present in this section a more organized account of all the major thalamic nuclei and related fiber systems.

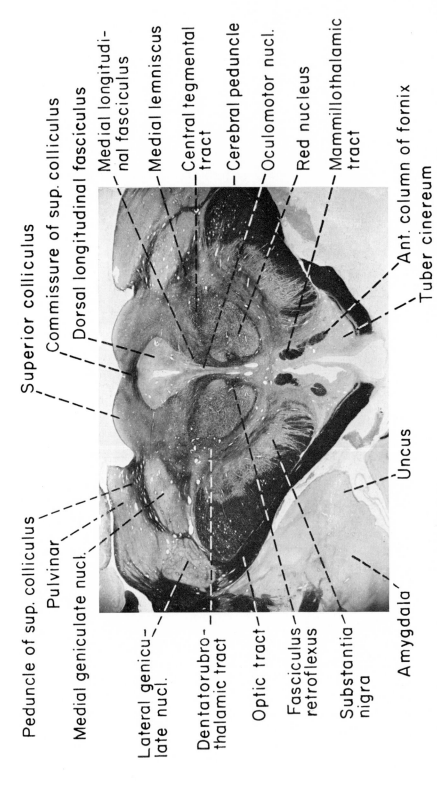

Peduncle of sup. colliculus
Pulvinar
Medial geniculate nucl.

Superior colliculus
Commissure of sup. colliculus
Dorsal longitudinal fasciculus
Medial longitudinal fasciculus
Medial lemniscus
Central tegmental tract
Cerebral peduncle
Oculomotor nucl.
Red nucleus
Mammillothalamic tract

Ant. column of fornix
Tuber cinereum

Uncus

Amygdala

Lateral geniculate nucl.
Dentatorubrothalamic tract
Optic tract
Fasciculus retroflexus
Substantia nigra

Fig. 169. Photomicrograph of transverse section through the rostral part of the superior collicular level of the midbrain which passes through the posterior thalamic nuclei. Weil stain.

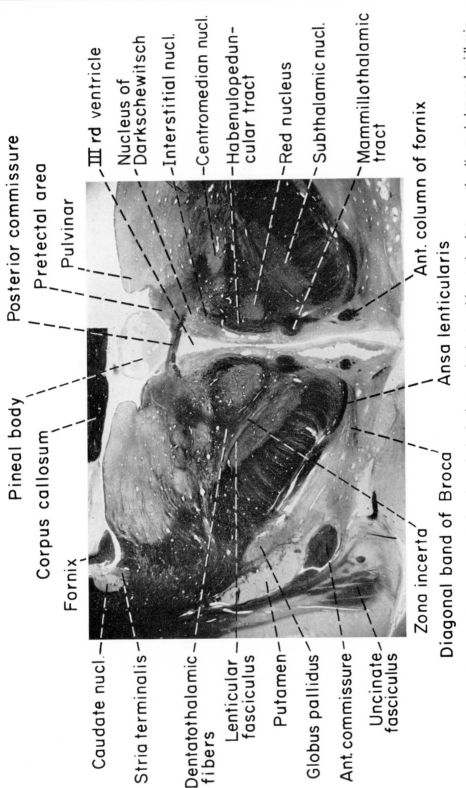

Posterior commissure

Pineal body

Corpus callosum

Fornix

Pretectal area

Pulvinar

IIIrd ventricle

Nucleus of Darkschewitsch

Interstitial nucl.

Centromedian nucl.

Habenulopeduncular tract

Red nucleus

Subthalamic nucl.

Mammillothalamic tract

Ant. column of fornix

Ansa lenticularis

Diagonal band of Broca

Zona incerta

Uncinate fasciculus

Ant. commissure

Globus pallidus

Putamen

Lenticular fasciculus

Dentatothalamic fibers

Stria terminalis

Caudate nucl.

FIG. 170.   Photomicrograph of a transverse section through the brain stem in the transition region between the diencephalon and midbrain. In addition to thalamic nuclei, several subthalamic structures are shown.   Weil stain.

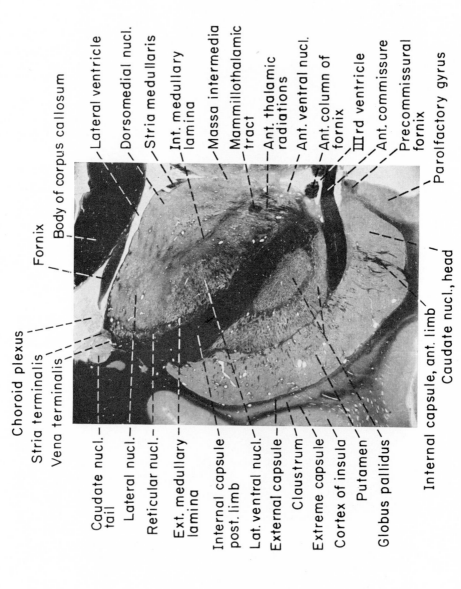

Choroid plexus
Stria terminalis
Vena terminalis

Fornix
Body of corpus callosum

Lateral ventricle
Dorsomedial nucl.
Stria medullaris
Int. medullary lamina
Massa intermedia
Mammillothalamic tract
Ant. thalamic radiations
Ant. ventral nucl.
Ant. column of fornix
IIIrd ventricle
Ant. commissure
Precommissural fornix

Parolfactory gyrus

Caudate nucl. tail
Lateral nucl.
Reticular nucl.
Ext. medullary lamina
Internal capsule post. limb
Lat. ventral nucl.
External capsule
Claustrum
Extreme capsule
Cortex of insula
Putamen
Globus pallidus

Internal capsule, ant. limb
Caudate nucl., head

Fig. 171. Photomicrograph of an oblique section through the diencephalon and basal telencephalon illustrating the thalamus and basal ganglia. The section passes through the middle third of the thalamus. Weil stain.

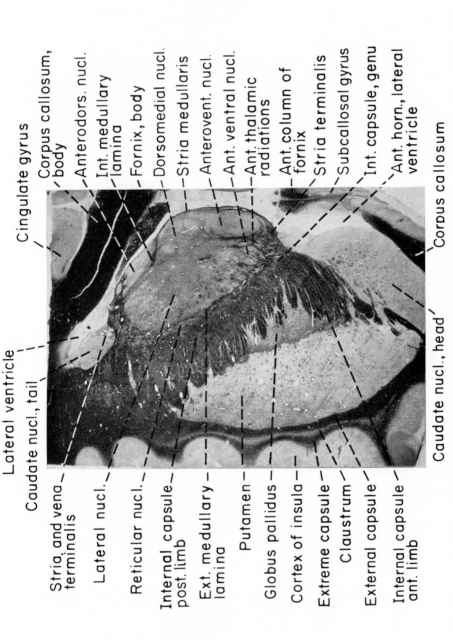

Lateral ventricle

Caudate nucl., tail

Cingulate gyrus

Corpus callosum, body

Anterodors. nucl.

Int. medullary lamina

Fornix, body

Dorsomedial nucl.

Stria medullaris

Anterovent. nucl.

Ant. ventral nucl.

Ant. thalamic radiations

Ant. column of fornix

Stria terminalis

Subcallosal gyrus

Int. capsule, genu

Ant. horn, lateral ventricle

Stria, and vena terminalis

Lateral nucl.

Reticular nucl.

Internal capsule post. limb

Ext. medullary lamina

Putamen

Globus pallidus

Cortex of insula

Extreme capsule

Claustrum

External capsule

Internal capsule ant. limb

Caudate nucl., head

Corpus callosum

FIG. 172. Photomicrograph of an oblique section through the rostral third of the thalamus which shows the relation of the thalamus to internal capsule, lentiform nucleus and head of caudate.

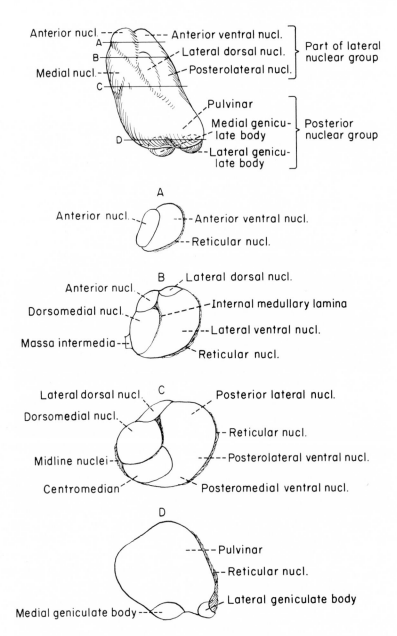

FIG. 173. The upper drawing is a schematic representation of the human thalamus which shows the positional relations of the major thalamic nuclei. *A-C* are cross-section diagrams of the thalamus at the levels indicated.

The thalamus consists in large part of gray matter which may be divided into 5 major nuclear groups, *anterior, midline, medial, lateral* and *posterior* (Figs. 169-173). This division, which is based upon the studies of Walker (1938) for the monkey, has been shown to be applicable for man (Sheps, 1945; Toncray and Krieg, 1946) and is used quite generally for all primates. The following list of thalamic nuclei, which is in accord with that of Walker, is very similar to the listing of Sheps for man. Not all of the described nuclei are included here since our knowledge of their connections and functions is incomplete.

I. Anterior nuclei

These are enclosed by the diverging limbs of the internal medullary lamina which separates this group from the other thalamic nuclei (Fig. 173). Of the three described nuclei in this group, *anteromedial, anterodorsal* and *anteroventral,* the latter is best developed in man (Fig. 172). The anterior nuclei receive connections via the *mammillothalamic tract* and project to gyrus cinguli (Fig. 199), especially to areas 23 and 24 of Brodmann.

II. Midline nuclei

These include groups of cells adjacent to the wall of the third ventricle as well as cells in the *massa intermedia* (Figs. 171 and 173). The latter is absent in about 25 per cent of human brains. The midline nuclei receive fibers from the major ascending sensory tracts (spinothalamic, trigeminothalamic and medial lemniscus), from the reticular formation and from other thalamic nuclei. Midline nuclei have efferent projections to the hypothalamus, to the cortex of the anterior rhinencephalon and probably to the basal ganglia. Efferent connections are also made with other thalamic nuclei. Walker (1938) expressed the view that these nuclei receive impulses from the axial part of the body and that they may be able to integrate some of the information received.

III. Medial nuclei

Of the seven medial nuclei which have been described between the midline nuclei and the internal medullary lamina, only two are considered here, the *dorsomedial* and *centromedian* (Figs. 170, 171 and 173, *C*). The prominent dorsomedial nucleus receives fibers from other thalamic nuclei, from the hypothalamus, septal areas, and from the prefrontal and temporal pole cortex. The major projections are to the prefrontal cortex and to the hypothalamus. Since this nucleus receives fibers from many of the surrounding nuclei, it probably serves to integrate much of the visceral and somatic information coming into the thalamus and then projects it to the frontal lobe (Walker, 1959). In this context it is significant that destruction of the dorsomedial nucleus, thalamotomy, is an effective surgical procedure for the treatment of certain patients with severe personality disorders (Spiegel, 1952).

The centromedian nucleus is large and easily recognized since it is partially surrounded by fibers of the internal medullary lamina. Little is known about the connections of this nucleus in man, although connections to other thalamic nuclei and to the putamen and caudate nucleus have been described (McLardy, 1948). Although the literature relative to the connections of nucleus centromedian is quite controversial, it is generally agreed that it does not project to the cortex. Since it has many connections with other thalamic nuclei, it is probable that its primary role is that of intrathalamic correlation. In addition to nucleus centromedian, three other small nuclei are described which are within the internal medullary lamina. All of these are often referred to as the *intralaminar group.* The nuclei in this group are generally considered to be a part of the nonspecific or *diffuse thalamocortical system* (Morison and Dempsey, 1942; Jasper, 1949). A further discussion of this system is given on page 238.

IV. Lateral nuclei

This is a large group located between the internal and external medullary laminae and extending to the *pulvinar* posteriorly (Figs. 171-173). The group also includes the reticular nucleus which is outside the external medullary lamina. Nuclei of the lateral group to be considered are the *anterior ventral, lateral ventral, posterolateral ventral, posteromedial ventral, dorsal lateral, posterior lateral* and *reticular.*

The anterior ventral nucleus receives fibers from the globus pallidus through the thalamic fasciculus and sends fibers to the corpus striatum (see Chapter 16). Connections of this nucleus with the premotor cortex have been reported (Bucy, 1949).

The lateral ventral nucleus receives fibers from the cerebellum through the superior cerebellar peduncle (Fig. 166) and from the globus pallidus via the thalamic fasciculus (Fig. 140). The efferent fibers course through the posterior limb of the internal capsule to the motor and premotor areas of the cerebral cortex (Fig. 166). In monkeys, fibers from the premotor cortex to the lateral ventral nucleus have been described (Mettler, 1947).

As discussed in Chapter 5, the posterolateral ventral nucleus is the terminus of the spinothalamic tracts and of the medial lemniscus. Fibers from the cervical segments end medially and those from more caudal segments end more laterally in the nucleus (Fig. 174). The posteromedial ventral nucleus, also called *semilunar nucleus,* is the terminus of the secondary trigeminal fibers and of the secondary taste fibers. These two nuclei, in which there is a topographic arrangement of the terminating fibers, project through the posterior limb of the internal capsule (Fig. 175) to cortical areas 3, 1 and 2 of the postcentral gyrus where the topographic pattern is maintained (Fig. 174).

The dorsal lateral and the posterior lateral nuclei receive fibers from other thalamic nuclei and project to parietal lobe cortex. Fibers from the parietal lobe to these nuclei have also been described.

The reticular nucleus receives fibers from the nuclei of the midline and medial group, and projects to all parts of the cerebral cortex. The pattern of cortical projection has been shown to be organized in a rostrocaudal direction (Walker, 1938; Chow and Pribram, 1956).

V. Posterior nuclei *(medial and lateral geniculate and pulvinar)*

The medial geniculate nucleus (Fig. 169) receives auditory information through the brachium of the inferior colliculus and projects to the auditory cortex through the acoustic radiations which course in the sublenticular part of the internal capsule (Fig. 175) (see Chapter 8).

The lateral geniculate nucleus (Fig. 169) relays visual impulses to the visual cortex. The nucleus receives optic tract fibers, and the cortical projections are via the sub- and retrolenticular part of the internal capsule (Fig. 175). The medial part of the lateral geniculate nucleus receives fibers from the upper retinal quadrants and projects to the

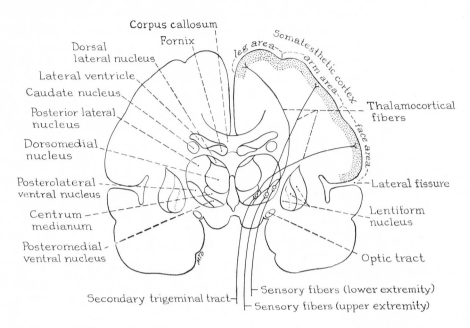

FIG. 174. Diagram showing the termination of sensory tracts in the nuclei of the lateral part of the thalamus and the projection of these nuclei upon the somatesthetic cortex by way of the internal capsule (modified from Ranson).

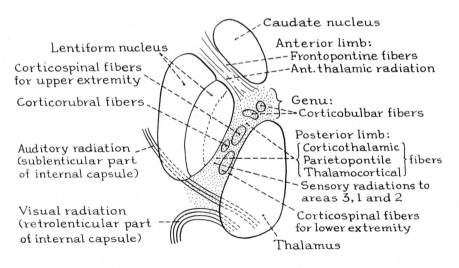

FIG. 175. Diagram to illustrate the parts of the internal capsule and the various fiber systems in the respective parts as seen in horizontal section.

upper lip of the calcarine cortex. The lateral part of the nucleus receives fibers from the lower retinal quadrants and projects to the lower lip of the calcarine cortex. Macular fibers end in the caudal part of the geniculate nucleus which projects to the posterior part of the visual cortex (Polyak and Hayashi, 1936). Representation of the more peripheral fields is on the anterior part of the visual cortex (Chapter 8).

The pulvinar (Figs. 169 and 170) is generally considered to receive fibers from adjacent nuclei, the lateral group in particular, and from the medial and lateral geniculate nuclei. The pulvinar projects to the cortex of the parietal, temporal and occipital lobes and probably receives fibers from these cortical areas.

On the basis of known connections, the thalamic nuclei can be classified as *cortical relay, association* and *subcortical.* The primary sensory relay nuclei are the posteromedial ventral, posterolateral ventral, medial geniculate and lateral geniculate. Other cortical relay nuclei are the lateral ventral and probably the anterior ventral. The association nuclei receive stimuli primarily from other nuclei and project to the so-called association areas of the cerebral cortex. Included in this group are the dorsomedial, dorsal lateral, posterior lateral and the pulvinar. The nuclei without known direct cortical connections (subcortical group) are those of the midline and centromedian. The cortical relay and the association nuclei, because of their specific projections, are considered as specific thalamocortical projection nuclei.

Other thalamic nuclei have been shown to project diffusely to wide areas of the cerebral cortex and are considered a part of the diffuse thalamocortical system which provides the substrate for widespread cortical activity of the recruiting type (Morison and Dempsey, 1942).

The reticular nucleus, midline nuclei and some intralaminar nuclei belong to this diffuse system and are considered to be the cephalic components of the brain stem reticular formation. Moruzzi and Magoun (1949) and others have shown the ascending reticular formation to be concerned with maintenance of the waking state. Stimulation of the reticular formation awakens the animal and changes the electrical activity of the cortex from the random sleep-like pattern to that of the waking condition. Lindsley (1957), in reviewing the possible roles of the ascending reticular system, includes general arousal, attention and focused attention. Additional evidence is provided that this system is concerned with perception and simple discriminations. There is convincing anatomical evidence for ascending pathways from the reticular formation of the brain stem which are probably responsible for the diffuse influence at thalamic and cortical levels (Nauta and Kuypers, 1957; Scheibel and Scheibel, 1957). In brief, these and other studies show that the primary sensory pathways give off collaterals to the central reticular core of the brain stem. The reticular neurons in turn, through multisynaptic relays, form ascending pathways which likely provide the anatomical substrate for the diffuse cortical responses which have been demonstrated by neurophysiological methods.

The **hypothalamus** is the most ventral part of the diencephalon. Its rostral and caudal boundaries are marked on the ventral surface by the *optic chiasm* and the *mammillary bodies,* respectively, and the region between these is the *tuber cinereum* (Fig. 176). Internally the hypothalamus is divided into halves by the third ventricle, and is continuous rostrally with the telencephalic *preoptic area* and caudally with the midbrain tegmentum. Dorsally the hypothalamic sulcus marks

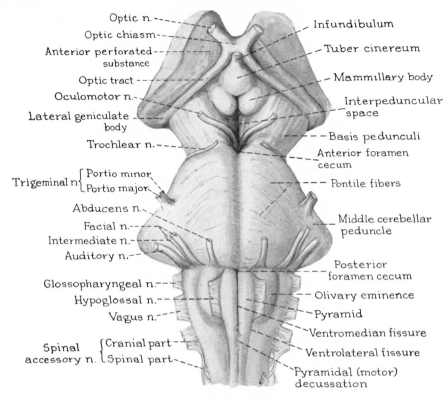

Optic n.
Optic chiasm
Anterior perforated substance
Optic tract
Oculomotor n.
Lateral geniculate body
Trochlear n.
Trigeminal n. { Portio minor / Portio major
Abducens n.
Facial n.
Intermediate n.
Auditory n.
Glossopharyngeal n.
Hypoglossal n.
Vagus n.
Spinal accessory n. { Cranial part / Spinal part

Infundibulum
Tuber cinereum
Mammillary body
Interpeduncular space
Basis pedunculi
Anterior foramen cecum
Pontile fibers
Middle cerebellar peduncle
Posterior foramen cecum
Olivary eminence
Pyramid
Ventromedian fissure
Ventrolateral fissure
Pyramidal (motor) decussation

FIG. 176.   Drawing of the brain stem, ventral view.

the boundary between the thalamus and hypothalamus (Figs. 167 and 177).

Each half of the hypothalamus can be divided arbitrarily into three longitudinal zones, the *periventricular region* adjacent to the third ventricle, a *medial region* just lateral to this which contains several nuclear groups, and a *lateral zone* or area roughly separated from the medial region by the path of the *fornix* (Fig. 177). The lateral hypothalamic area contains fewer cells than the medial region but has many thinly myelinated fibers which run longitudinally. The nuclei of the ventral thalamus (subthalamus) form the lateral boundary of the hypothalamus (Fig. 170). The hypothalamus can also be subdivided, for purposes of localizing the nuclear groups, into three rostrocaudal parts, a *supraoptic* area at the level of the optic chiasma, a middle or *tuberal*

region, and a *mammillary area* at the level of the mammillary bodies (Fig. 177, *A*, *B*, and *C*).

The nuclei in the medial part of the supraoptic area (Fig. 177, *A*) include the *anterior hypothalamic, paraventricular* and *supraoptic*. The anterior hypothalamic nucleus in man is composed of an irregular mass of small cells and is more appropriately called *anterior hypothalamic area*. The paraventricular nucleus is an elongated group of cells along the sides of the third ventricle, and the supraoptic nucleus overlies the optic tract. The paraventricular and supraoptic nuclei contain neurosecretory material and send their axons into the neurohypophysis (Fig. 178). While the anterior hypothalamic area and the lateral hypothalamic area cannot be distinguished histologically from the preoptic

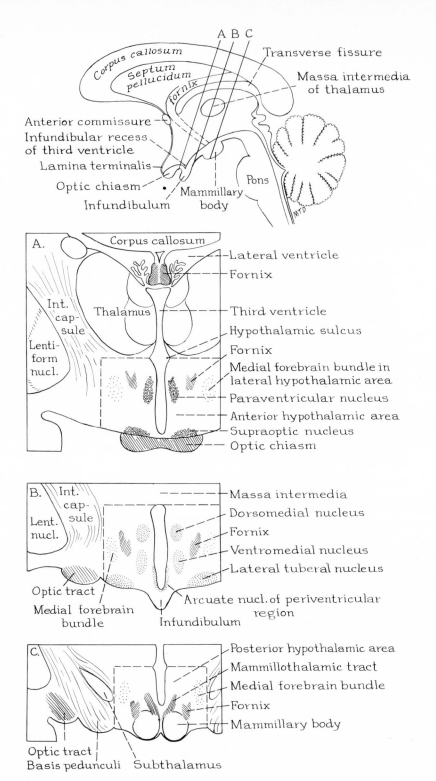

FIG. 177. The upper schematic drawing is a sagittal section of the brain stem to show the relations of the hypothalamus to surrounding brain structures. The lines, *A, B* and *C,* show the levels at which the 3 sections below were made. Section *A,* is through the supraoptic area, *B* is through the tuberal area and *C* is through the mammillary area of the hypothalamus.

(240)

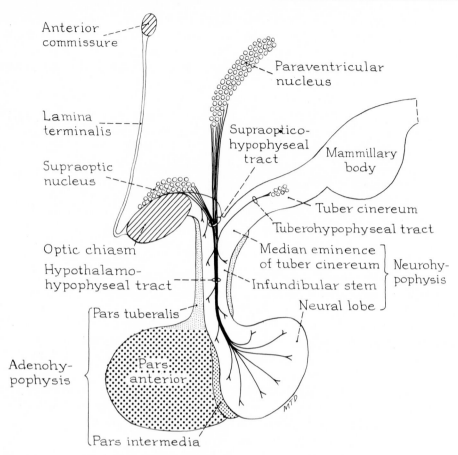

Anterior commissure

Paraventricular nucleus

Lamina terminalis

Supraoptico-hypophyseal tract

Mammillary body

Supraoptic nucleus

Tuber cinereum

Tuberohypophyseal tract

Optic chiasm

Median eminence of tuber cinereum

Hypothalamo-hypophyseal tract

Infundibular stem

Neurohypophysis

Neural lobe

Pars tuberalis

Adenohypophysis

Pars anterior

Pars intermedia

FIG. 178. Sagittal section through the hypothalamus and hypophysis to show origin and distribution of the hypothalamo-hypophyseal tract.

area, it is customary to limit the supraoptic portion of the hypothalamus by a transverse plane rostral to the optic chiasm.

Nuclei in the tuberal region of the hypothalamus (Fig. 177, *B*) include the *arcuate nucleus* within the ventral part of the periventricular gray, the *ventromedial* and *dorsomedial nuclei* of the medial zone, and the *lateral tuberal nuclei* which are located ventrally in the lateral zone. The dorsomedial nucleus is not well defined in man.

The nuclei of each mammillary body, a large medial and small lateral nucleus, are considered in this text without subdivisions (Fig. 177, *C*).

The **hypophysis** or **pituitary gland** is attached to the hypothalamus at the rostral part of the tuber cinereum, the region known as the *median eminence*, (Fig. 178). The hypophysis is comprised of two major divisions, *neurohypophysis* and *adenohypophysis,* which have separate embryonic origins. The neurohypophysis arises from the embryonic infundibular process of the diencephalic floor and in the adult includes the *neural lobe, infundibular stem* and *median eminence.* The adenohypophysis differentiates from a diverticulum of the stomadaeal roof (Rathke's pouch) and in the adult is composed of the *pars distalis, pars intermedia* and *pars tuberalis* (Fig. 178).

Of the numerous described fiber systems which interconnect the hypothalamus with other areas of the brain, only the major systems will be described. One of these, discussed in connection with the rhinencephalon (Chapter 23) is the *medial forebrain bundle* (Figs. 178 and 199). This bundle includes both ascending and descending fibers which connect the septal or medial olfactory area with the preoptic and hypothalamic areas and with the tegmental areas of the midbrain. Several hypothalamic nuclei, particularly the ventromedial nucleus, are believed to have connections with the medial forebrain bundle.

The *mammillary peduncle,* described as taking origin from the medial lemniscus at midbrain levels, ends in the mammillary nuclei. A number of fibers from the tegmental gray are believed to be incorporated in the mammillary peduncle. It is probable that this system includes descending as well as ascending fibers.

The most prominent fiber system of the hypothalamus is the fornix which, in the main, arises in the hippocampus (Fig. 194) and terminates in the mammillary nuclei (Figs. 177 and 196). It is considered in relation to the rhinencephalon (Chapter 23). As the fornix approaches the anterior commissure, it divides into a small precommissural and a large postcommissural division. The precommissural fornix connects with the preoptic and the anterior hypothalamic area (Fig. 199). The postcommissural fornix terminates in the anterior hypothalamic area, mammillary nuclei and possibly other hypothalamic nuclei. There is evidence that fibers of the fornix arise in the septal area and conduct via the hippocampus to the cortex of the temporal pole.

The stria terminalis arises from the amygdala and connects with the preoptic and anterior hypothalamic areas.

Adjacent to the ventricle throughout the diencephalon is a system of finely medullated and nonmedullated fibers known as the periventricular fiber system. Many of the fibers are arranged obliquely and others course in a rostrocaudal direction. The rostral part of the system connects the preoptic and anterior hypothalamic areas with the dorsomedial and midline nuclei of the thalamus. The caudally directed fibers which have connections with essentially all areas of the hypothalamic gray extend to the tegmental gray of the midbrain and reticular areas of more caudal levels. The *dorsal longitudinal fasciculus,* a fairly discrete grouping of fibers in the periaqueductal region of the midbrain, is generally considered to be part of the periventricular system (Figs. 169 and 199). The connections to the dorsomedial thalamic nuclei provide for connections between the hypothalamus and the frontal cortex. In addition to these indirect connections, direct fibers from the preoptic and anterior hypothalamic areas to the orbitofrontal areas have been described.

The *mammillothalamic tract* (tract of Vicq d'Azyr) is a conspicuous bundle of fibers which projects from the mammillary nuclei to the anterior thalamic nuclei (Figs. 177 and 171). The *mammillotegmental tract* arises from the mammillothalamic tract and courses dorsocaudally to the dorsal tegmental nucleus (Figs. 196 and 199).

Connections of the hypothalamus with the basal ganglia were mentioned in Chapter 16. Pathways establishing these connections include the pallidohypothalamic tract to the ventromedial hypothalamic nucleus, and fibers from the ansa lenticularis and subthalamic nucleus to the hypothalamus.

The *hypothalamohypophyseal tract,* which is composed of two parts, relates the hypothalamus with the neurohypophysis (Fig. 178). The larger component, *supraopticohypophyseal tract,* arises from the supraoptic and paraventricular nuclei. The lesser component, the *tuberohypophyseal tract,* arises from the basal tuberal and mammillary regions of the hypothalamus. Near their origin, these two tracts join to form the hypothalamohypophyseal tract, which courses centrally in the pituitary stalk to the neurohypophysis (Fig. 178). The fibers probably terminate in relation to blood vessels.

It has been established, primarily through lesions and electrical stimulation, that the hypothalamus plays an important role in the regulation of metabolic activities and in controlling the many functions of the autonomic nervous system. Related to the control of autonomic functions is the involvement of the hypothalamus in the behavioral responses to emotional states.

The many hypothalamic regulatory mechanisms are mediated primarily through the neuronal connections described above. In the case of the hypophysis, humoral factors as well as nerve fibers are involved. Both major divisions of the hypophysis (adenohypophysis and neurohypophysis) come under hypothalamic control, although there is no satisfactory evidence for fibers from the hypothalamus to the adenohypophysis. (It is recalled that the adenohypophysis through its hormones controls most of the endocrine glands and thus has a widespread influence over reproductive, metabolic and related processes.) There is good evidence that venous connections from the median eminence to the adenohypophysis (hypophyseal portal system) provide the functional relationship between the hypothalamus and adenohypophysis (Green and Harris, 1947; Harris, 1955; and others). Harris (1955) demonstrated by transplantation experiments that the adenohypophysis must establish a vascular relationship with the hypothalamus before normal gonado-

tropic, adrenocorticotropic and thyrotropic functions are restored.

It is, in fact, now well established that the release of adrenocorticotropic, thyrotropic and gonadotropic hormones of the adenohypophysis is regulated by hypothalamic "centers" (Harris, 1960; Sawyer, 1960, 1962; D'Angelo, 1963; Everett and Nikitovitch-Winer, 1963; Flerkó, 1963; Ganong, 1963; Meites *et al.,* 1963). Although it has not always been possible to outline precisely specific hypothalamic nuclei controlling the release of each pituitary tropin, largely because of the relatively small size of the hypothalamus and its many connections, it is generally accepted that overlapping pituitary regulating mechanisms exist in the more ventral portions of the hypothalamus throughout its rostrocaudal extent.

The neurohypophysis liberates an antidiuretic hormone (vasopressin) which mediates the resorption of water in the renal tubules, and *oxytocin* which causes uterine contractions and the ejection of milk from lactating mammary glands. The supraoptic and paraventricular neurons of the hypothalamus secrete these two neurohypophyseal hormones which are transported by the supraopticohypophyseal tract to the neurohypophysis where they are stored (Bargmann, 1949, 1955; Scharrer and Scharrer, 1954; Lundberg, 1957; Ortmann, 1960). Injury to the supraopticohypophyseal system produces *diabetes insipidus* in which large volumes of dilute urine are formed (polyuria). The excessive loss of water in the urine causes pronounced thirst and excessive intake of water (polydipsia).

With respect to the hypothalamic control of functions of the autonomic nervous system, descending nervous pathways described above provide for relaying the information from the integrative centers (hypothalamic nuclei) to the motor centers of the brain stem and spinal cord.

Autonomic functions in which the hypothalamus apparently has an integrative or regulative role include both sympathetic and parasympathetic phenomena. As reviewed by Ingram (1960), sympathetic responses which have been obtained by electrically stimulating the hypothalamus include cardiac acceleration, increased blood pressure, piloerection, pupillary dilatation, sweating, hyperglycemia and cessation of gastrointestinal movement. Parasympathetic responses which have been elicited, particularly from stimulating the more anterior hypothalamic regions, include cardiac depression, vasodilation, bladder contraction and increased gastrointestinal movement. These responses following anterior hypothalamic stimulation suggest that separate areas are concerned with sympathetic and parasympathetic regulation. It has been pointed out by Ingram (1960), however, that there is considerable intermingling of the elements responsible for these responses throughout the hypothalamus. Furthermore, the responses are generally more easily elicited from the lateral hypothalamic area which contains many fibers and few neurons.

Other functions under hypothalamic influence include control of body temperature, thirst or drinking, hunger, sleep and wakefulness, and emotional expression. It is to be appreciated that these may involve one or more of the autonomic responses, for example, sweating and vasodilation in the dissipation of body heat. Animals with lesions of the anterior hypothalamus dorsal to the optic chiasm and infundibulum (including the preoptic region) are unable to avoid extreme rises in body temperature when in a warm environment (Ranson, 1940). Heating this region through electrodes has long been known to activate heat loss mechanisms such as panting and sweating (Magoun et al., 1938). Lesions in the caudal hypothalamus, dorsolateral to the

mammillary bodies, render animals incapable of maintaining normal body temperature in either a warm or cold environment. It is believed that the dorsomedial portion of the posterior hypothalamus is responsible, in part, for cold-induced shivering, and that a more dorsolateral region of the posterior hypothalamus is involved in other motor responses to cold (Stuart et al., 1961, 1962). It seems likely that the changes in thermoregulatory responses which follow posterior hypothalamic lesions may be due to the interruption of traversing fibers as well as to the destruction of cells therein.

A number of recent studies support the view that the preoptic-anterior hypothalamic regions contain thermosensitive elements that are involved in the regulation of body temperature (von Euler, 1961; Hardy, 1961, 1962; Benzinger, 1962).

With respect to the role of the preoptic area in thermal regulation, it is significant that Andersson et al. (1962a) found that local cooling of this region in goats activated the thyroid gland along with the development of marked core hyperthermia. These same investigators subsequently demonstrated that the thyroid response to cold was blocked by local warming of the preoptic area (Andersson et al., 1962b).

It seems well established that neural mechanisms reside in the hypothalamus which regulate food and water intake (Brobeck, 1960), although specific functions cannot easily be ascribed to any one isolated nuclear group. Rather, it appears that separate but interconnected widespread regions control the many aspects of eating and drinking behavior. For example, while Andersson and McCann (1955, 1956) have shown that stimulation of the region between the columns of the fornix and mammillothalamic tracts produces polydipsia and pronounced over-hydration, and that lesions in this general region caused temporary adipsia; impairment of drinking has also been obtained by lateral hypothalamic lesions (Montemurro and Stevenson, 1955 and others). With regard to the regulation of food intake, a variety of experiments have indicated that the lateral hypothalamic area is a feeding center and the medial hypothalamic region a satiety center (Anand, 1961). Hyperphagia and resultant obesity ensue from lesions of the ventromedial nucleus, while lesions of the lateral hypothalamus result in aphagia and eventual starvation unless the animals are force fed. Correspondingly, food intake is decreased by electrical stimulation of the medial hypothalamus and increased by stimulating the lateral hypothalamus.

While there is considerable overlap between areas regulating feeding and drinking, it has been shown that these areas are partially separable. For example, Andersson et al. (1962a) have shown that chronic cooling of the preoptic-anterior hypothalamic region causes an inhibition of water intake with little effect on food intake, while cooling more caudal areas in the anterior hypothalamus results in a considerable increase in food intake but does not affect drinking.

It can readily be seen that many parts of the hypothalamus enter into the regulation of food and water intake. While it seems justifiable to call the ventromedial nucleus a satiety center, Andersson et al. (1963) have emphasized that the lateral hypothalamus does not have the character of a center due to its scarcity of neurons. These authors suggest that ascending tracts in the lateral zone may transmit to higher centers the urges to eat and drink. Morgane (1961a, b) has suggested that the medial forebrain bundle and pallidofugal systems of fibers play a role in the neural organization of the feeding center. Teitlebaum and Epstein (1963) have further stressed that

motivational factors must be considered when studying alterations in eating and drinking behavior due to hypothalamic interference.

Bilateral lesions in the hypothalamus of monkeys have produced somnolence (Ranson, 1939), and it has been suggested that in the rat there is a cephalic hypothalamic sleep center and a more caudal waking center (Nauta, 1956). Additionally, Hess (1956) has produced sleep in cats by diencephalic stimulation and has shown that the frequency of stimulation is important. Although these and a number of other studies have suggested the presence of an active sleep center in the hypothalamus, it seems questionable that this is the case.

As pointed out by Ingram (1960) it would seem more propitious to direct attention to wakefulness since sleep is at least in part the condition which occurs in the absence of wakefulness. The studies of Magoun (1952) and associates in relation to the reticulocortical activating system provide substantial support for the view that sleep ensues from the decreased flow of afferent impulses to the cerebral cortex. It has been reported, however, that stimulation of the basal forebrain in cats produces behavioral and electroencephalographic manifestations of sleep (Sterman and Clemente, 1962). Moreover, the studies of Moruzzi (1964) suggest that in addition to the activating system there are deactivating structures in the brain stem, primarily medulla and pons, which are responsible for deep sleep without EEG synchronization.

It is readily appreciated that the hypothalamus is involved in the expression of emotional states since it serves as a regulatory center for both parasympathetic and sympathetic divisions of the autonomic nervous system. Stimulation or the placement of lesions in localized regions of the hypothalamus have produced responses not unlike those produced by comparable procedures applied to rhinencephalic and related cortical areas. For example, lesions of the ventromedial nuclei of the hypothalamus elicit rage and savageness in animals (Wheatley, 1944) and "sham" rage has been produced by ablating the orbital cortex (Kennard, 1945). A variety of responses may, in fact, be elicited from stimulating the hypothalamus in unanesthetized animals which mimic normal defense reactions (Hess, 1956). It is probable, however, that the role of the hypothalamus is that of integrating the activity from cortical centers, thus controlling the expressive or motor aspects of emotion.

BIBLIOGRAPHY

ANAND, B. K., 1961: Nervous regulation of food intake. Physiol. Rev., *41*, 677-708.

ANDERSSON, B. and MCCANN, S. M., 1955: Drinking, antidiuresis and milk ejection from electrical stimulation within the hypothalamus of the goat. Acta Physiol. Scand., *35*, 191-201.

———— 1956: The effect of hypothalamic lesions on the water intake of the dog. Acta Physiol. Scand., *35*, 312-320.

ANDERSSON, B. EKMAN, L., GALE, C. C. and SUNDSTEN, J. W., 1962a: Activation of the thyroid gland by cooling of the preoptic area in the goat. Acta Physiol. Scand., *54*, 191-192.

———— 1962b: Blocking of the thyroid response to cold by local warming of the preoptic region. Acta Physiol. Scand., *56*, 94-96.

ANDERSSON, B., GALE, C. C. and SUNDSTEN, J. W., 1963: The relationship between body temperature and food and water intake. Proc. First Intern. Symp. on Olfaction and Taste. Y. ZOTTERMAN, ed., Pergamon Press, Oxford, London, New York, pp. 361-375.

BARGMANN, W., 1949: Über die neurosekretorische Verknüpfung von Hypothalamus und Neurohypophyse. Z. Zellforsch., *34*, 610-634.

———— 1955: Die funktionelle Morphologie der Hormonbildungsstätten. Klin. Wochschr., *33*, 322-328.

BENZINGER, T. H., 1962: The thermostatic regulation of human heat production and heat loss. Proc. XXII Intern. Congr. Physiologic Sci., Leiden, Vol. I, pp. 415-438.

BROBECK, J. R., 1960: Regulation of feeding and drinking. In *Handbook of Physiology*, Vol. II, Section I, Neurophysiology. JOHN FIELD, ed.-in-chief, Williams & Wilkins, Baltimore, Chap. 47, pp. 1197-1206.

BUCY, P. C., 1949: Relation to abnormal involuntary movements. In *The Precentral Motor Cortex*, 2nd Ed., P. C. BUCY, ed., University of Illinois Press, Urbana, Chap. 15, pp. 395-408.

CHOW, K. L. and PRIBRAM, K. H., 1956: Cortical projection of the thalamic ventrolateral nuclear group in monkeys. J. Comp. Neurol., *104*, 57-75.

D'ANGELO, S. A., 1963: Central nervous regulation of the secretion and release of thyroid stimulating hormone. In *Advances in Neuroendocrinology*, A. V. NALBANDOV, ed., University of Illinois Press, Urbana, pp. 158-210.

EVERETT, J. W. and NIKITOVITCH-WINER, M., 1963: Physiology of the pituitary gland as affected by transplantation of stalk transection. In *Advances in Neuroendocrinology*, A. V. NALVANDOV, ed., University of Illinois Press, Urbana, pp. 289-312.

FLERKÓ, B., 1963: The central nervous system and the secretion and release of luteinizing hormone and follicle stimulating hormone. In *Advances in Neuroendocrinology*, A. V. NALBANDOV, ed., University of Illinois Press, Urbana, pp. 211-237.

GANONG, W. F., 1963: The central nervous system and the synthesis and release of adrenocorticotropic hormone. In *Advances in Neuroendocrinology*, A. V. NALBANDOV, ed., University of Illinois Press, Urbana, pp. 92-157.

GREEN, J. D. and HARRIS, G. W., 1947: The neurovascular link between neurohypophysis and adenohypophysis. J. Endocrinol., *5*, 136-146.

HARDY, J. D., 1961: Physiology of temperature regulation. Physiol. Rev., *41*, 521-606.

———— 1962: Homeostatic temperature regulation. Proc. XXII Intern. Congr. Physiologic Sci., Leiden, Vol. I, pp. 403-414.

HARRIS, G. W., 1955: Neural control of the pituitary gland. Physiol. Soc. Monograph No. 3, Edward, Arnold, London.

———— 1960: Central control of pituitary secretion. In *Handbook of Physiology*, Vol. II, Section I, Neurophysiology, JOHN FIELD, ed.-in-chief, Williams & Wilkins Co., Baltimore, Chap. 39, pp. 1007-1038.

HESS, W. R., 1956: *Hypothalamus and Thalamus*, Thieme, Stuttgart.

INGRAM, W. R., 1960: Central autonomic mechanisms. In *Handbook of Physiology*, Vol. II, Section I, Neurophysiology, JOHN FIELD, ed.-in-chief, Williams & Wilkins Co., Baltimore, Chap. 37, pp. 951-978.

JASPER, H. H., 1949: Diffuse projection systems. The integrative action of the thalamic reticular system. Electroencephalo. Clin. Neurophysiol., *1*, 405-419.

KELLY, D. E., 1962: Pineal organs: photoreception, secretion and development. Am. Scientist, *50*, 597-625.

KENNARD, MARGARET A., 1945: Focal autonomic representation in the cortex and its relation to sham rage. J. Neuropathol. Exptl. Neurol., *4*, 295-304.

LINDSLEY, D. B., 1957: The reticular system and preceptual discrimination. In *Reticular Formation of the Brain*, H. H. JASPER et al., eds., Henry Ford Hosp. Intern. Symposium, Little, Brown & Co., Boston, pp. 513-534.

LUNDBERG, P. O., 1957: A study of neurosecretory and related phenomena in the hypothalamus and pituitary of man. Acta Morphol. Neerl. Scand., *1*, 256-285.

MAGOUN, H. W., 1952: The ascending reticular activating system. Assoc. Res. Nerv. Ment. Dis., *30*, 480-492.

MAGOUN, H. W., HARRISON, F., BROBECK, J. R. and RANSON, S. W., 1938: Activation of heat loss mechanisms by local heating of the brain. J. Neurophysiol., *1*, 101-114.

McLARDY, T., 1948: Projection of the centromedian nucleus of the human thalamus. Brain, *71*, 290-303.

MEITES, J., NICOLL, C. S. and TALWALKER, P. K., 1963: The central nervous system and the secretion and release of prolactin. In *Advances in Neuroendocrinology*, A. V. NALBANDOV, ed., University of Illinois Press, Urbana, pp. 238-288.

METTLER, F. A., 1947: Extracortical connections of the primate frontal cerebral cortex. II. Corticifugal connections. J. Comp. Neurol., *86*, 119-166.

MONTEMURRO, D. G. and STEVENSON, J. A. F., 1955-56: The localization of hypothalamic structures in the rat influencing water consumption. Yale J. Biol. Med., *28*, 396-403.

MORGANE, P. J., 1961a: Medial forebrain bundle and "feeding centers" of the hypothalamus. J. Comp. Neurol., *117*, 1-25.

———— 1961b: Alterations in feeding and drinking behavior of rats with lesions in globi pallidi. Am. J. Physiol., *201*, 420-428.

MORISON, R. S. and DEMPSEY, E. W., 1942: A study of thalamo-cortical relations. Am. J. Physiol., *135*, 281-292.

MORUZZI, G., 1964: Reticular influences on the EEG. Electroencephalo. Clin. Neurophysiol., *16*, 2-17.

MORUZZI, G. and MAGOUN, H. W., 1949: Brain stem reticular formation and activation of the EEG. Electroencephalo. Clin. Neurophysiol., *1*, 455-473.

NAUTA, W. J. H., 1956: An experimental study of the fornix system in the rat. J. Comp. Neurol., *104*, 247-271.

NAUTA, W. J. H. and KUYPERS, H. G. J. M., 1957: Some ascending pathways in the brain stem reticular formation. In *Reticular Formation of the Brain*, H. H. JASPER, et al., eds. Henry Ford Hosp. Intern. Symposium, Little, Brown & Co., Boston, pp. 3-30.

ORTMANN, R., 1960: Neurosecretion. In *Handbook of Physiology*, Vol. II, Section I, Neurophysiology, JOHN FIELD, ed.-in-chief, Williams & Wilkins Co., Baltimore, Chap. 40, pp. 1039-1065.

POLYAK, S. and HAYASHI, R., 1936: The cerebral representation of the retina in the chimpanzee. Brain, *59*, 51-60.

RANSON, S. W., 1939: Somnolence caused by hypothalamic lesions in the monkey. A.M.A. Arch. Neurol. Psychiat., *41*, 1-23.

———— 1940: Regulation of body temperature. Assoc. Res. Nerv. Ment. Dis., *20*, 342-399.

SAWYER, C. H., 1960: Reproductive behavior. In *Handbook of Physiology*, Vol. II, Section I, Neurophysiology, JOHN FIELD, ed.-in-chief, Williams & Wilkins Co., Baltimore, Chap. 49, pp. 1225-1240.

———— 1962: Gonadal hormone feed-back and sexual behavior. Proc. XXII Intern. Congr. Physiologic Sci., Leiden, Vol. I, pp. 642-649.

SCHARRER, E. and SCHARRER, B., 1954: Hormones produced by neurosecretory cells. Progress in Hormone Research, GREGORY PINCUS, ed., *10*, 183-240.

SCHEIBEL, M. E. and SCHEIBEL, A. B., 1957: Structural substrates for integrative patterns in the brain stem reticular core. In *Reticular Formation of the Brain*, H. H. JASPER *et al.*, eds., Henry Ford Hosp. Intern. Symposium, Little, Brown & Co., Baltimore, pp. 31-55.

SHEPS, J. G., 1945: The nuclear configuration and cortical connections of the human thalamus. J. Comp. Neurol., *83*, 1-56.

SPIEGEL, E. A., 1952: *Stereoencephalotomy, Thalamotomy and Related Procedures.* Grune & Stratton, New York.

STERMAN, M. B. and CLEMENTE, C. D., 1962: Forebrain inhibitory mechanisms: Sleep patterns induced by basal forebrain stimulation in the behaving cat. Exptl. Neurol., *6*, 103-117.

STUART, D. G., KAWAMURA, Y. and HEMINGWAY, 1961: Activation and suppression of shivering during septal and hypothalamic stimulation. Exptl. Neurol., *4*, 485-506.

STUART, D. G., KAWAMURA, Y., HEMINGWAY, A. and PRICE, W. M., 1962: Effects of septal and hypothalamic lesion on shivering. Exptl. Neurol., *5*, 335-347.

TEITELBAUM, P. and EPSTEIN, A. N., 1963: The role of taste and smell in the regulation of food and water intake. In *Olfaction and Taste*, Y. ZETTERMAN, ed., Pergamon Press, Oxford, pp. 347-360.

TONCRAY, J. E. and KRIEG, W. J. S., 1946: The nuclei of the human thalamus. A comparative approach. J. Comp. Neurol., *85*, 421-459.

VON EULER, C., 1961: Physiology and pharmacology of temperature regulation. Pharmacol. Rev., *13*, 361-398.

WALKER, A. E., 1938: *The Primate Thalamus.* University of Chicago Press, Chicago.

————— 1959: Normal and pathological physiology of the thalamus. In *Introduction to Stereotaxis with an Atlas of the Human Brain.* I. G. SCHALTENBRAND and P. BAILEY, eds., Thieme, Stuttgart, pp. 291-330.

WHEATLEY, M. D., 1944: The hypothalamus and affective behavior in cats. A.M.A. Arch. Neurol. Psychiat., *52*, 296-316.

Chapter 21

The Autonomic (Visceral) Nervous System

THE autonomic (visceral) nervous system is that system of nerve cells and fibers which is distributed to "visceral" structures, *i.e.*, to smooth muscle, cardiac muscle and glands. As such it consists of both afferent and efferent divisions. *Visceral afferent neurons*, like those with somatic afferent functions, have their cell bodies in the sensory ganglia of spinal and cranial nerves; specific locations, distribution of peripheral processes, and termination of central processes of these neurons have been discussed.

The *visceral efferent* or *autonomic system* is divided, on the basis of function and outflow from the central nervous system, into *thoracolumbar* and *craniosacral* portions. The former is also classified as *sympathetic* and the latter as *parasympathetic* (Fig. 179). It has been pointed out (Chapter 20) that both sympathetic and parasympathetic divisions are influenced by nervous impulses from the hypothalamus through the medium of descending hypothalamic pathways. Direct and indirect corticohypothalamic connections have been described and the role of the hypothalamus in integrating activity from cortical centers and thus controlling motor aspects of emotion has been indicated.

Both divisions of the autonomic system (sympathetic and parasympathetic) employ two neurons for the transmission of impulses from the central nervous system to the structures innervated. The first or *preganglionic neuron* is located in the spinal cord or brain stem; the second or *ganglionic neuron* has its cell body in either a vertebral or a collateral ganglion.

Examples of *collateral ganglia* are the ciliary, otic, submandibular and sphenopalatine in the head region and the celiac, aorticorenal and superior and inferior mesenteric in the abdominal cavity. *Intrinsic ganglia,* situated in the walls of the visceral organs, may be included in the collateral classification. Nerve cells in the adrenal medulla, which are derived from the neural crest, may be included also since preganglionic fibers from the spinal cord reach them by way of the splanchnic nerves.

The **vertebral** or **chain ganglia** consist of paired ganglionated trunks located lateral to the vertebral column; they extend from the base of the skull to the coccyx where the two trunks fuse in the ganglion impar (Fig. 180).

Preganglionic fibers—axons of centrally located neurons—proceed to the peripheral ganglia by way of spinal or cranial nerves and synapse upon the ganglionic cells whose axons are then distributed as *postganglionic fibers* to the visceral structures (Fig. 179). Preganglionic fibers in spinal nerves reach the sympathetic ganglia via white rami communicantes (Fig. 2). Postganglionic fibers traverse the gray rami communicantes from sympathetic ganglia to the spinal nerves with which they are distributed.

Most visceral organs have a dual innervation, *i.e.*, they receive both sympathetic and parasympathetic impulses. It is still not definitely known whether the peripheral blood vessels have a dual innervation, although it is well established that all of them receive fibers from the

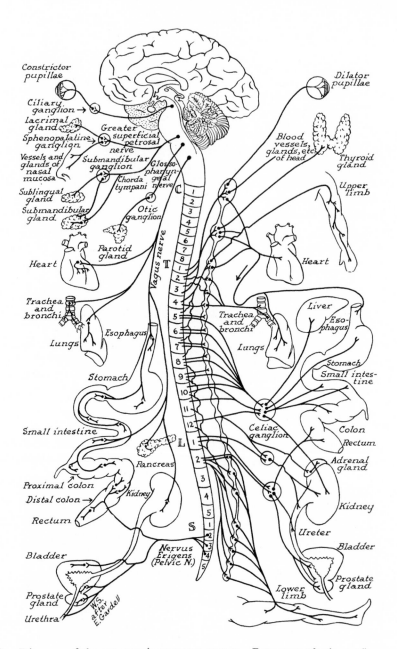

FIG. 179. Diagram of the autonomic nervous system. Parasympathetic outflow and distribution are shown on the left and sympathetic outflow and distribution on the right. The nuclei within the brain stem indicated as giving rise to preganglionic fibers, in rostro-caudal order, are nucleus of Edinger-Westphal, superior salivary nucleus, inferior salivary nucleus, and dorsal motor nucleus of vagus nerve.

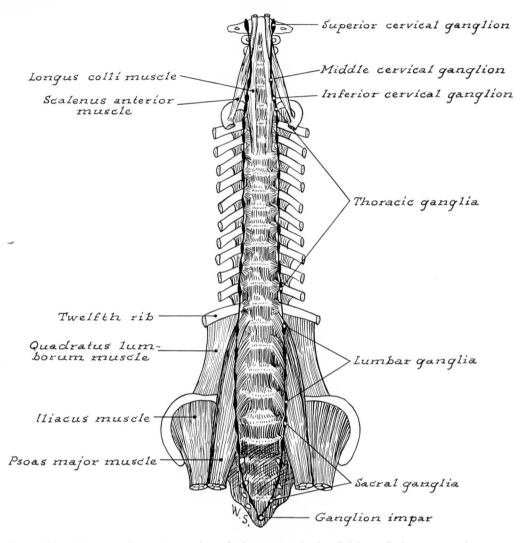

Longus colli muscle

Scalenus anterior muscle

Twelfth rib

Quadratus lum-borum muscle

Iliacus muscle

Psoas major muscle

W. S.

Superior cervical ganglion

Middle cervical ganglion

Inferior cervical ganglion

Thoracic ganglia

Lumbar ganglia

Sacral ganglia

Ganglion impar

FIG. 180. The ganglionated trunks of the sympathetic division of the autonomic system.

sympathetic division of the autonomic system.

Pupillary constriction is produced by parasympathetic nerve impulses. The preganglionic neurons have their cell bodies in the *Edinger-Westphal nucleus* in the mesencephalon (Fig. 63). The nucleus is dorsolateral to the rostral half of the oculomotor nucleus and extends forward to a level slightly beyond the rostral limit of the latter nucleus. *Preganglionic fibers* reach the *ciliary ganglion* by way of the oculomotor nerve and synapse upon ganglionic cells whose axons are distributed, as postganglionic fibers through the short ciliary nerves to the sphincter muscle of the pupil and to the ciliary body (Fig. 179). Naquin (1954) postulated that some of the parasympathetic fibers from the Edinger-Westphal nucleus pass to the iris sphincter without synapse in the ciliary ganglion but Warwick (1954) observed that section of the short ciliary nerves results in retrograde changes in

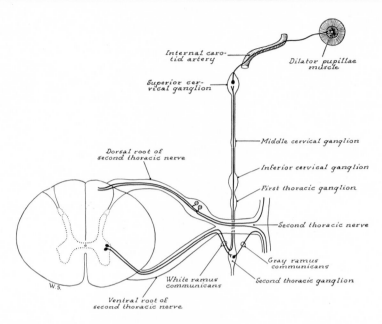

Internal caro-
tid artery

Dilator pupillae
muscle

Superior cer-
vical ganglion

Middle cervical ganglion

Dorsal root of
second thoracic nerve

Inferior cervical ganglion

First thoracic ganglion

Second thoracic nerve

Gray ramus
communicans

W.S.

White ramus
communicans

Second thoracic ganglion

Ventral root of
second thoracic nerve

FIG. 181.   Diagram of the sympathetic pathway to the iris.

97 per cent of ciliary ganglion cells without such changes in oculomotor or other mesencephalic nuclei.

Dilatation of the pupil is effected by sympathetic impulses. The preganglionic neurons are located in the *intermediate gray column* of the upper two thoracic segments of the spinal cord; preganglionic fibers emerge from the cord over the anterior roots of the corresponding spinal nerves, proceed to the sympathetic trunk by way of the *white rami communicantes,* and then course upward in the trunk to finally synapse upon cells in the *superior cervical ganglion* (Fig. 181). Postganglionic fibers from this ganglion reach the dilator pupillae muscle by way of the sympathetic plexus surrounding the internal carotid artery; they enter the orbit through the superior orbital fissure and pass through or near the ciliary ganglion without interruption therein. Sympathetic fibers complete their course to the iris and ciliary body by way of the short ciliary nerves.

Ward and Reed (1946) have demon-strated conclusively, in the monkey, that pupillary dilatation elicited by electrical stimulation of Area 8 is a sympathetic response which is mediated by indirect cortico-hypothalamic and hypothalamico-spinal connections. The response was abolished by section of the cervical sympathetic chain.

The **submandibular** and **sublingual glands** receive their *parasympathetic* innervation by way of a two-neuron pathway which begins with preganglionic cells in the *superior salivary nucleus* in the pontile tegmentum. Preganglionic fibers pass to the *submandibular ganglion* through the *nervus intermedius* and *chorda tympani.* Postganglionic fibers, axons of cells in the ganglion, are distributed to the glands (Fig. 179).

The **lacrimal gland** and the **glands of the nose and palate** also receive *parasympathetic* impulses from the *superior salivary nucleus.* Preganglionic fibers from the nucleus traverse the *nervus intermedius* and *greater superficial petrosal* nerve to reach the *sphenopalatine gan-*

glion in the pterygopalatine fossa. Postganglionic fibers from the ganglion are distributed to the glands.

The **parotid gland** is innervated by preganglionic parasympathetic fibers which originate in the *inferior salivary nucleus,* in the reticular formation of the medulla; they reach the *otic ganglion* by way of the *glossopharyngeal nerve;* postganglionic fibers from the otic ganglion are distributed to the gland through the *auriculotemporal nerve* (Fig. 179).

Direct parasympathetic innervation of secretory cells in parotid and submandibular glands (from otic and submandibular ganglia) has been demonstrated anatomically to satisfactorily explain the copious secretory effects produced by parasympathetic stimulation (Richins and Kuntz, 1953). The sympathetic nerves supplying these glands are distributed predominantly or exclusively to the intraglandular blood vessels which implies that salivary secretion in response to sympathetic stimulation is the result of vasomotor activity. This concept coincides with the observation that occlusion of arteries supplying the glands prevents secretion due to sympathetic stimulation.

The **salivary nuclei** are not distinguishable in sections through the brain stem but their approximate locations have been determined through stimulation experiments. The superior salivary nucleus has been found to be dorsolaterally placed in the caudal end of the pontile tegmentum with the inferior nucleus directly caudal to it in the reticular formation of the medulla.

Magoun and Beaton (1942) investigated the distribution of points in the brain stem of the monkey which were responsible, when stimulated electrically, for salivary secretion. They found an excitable region in the dorsal midline area which extended from the genu of the facial nerve to the hypoglossal nucleus. Salivary secretion was also elicited from the reticular formation between this area and the emerging fibers of the seventh and ninth nerves. Although there was considerable overlap, responses of the homolateral submandibular gland were elicited predominantly from the rostral part of the excitable area and those of the homolateral parotid gland from the caudal part. Wang (1943) found a similar distribution of preganglionic salivary neurons in the cat.

The **sympathetic supply to all the salivary glands** and to other glands in the head region comes from preganglionic cells in the upper two thoracic segments of the spinal cord. Preganglionic fibers pass through the first and second thoracic nerves, the white rami communicantes, and the sympathetic trunk to the *superior cervical ganglion* (Fig. 181); postganglionic fibers from the ganglion are distributed to the glands by way of the plexuses which accompany the internal and external carotid arteries (Fig. 179).

The **upper extremity** derives its *sympathetic supply* from preganglionic cells located in the *intermediate gray column* of the upper seven or eight thoracic segments of the spinal cord. Axons of these cells reach the sympathetic trunk in the usual manner and, after ascending in the trunk, synapse upon cells in the middle and inferior cervical and upper two thoracic ganglia. Postganglionic fibers, through the gray rami communicantes, join the lower four cervical and first thoracic nerves and are distributed to the vascular and glandular structures and arrector pili muscles of the upper extremity by way of the brachial plexus and its branches (Fig. 182). Sweating, pilo-erection and vasoconstriction are produced by impulses traversing these fibers. If there are vasodilator fibers to the blood vessels of the extremities they have still to be conclusively demonstrated.

A *sympathetic vasodilator outflow* from the motor cortex to skeletal muscles, by way of the hypothalamus, has been demonstrated in the dog (Eliasson *et al.*, 1953; Uvnäs, 1954). Such a pathway probably exists in the cat as well but is said to be lacking in rabbits and monkeys and its existence in man is doubtful. Uvnäs found the sympathetic vasodilator fibers to be cholinergic rather than adrenergic and suggested that they are capable of increasing blood flow to skeletal (and possibly to cardiac) muscle in situations of emergency or other conditions requir-

ing sudden muscular effort. In connection with humoral mediation between autonomic nerves and effector mechanisms it is to be noted that the sympathetic fibers to sweat glands are also cholinergic. As a general rule sympathetics are adrenergic and parasympathetics are cholinergic. Within peripheral ganglia, however, transmission from preganglionic fiber to ganglionic neuron is supposed to be facilitated by acetylcholine regardless of whether that neuron depends upon

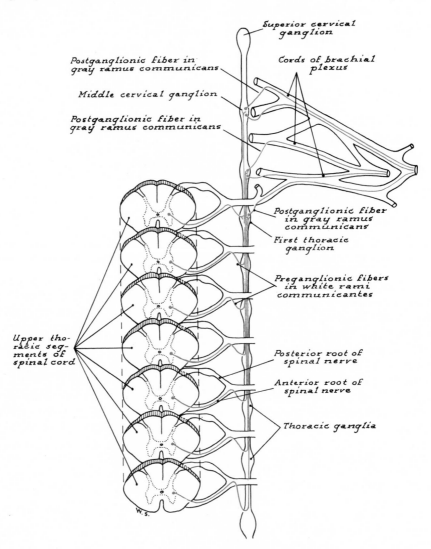

FIG. 182. Diagram of the sympathetic innervation of the upper extremity by way of the brachial plexus.

adrenin or acetylcholine for its functional contact with an effector.

The **lower extremity** receives its sympathetic supply from preganglionic cells in the intermediate gray column of the lower five thoracic and the upper two lumbar segments of the spinal cord. After reaching the sympathetic trunk by way of white rami communicantes the preganglionic fibers course downward within the trunk and synapse upon ganglion cells in the lower lumbar and sacral ganglia (Fig. 185). Postganglionic fibers from

these ganglia join the lumbar and sacral nerves as gray rami communicantes and, through the branches of the lumbar and sacral plexuses, are distributed to the blood vessels, arrector pili muscles and sweat glands of the lower extremity.

The **thoracic viscera** are innervated by *sympathetic preganglionic neurons* in the intermediate gray columns of the upper five thoracic segments of the spinal cord. Preganglionic fibers enter and course upward in the sympathetic trunk where they synapse upon cells in

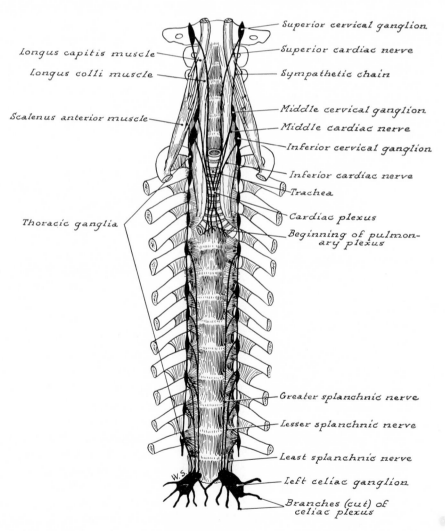

Longus capitis muscle
Longus colli muscle
Scalenus anterior muscle
Thoracic ganglia

Superior cervical ganglion
Superior cardiac nerve
Sympathetic chain
Middle cervical ganglion
Middle cardiac nerve
Inferior cervical ganglion
Inferior cardiac nerve
Trachea
Cardiac plexus
Beginning of pulmonary plexus
Greater splanchnic nerve
Lesser splanchnic nerve
Least splanchnic nerve
Left celiac ganglion
Branches (cut) of celiac plexus

FIG. 183.   Diagram to show the origin of cardiac and splanchnic nerves from the sympathetic chains.

the superior, middle and inferior cervical ganglia. Postganglionic fibers enter the thorax by way of the *superior, middle* and *inferior cardiac nerves* and are distributed to the heart and lungs through the *cardiac* and *pulmonary plexuses* (Fig. 183). Some postganglionic fibers reach the pulmonary plexuses by passing directly forward from the third, fourth and fifth thoracic ganglia. All cardiac nerves contain both efferent and afferent fibers with the exception of the superior one (derived from the superior cervical ganglion) which has only efferent fibers (Mitchell, 1953). This is of importance in operations devised for the relief of cardiac pain.

The **sympathetic supply to the abdominal viscera** comes from preganglionic neurons with cell bodies in the lower six thoracic segments of the spinal cord. Their axons reach the sympathetic trunk over the corresponding ventral roots and white rami communicantes. They pass through the trunk ganglia without synapsing therein and form the splanchic nerves (greater, lesser and least). The *splanchnic nerves* (Fig. 183) pierce the diaphragm and their component fibers (preganglionic) synapse upon ganglionic cells in the *celiac, aorticorenal, superior mesenteric* and *inferior mesenteric ganglia.* Postganglionic fibers from the ganglia are distributed with the branches of the aorta to smooth muscle in the abdominal and pelvic organs and in the blood vessels which supply the organs.

The **parasympathetic supply to the thoracic and abdominal viscera,** including the digestive tract as far down as the transverse colon, originates in the *dorsal motor nucleus* of the *vagus nerve.* The nucleus is located in the medulla, just beneath the floor of the fourth ventricle and immediately lateral to the hypoglossal nucleus; the area of the rhomboid fossa overlying it is called the *vagal trigone* (Fig. 184). Preganglionic fibers

are distributed by way of the vagus nerve and the cardiac, pulmonary, celiac and hypogastric plexuses to intrinsic ganglia which have been previously described as being within the walls of the visceral structures (Fig. 179).

The **descending colon,** the **pelvic viscera** (pelvic colon, rectum, bladder and uterus) and the **external genitalia** receive parasympathetic fibers from the intermediate (parasympathetic) gray column of the middle sacral segments of the spinal cord. Preganglionic fibers emerge from the cord through the anterior roots of the corresponding sacral nerves and, without passing through the sympathetic trunk, unite to form the *pelvic nerve (nervus erigens)* which is distributed through the *pelvic (inferior hypogastric) plexuses,* to the intrinsic ganglia in the pelvic viscera and external genitalia (Fig. 179).

Operative procedures upon the visceral nervous system are carried out for the relief of pain, to correct circulatory disorders which appear to be due to abnormal vasomotor stimuli, and to adjust apparent motor imbalances in the smooth musculature of the colon and uterus. Pain is frequently associated with muscular spasm due to excessive autonomic impulses.

Cervicothoracic ganglionectomy has been performed for the relief of vascular spasm of the upper extremity of such degree as to interfere seriously with oxygenation of the tissues. The inferior cervical and upper two thoracic ganglia are excised; the preganglionic fibers from the upper two thoracic segments and the postganglionic fibers from these ganglia to the brachial plexus are thus severed, together with the removal of a large number of ganglionic cells (Fig. 182). The procedure promotes vasodilatation by decreasing the vasoconstrictor impulses to the extremity.

Horner's syndrome, on the side of the operation, is an unavoidable sequel of cervicothoracic ganglionectomy since all preganglionic sympathetic fibers to the head region course upward through that part of the sympathetic chain which is excised. The syndrome is characterized by ipsilateral miosis, ptosis, enophthalmos and anhidrosis and blushing of the face. *Miosis* (constriction of the pupil) occurs as the result of having interrupted the nerve supply to the dilator pupillae muscle. *Ptosis* of slight, but noticeable, degree results from paralysis of the smooth muscle (of Horner) which is associated with the levator palpebrae superioris in the upper eyelid. *Enophthalmos* may be due to paralysis of Mueller's muscle which bridges the inferior orbital fissure but has been termed an optical illusion due to narrowing of the palpebral fissure (Craig and Fuller, 1948). *Anhidrosis*

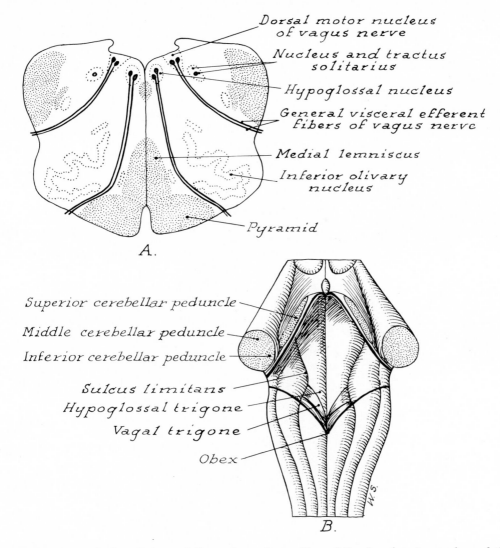

Fig. 184. *A,* Section of the medulla to show the position of the dorsal motor nucleus of the vagus nerve; *B,* Diagram to show the position of the vagal trigone in the floor of the fourth ventricle (rhomboid fossa).

(absence or diminution of sweating) is due to interruption of the sympathetic nerves to the sweat glands and *blushing* results from vasodilatation of peripheral vessels whose sympathetic innervation has been interrupted.

The oculopupillary features of Horner's syndrome can be avoided if, instead of performing cervicothoracic ganglionectomy, only the second or second and third thoracic ganglia are removed (Goetz, 1948 and others). Preganglionic sympathetic fibers to the upper extremity have been shown to come from the intermediate gray column of the first thoracic segment of the spinal cord in only about 10 per cent of individuals. A theoretical advantage of second thoracic ganglionectomy, so far as sympathectomy of the upper extremity is concerned, is

that the procedure is essentially a preganglionic resection with respect to the ganglion cells in the lower two cervical and first thoracic ganglia whose cells actually distribute postganglionic fibers to the upper extremity; sensitization to circulating epinephrine which has been supposed to be responsible for unsatisfactory results when the cervicothoracic ganglion cells are removed, is thus reduced or eliminated. Ray (1953) dismissed the existence of significant differences in sensitivity to epinephrine after pre- and postganglionic sympathectomy in man and advocated removal of the first thoracic and inferior cervical ganglia for effective and lasting denervation of the blood vessels of the upper extremity.

Lumbar ganglionectomy is performed for the relief of disorders of the circula-

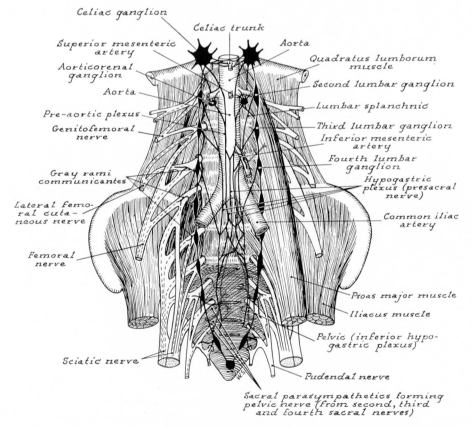

FIG. 185.   The hypogastric plexus and the sympathetic supply to the lower extremity
(in part after Gask and Ross).

tion in the lower extremities and is particularly applicable to cases of thromboangitis obliterans which are not too far advanced. The second and third and, frequently, the fourth lumbar ganglia are removed and this, in addition to removing some ganglionic cells, interrupts all the preganglionic fibers from the lower thoracic and upper lumbar segments of the cord which have to do with the sympathetic innervation of the lower extremity (Fig. 185). The relief of the excruciating pain usually associated with thromboangitis obliterans, by lumbar ganglionectomy, may be due to the interruption of visceral afferent fibers, to the increased blood supply to the extremity, or to a combination of both factors. Randall et al. (1953), on the basis of electrical stimulation of the sympathetic trunk, found preganglionic fibers, innervating the most distal portion of the lower extremity, entering the trunk at levels varying from first to fourth or fifth lumbar ganglia; they showed that, in some patients, a single ganglion left intact at the first lumbar level may afford sufficient innervation to elicit profound vasomotor and sudomotor reactions in the lower extremity and that, in others, complete removal of all the lumbar ganglia failed to abolish such responses.

It has been generally believed that bilateral removal, in the male, of the upper lumbar ganglia would result in sterility because of the location in the lumbar cord of the ejaculatory center, responsible for the sympathetic innervation of the ejaculatory mechanism (seminiferous tubules, vas deferens and ejaculatory ducts). Rose (1953) followed 30 cases of bilateral lumbar ganglionectomy in which the first, second and third ganglia were removed; only 3 were found to be sterile. On the contrary, 7 of 8 cases of hypertension in whom the sympathetic chain from ninth thoracic to third lumbar was removed, had complete absence of ejaculation. Rose explained these observations by the assumption that *postganglionic* ejaculatory innervation arises in the twelfth thoracic ganglion and reaches the pelvis via the least splanchnic and *presacral nerves* (Fig. 185).

The **hypogastric plexus (presacral nerve),** through which the distal part of the colon, rectum, bladder and uterus receive their sympathetic supply, is formed by three roots (Fig. 185). The central root descends over the bifurcation of the aorta from the pre-aortic plexus and is joined on each side by a lateral root. The lateral roots are formed by the union, on each side, of the lumbar splanchnics which arise from the upper lumbar segments of the spinal cord. The *lumbar splanchnics* pass through the sympathetic trunks without synapsing upon ganglionic cells and eventually synapse upon cells in ganglia scattered among the fibers of the pelvic plexuses. The hypogastric plexus is located between the common iliac arteries, anterior to the fifth lumbar vertebra and the sacral promontory. It continues into the pelvis and divides into right and left *pelvic (inferior hypogastric) plexuses* which course downward on either side of the rectum. The pelvic nerves, or sacral parasympathetics, as previously noted, also enter into the pelvic plexuses.

Hirschsprung's disease or **congenital megacolon** was formerly thought to be due to an autonomic imbalance; *i.e.,* the sympathetic impulses to the colon were supposed to be in excess of the parasympathetic. Since the sympathetics have been shown to inhibit peristalsis and the parasympathetics to increase it, the imbalance would result in stasis of intestinal content with the tremendous dilatation of the colon which is characteristic of the condition.

Adson (1937) treated Hirschsprung's disease by resection of the hypogastric plexus in combination with bilateral removal of the second, third and fourth lumbar sympathetic ganglia. He stated that the extent of sympathectomy should be adjusted to the degree of the existing disease and should "include sufficient sympathetic fibers to balance the neuromuscular mechanism of filling and emptying the colon."

More recently it has been demonstrated that there is, in most cases of congenital megacolon, an absence of ganglion cells in the myenteric (Auerbach's) plexuses of the distal colon (Zuelzer and Wilson, 1948; Whitehouse and Kernohan, 1948; Swenson et al., 1949; Swenson, 1954; Davidson et al., 1955; others). It appears that the aganglionic portion of the colon is tonically contracted and that there is absence, in this segment, of propulsive peristaltic activity, leading to accumulation of intestinal content in the proximal colon; this results in thinning out of the muscular layers and, eventually, loss of propulsive activity with stasis in this segment.

Kamijo (1953) found high concentrations of cholinesterase in the bundles of unmyelinated nerve fibers in the acellular myenteric plexuses of the spastic segments of colons from subjects suffering from megacolon; they reasoned that the presence of the enzyme indicated that the fibers were cholinergic and that the lack of myelinization placed them in the postganglionic category. They hypothesized that cholinergic ganglion cells are present but are outside the colon in a location "more central than normal" and that their axons may extend to their usual sites of termination.

The myenteric plexuses may contain, normally, both excitatory (cholinergic) and inhibitory (adrenergic) neurons, the participation of both of which is necessary for the integration of peristaltic activity (Ambache, 1951). If this is true of the human colon, it is possible that the physiologic defect in the spastic segment in congenital megacolon might consist of an absence or paucity of adrenergic neurons which, in the presence of a nor-

mal component of centrally situated cholinergic ganglion cells, could result in the net effect of unopposed tonic contraction (Kamijo et al., 1953). Swenson et al., (1949) have reported excellent results in 33 patients with megacolon from removal of the narrowed, spastic portions of distal colon and proximal rectum, or those areas quite regularly found to be lacking in ganglionic cells.

Dysmenorrhea (painful menstruation) has been successfully treated by *presacral neurectomy* (excision of the hypogastric plexus). The relief of pain may be dependent upon the division of visceral afferent fibers but it is probable that the division of efferent fibers, necessarily a part of the procedure, may be a potent factor through lessening of the severe smooth muscle spasm which accounts for the pain.

Hendrick (1941) has reported favorable results from presacral neurectomy in a fairly large series of patients with dysmenorrhea. At least 16 of his patients subsequently delivered one or more children without difficulty. Frequency of urination for two or three days following the operation occurred in practically all cases; after this brief interval, however, bladder function returned to normal.

It is generally conceded that the parasympathetics produce contraction of the detrusor muscle of the bladder and relaxation of the internal sphincter (van Duzen and Duncan, 1953). The sympathetics are responsible for contraction of the internal sphincter and relaxation of the detrusor muscle, thus promoting filling of the bladder. Langworthy (1943) considered the sympathetic innervation of the urinary bladder to be relatively unimportant since, in his experience, the organ continued to function normally following section of its sympathetic supply as has been "repeatedly demonstrated in cases of presacral neurectomy." In summarizing his views on the subject of bladder innervation Langworthy stated, "The parasympathetic influence controls the tone and contractions of the vesical muscle during the period of vesical filling. It is possible voluntarily to suppress waves of vesical contraction through the mediation of the parasympathetic pathway. The parasympathetic influence can induce a sustained contraction of the muscle which empties the bladder completely. Influences through the sympathetic pathway appear to have no part in the control of these activities."

BIBLIOGRAPHY

ADSON, A. W., 1937: Hirschsprung's disease; indications for and results obtained by sympathectomy. Surgery, 1, 859-877.

AMBACHE, N., 1951: Unmasking, after cholinergic paralysis by Botulinum toxin, of a reversed action of nicotine on the mammalian intestine, revealing the probable presence of local inhibitory ganglion cells in the enteric plexuses. Brit. J. Pharmacol., 6, 51-67.

CRAIG, J. D. and FULLER, R. C., 1948: Cervical sympathetic paralysis. Brit. Med. J., 1, 1182-1184.

DAVIDSON, M., SLEISENGER, M. H., STEINBERG, H. and ALMY, T. P., 1955: Studies of distal colonic motility in children. III. The pathologic physiology of congenital megacolon (Hirschsprung's disease). Gastroenterology, 29, 803-824.

ELIASSON, S., LINDGREN, P. and UVNÄS, B., 1953: Representation in the hypothalamus and the motor cortex in the dog of the sympathetic vasodilator outflow to the skeletal muscles. Acta Physiol. Scand., 27, 18-37.

GOETZ, R. H., 1948: The surgical physiology of the sympathetic nervous system with special reference to cardiovascular disorders. Intern. Abstr. Surg., 87, 417-439.

HENDRICK, J. W., 1941: Resection of the presacral nerve for dysmenorrhea and pelvic pain. Texas State J. Med., 37, 26-29.

KAMIJO, K., HIATT, R. B. and KOELLE, G. B., 1953: Congenital megacolon. A comparison of the spastic and hypertrophied segments with respect to cholinesterase activities and sensitivities to acetylcholine, DFP and the barium ion. Gastroenterology, 24, 173-185.

LANGWORTHY, O. R., 1943: General principles of autonomic innervation. A.M.A. Arch. Neurol. Psychiat., 50, 590-602.

MAGOUN, H. W. and BEATON, L. E., 1942: The salivatory motor nuclei in the monkey. Am. J. Physiol., 136, 720-725.

MITCHELL, G. A. G., 1953: The innervation of the heart. Brit. Heart J., 15, 159-171.

NAQUIN, H. A., 1954: Argyll Robertson pupil following herpes zoster ophthalmicus: with remarks on the efferent pupillary pathways. Am. J. Ophthalmol., 38, 23-33.

RANDALL, W. C., COX, J. W., ALEXANDER, W. F. COLDWATER, K. B. and HERTZMAN, A. B., 1953: Direct electrical stimulation of the sympathetic trunk in man. XIX Intern. Physiol. Congress, Montreal, pp. 692-693.

RAY, B. S., 1953: Sympathectomy of the upper extremity. Evaluation of surgical methods. J. Neurosurg., 10, 624-633.

RICHINS, C. A. and KUNTZ, A., 1953: Role of sympathetic nerves in the regulation of salivary secretion. Am. J. Physiol., 173, 471-473.

ROSE, S. S., 1953: An investigation into sterility after lumbar ganglionectomy. Brit. Med. J., 1, 247-250.

SWENSON, O., RHEINLANDER, H. F. and DIAMOND, I., 1949: Hirschsprung's disease: a new concept of the etiology. Operative results in thirty-four patients. New England J. Med., 241, 551-556.

SWENSON, O., 1954: Modern treatment of Hirschsprung's disease. J. Am. Med. Assoc., 154, 651-653.

UVNÄS, B., 1954: Sympathetic vasodilator outflow. Physiol. Rev., 34, 608-618.

VAN DUZEN, R. E. and DUNCAN, C. G., 1953: Anatomy and nerve supply of urinary bladder. J. Am. Med. Assoc., 153, 1345-1347.

WANG, S. C., 1943: Localization of the salivatory center in the medulla of the cat. J. Neurophysiol., 6, 195-202.

WARD, A. A. and REED, H. L., 1946: Mechanism of pupillary dilatation elicited by cortical stimulation. J. Neurophysiol., 9, 329-335.

WARWICK, R., 1954: The ocular parasympathetic nerve supply and its mesencephalic sources. J. Anat., 88, 71-93.

WHITEHOUSE, F. R. and KERNOHAN, J. W., 1948: Myenteric plexus in congenital megacolon. Study of eleven cases. A.M.A. Arch. Int. Med., 82, 75-111.

ZUELZER, W. W. and WILSON, J. L., 1948: Functional intestinal obstruction on a congenital neurogenic basis in infancy. Am. J. Diseases Children, 75, 40-64.

Chapter 22

Visceral Reflex Arcs

VISCERAL reflex arcs, including *viscerovisceral, viscerosomatic* and *somatovisceral,* facilitate automatic adjustments of the entire organism to its internal and external environments. When food is ingested the visceral blood supply is increased at the expense of that to the periphery in order to promote digestion. When muscular activity results in increased demand for oxygen, respiration is correspondingly increased in rate and depth. In a cold environment the peripheral vessels are constricted to prevent loss of heat from the body surface.

Many visceral reflex arcs are centered in the spinal cord; others have their centers in the medulla oblongata. In many instances the afferent limb of the arc includes the thalamus which may send impulses to the hypothalamus or to the cerebral cortex; thus, visceral reflexes may be centered at diencephalic or cortical levels. That the cortex functions in visceral reflex arcs is indicated by the fact that there are several cortical areas which, when stimulated electrically, give rise to visceral responses.

The **carotid sinus reflex** (Fig. 186) is an important example of the viscerovisceral type. The *carotid sinus* is a slight dilatation of the common carotid artery at its level of bifurcation into internal and external divisions or of the proximal portion of the internal carotid artery. Its walls contain specialized receptors which are stimulated by increases in intrasinus pressure. Peripheral processes of nerve cells in the petrosal ganglion of the glossopharyngeal nerve are distributed to the receptors by way of the *carotid sinus nerve.*

When the pressure within the carotid sinus is increased as the result of a general rise in blood pressure the nerve impulses thus initiated are conducted to the nucleus solitarius in the medulla. Direct or indirect connections from the nucleus solitarius to the dorsal motor nucleus of the vagus nerve complete a reflex arc through which a reduction in heart rate is produced. Other reflex connections from the nucleus solitarius to the vasomotor center in the reticular formation of the medulla inhibit the activity of the center (Bouckaert and Heymans, 1933) and thus allow dilatation of the circulatory system to occur. The combined effect resulting from decreased heart rate and dilatation of the vascular system is reduction in blood pressure.

When the blood pressure is low the number of nerve impulses reaching the vasomotor center from the receptors in the carotid sinus is correspondingly reduced; thus, the inhibitory effect upon the center is lessened and vasoconstriction occurs with a resultant increase in blood pressure.

Sympathetic impulses emanating from the vasomotor center may also increase the cardiac rate and thereby contribute to an increase in blood pressure. Vasoconstrictor and cardioaccelerator impulses from the vasomotor center are conducted to the proper cells in the intermediate gray columns of the spinal cord by way of reticulospinal fibers originating from cells within the center (Fig. 186). According to Baker *et al.* (1950), large reticular cells situated in the ventro-medial area of the reticular formation of the medulla, immediately dorsal to the inferior olivary nucleus, regulate circulation. Damage to these cells invariably produces clinical symptoms of vasomotor disturbance, such as irregular feeble pulse, low pulse pressure, irregularities of blood pressure and terminal shock. Matzke and Baker (1952), after detailed studies of the pons from each of 109 cases of bulbar poliomyelitis, described the vasomotor center as having its rostral half within large reticular cells in the caudal part of the pons. Involvement of this area resulted in circulatory collapse.

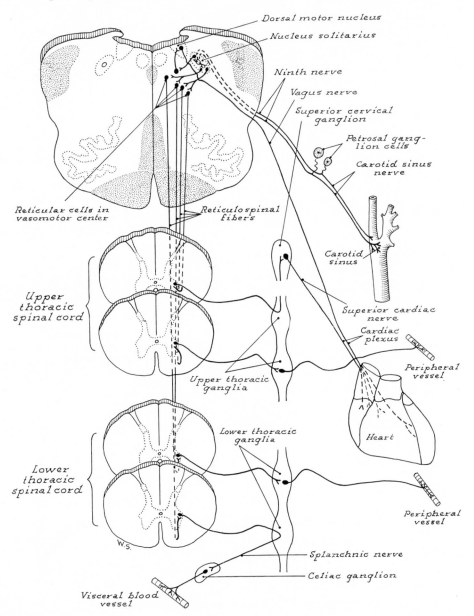

FIG. 186.   Diagram to show the probable reflex connections involved in the regulation of blood pressure by the carotid sinus.

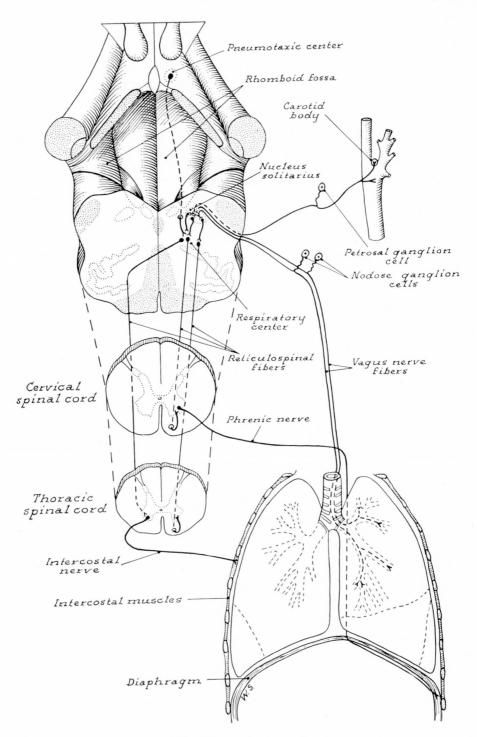

FIG. 187.　The respiratory reflex arc.

The **depressor nerve,** a branch of the vagus, functions as the afferent limb of another reflex arc through the nucleus solitarius, vasomotor center and dorsal motor nucleus which effects lowering of blood pressure. The depressor nerve consists of peripheral processes of nodose ganglion cells and is distributed to the proximal portion of the aortic arch. It is not as well defined in man as in some of the lower animals (cat, rabbit, dog). Currently, there is evidence that afferent connections from almost all divisions of the vascular system affect the vasomotor center and contribute to regulation of blood pressure.

Chemoreceptors in the carotid sinus and carotid body are stimulated by increases in carbon dioxide tension and decreases in oxygen tension of the blood. Impulses arising from stimulation of these special receptors serve to stimulate the respiratory center when it might otherwise fail to maintain respiration because of abnormal conditions such as deep anesthesia. It has been shown (Ray and Stewart, 1948) that the chemically induced part of the carotid sinus reflex is transmitted principally by nerves other than the glossopharyngeal (vagus, sympathetic).

The **respiratory reflex** functions through a viscerosomatic arc (Fig. 187) since the muscles responsible for respiration originate from mesodermal somites. Peripheral processes of nodose ganglion cells are distributed, by way of the vagus nerve and pulmonary plexuses, to special receptors in the lungs. Special receptors are found throughout the bronchial tree and as far distally as the atria (Larsell and Dow, 1933). Impulses originating in these receptors reach the nucleus solitarius from which they are conducted to the respiratory center in the reticular formation of the medulla; those initiated by inflation of the lungs inhibit, and those resulting from deflation excite, in-spiration. Many reticulospinal fibers from the respiratory center terminate in relation to anterior gray column cells in the third, fourth and fifth cervical segments of the spinal cord and thus serve, through the phrenic nerve, to activate the diaphragm; others terminate in relation to anterior gray column cells in the thoracic levels of the cord whose axons are distributed to the intercostal muscles through the intercostal nerves.

The **respiratory center** consists of a diffusely arranged group of reticular cells extending from the rostral part of the medulla to the level of the obex (Fig. 187). The cells in the more dorsal part of the reticular formation have been shown to be concerned with the expiratory phase of respiration and those in the ventral part with the inspiratory phase (Pitts *et al.,* 1939 a, b); Woldring and Dirken, 1951). Afferent impulses from the lungs by way of the vagus nerve and from the carotid sinus by way of the glossopharyngeal do not constitute the only sources of activation of the respiratory center; slight increases in the carbon dioxide tension of the blood circulating through the center augment its activity. The function of the vagi in limiting inspiration and permitting the inception of expiration may be shared to some extent by the so-called pneumotaxic center.

A **pneumotaxic center** and its location in the rostral pons or mesencephalon have been postulated from experiments in which the vagus nerves were sectioned bilaterally in association with transection of the brain stem at various levels. After section of both vagi, breathing continues although it is deep and slow; if, however, section of the vagi is combined with transection of the brain stem at a level slightly rostral to the brachia pontis, respiration ceases in a state of deep inspiration. Section of the brain stem at the same level without section of the vagi results

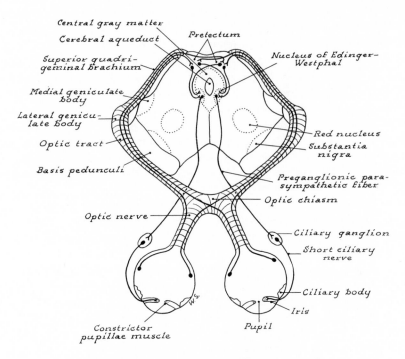

FIG. 188.   The light reflex arc.

in the same type of respiration as produced by vagal section alone (Pitts *et al,* 1939). Tang (1953) consistently failed to produce apneustic breathing in vagotomized cats, decerebrated at the midcollicular level after separate or seriatim ablation of inferior colliculi, central gray matter and tegmentum at the inferior collicular level, pontile central gray matter and central part of the anterior pontile tegmentum. However, small bilateral lesions in the extreme dorsolateral part of the anterior pontile tegmentum consistently produced apneustic breathing, indicating that this is the location of the pneumotaxic center.

Baker *et al.* (1950) studied the entire medulla from each of eighty cases of bulbar poliomyelitis. On the basis of their observations they concluded that small reticular cells in the ventrolateral area of the reticular formation of the medulla, just dorsal to the inferior olivary nucleus,

regulate respiratory function. Involvement of these cells by the virus resulted in irregularity of respiratory rhythm and depth, periods of apnea and, finally, cessation of respiration.

The **light reflex** is dependent upon a somatovisceral arc (Fig. 188). The receptors are the rods and cones of the retina. The course of the afferent impulses from the rod and cone cells through bipolar and ganglion cells, optic nerve, optic tract and superior quadrigeminal brachium was described in Chapter 8. Upon reaching the pretectum by way of the quadrigeminal brachium, the impulses are relayed to the Edinger-Westphal nuclei, ciliary ganglion and constrictor pupillae muscle as described in Chapter 21.

The **accommodation reflex** differs from the light reflex in that the cerebral cortex is included in its arc and in that both smooth and striated muscles are included in its effector mechanism. The reflex consists of the adjustments of the eyes which occur when they are rather suddenly focused on a near object after an interval of staring at a distant wall or landscape. The elicitation of the reflex, clinically, is accomplished by asking the patient to look at the farthest wall of the examining room or out of the window; when his eyes are well adjusted to distant vision, a pencil, pen or other small object is quickly placed in front of his eyes at a distance of twelve to fourteen inches and he is asked to focus upon it. Two important adjustments, reflex in character, occur when this procedure is carried out: the eyes converge to some extent (through contraction of the internal recti) and the

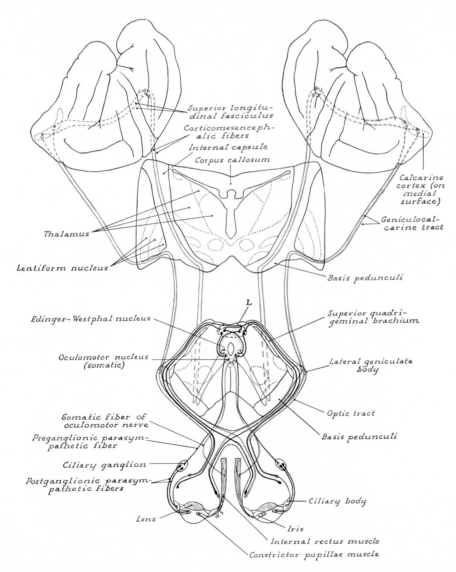

FIG. 189. Diagram to show the reflex connections responsible for the light reflex and those which may be involved in the accommodation reflex. The Argyll Robertson pupil, in which there is loss of the light reflex with preservation of accommodation would be explained by a lesion within the circle (L.).

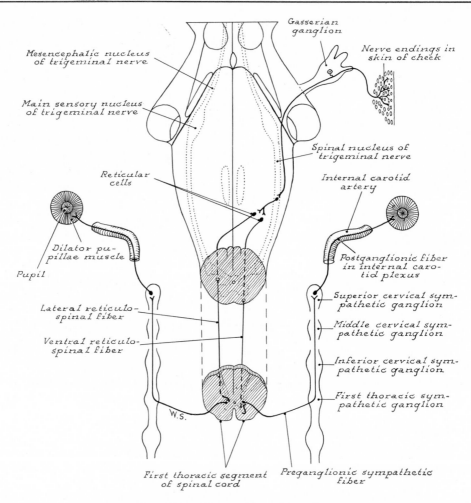

FIG. 190. The pupillary-skin reflex.

lenses are thickened through contraction of the ciliary muscles. These adjustments serve to properly focus the near object upon the retinae of the two eyes. Convergence and thickening of the lenses are accompanied by bilateral pupillary constriction which may or may not be essential to accommodation; it should serve to reduce the amount of light entering the eyes and thus produce more clearly defined images as is the case when the aperture in the diaphragm of a camera or microscope is reduced in diameter. Pupillary constriction in accommodation has sometimes been attrib-

uted to a failure of functional separation of the impulses from the Edinger-Westphal nuclei to ciliary and pupilloconstrictor muscles; it may be secondary to the convergence of the eyes and thus be dependent upon a separate reflex arc beginning with proprioceptors in the extrinsic muscles of the eyes.

Convergence of the eyes and constriction of the pupils constitute the observable reactions in the accommodation reflex. The arc traversed by the impulses responsible for the reflex has not been as definitely determined as has that for the light reflex. The receptors are the rods and cones from which impulses are conducted through the cell layers of the retina, the optic nerve and the optic tract. Since the reflex depends upon the conscious perception of an object or of objects within the visual fields it seems logical to assume that the afferent impulses are relayed from the lateral geniculate body to the visual cortex by way of the geniculo-calcarine tract. It is possible, and highly probable, that intracortical connections from the visual cortex to the frontal eye fields by way of the superior longitudinal fasciculus and between the visual cortex and Area 19 by way of short association fibers account for the inclusion of these areas in the accommodation reflex arc. Descending fibers from the various extrapyramidal areas of the cerebral cortex have been traced through the internal capsule to various subcortical centers (Chapter 16); those having to do with pupillary constriction and convergence as they occur in the accommodation reflex may enter the basis pedunculi of the mesencephalon and be distributed from it to the Edinger-Westphal and oculomotor nuclei (Fig. 189). It will be recalled, in this connection, that corticomesencephalic fibers from the frontal cortex have been traced to the oculomotor nuclei (Mettler, 1935). The efferent pathways from the oculomotor nuclei to the internal recti and from the Edinger-Westphal nuclei to the ciliary and constrictor pupillae muscles have been previously described.

The **Argyll Robertson pupil** is one in which there is no constriction of the pupil in response to light but normal constriction occurs in association with the accommodation reflex. It is obvious, since both reflexes have the same efferent pathway from the Edinger-Westphal nucleus to the constrictor pupillae muscle and since both have the same afferent pathway from retina to the lateral geniculate body, that the interruption in the light reflex

arc must occur at some point between the lateral geniculate body and the Edinger-Westphal nucleus (Fig. 189). If pupillary constriction in accommodation is effected by cortical projection fibers which reach the Edinger-Westphal nucleus by way of the basis pedunculi and mesencephalic tegmentum, the loss of the light reflex with preservation of accommodation is easily explained on the basis of a lesion in the rostrodorsal part of the mesencephalon (Fig. 189). Such a lesion would destroy the fibers from the pretectum to the Edinger-Westphal nucleus without damaging those from the basis pedunculi to the same nucleus (Merritt and Moore, 1933).

The **pupillary-skin reflex** is of the somatovisceral type (Fig. 190). It consists of pupillary dilatation in response to scratching or pinching the skin of the cheek or chin. The reflex arc begins with receptors in the skin to which peripheral processes of semilunar ganglion cells are distributed. Central processes of the ganglion cells terminate in the spinal nucleus of the trigeminal nerve and axons of cells in that nucleus synapse upon reticular cells whose axons course caudally through the spinal cord to synapse upon intermediate gray column cells in the upper two thoracic segments. Preganglionic fibers from the intermediate column cells enter the sympathetic trunk by way of the ventral roots and white rami communicantes of the first and second thoracic nerves, course upward in the trunk and end in relation to ganglionic cells in the superior cervical ganglion. Postganglionic fibers reach the dilator pupillae muscle by way of the internal carotid plexus and the ciliary nerves.

Langworthy (1943), Harris *et al.* (1944) and others have attributed reflex pupillodilatation to inhibition of the nucleus of Edinger-Westphal. Harris *et al.* stimulated the sciatic, splanchnic and trigeminal nerves in cats with progressively more rostral brain stem lesions. They found that lesions above the 'oculomotor' nucleus did not impair the response which was therefore "evidently completed at the midbrain level"; destruction at lower levels (spinal cord, medulla and pons) resulted in impairment or failure of the response. Their "oculomotor inhibitory pathway," as it ascends through the reticular formation, "seems to be distinct from the lateral spinothalamic throughout its course." Arieff and Pyzik (1953) showed,

in lesions of the cervical cord in which stimuli from above could not reach the sympathetic outflow in the spinal cord, that pupillary dilatation was absent, as observed in the ciliospinal (pupillary-skin) reflex, when the face was stimulated. However, when the chest below the level of the lesion was similarly stimulated, pupillary dilatation did occur, and could be mediated only through pathways causing sympathetic excitation. This work, in the opinion of the authors, led only to the one

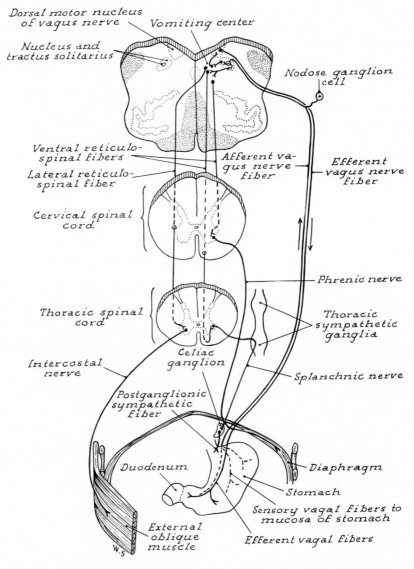

FIG. 191. Diagram of the connections involved in the vomiting reflex.

conclusion that, in man, pupillary dilatation in response to cutaneous stimulation is wholly sympathetic. They also concluded that dilatation of the pupil to darkness is not due to sympathetic stimulation by way of the ciliospinal center, but is most likely a reversal of the light reaction (based on parasympathetic inhibition of the Edinger-Westphal nucleus as described by Wilson, 1952).

The **vomiting reflex** (Fig. 191) begins with receptors in the mucosa of the stomach, gall bladder or duodenum. Irritative substances stimulate the receptors and the nerve impulses thus produced are carried by peripheral and central processes of nodose ganglion cells (vagus nerve) to the nucleus solitarius. From the nucleus the impulses are conducted to reticular cells whose axons course downward to anterior gray column cells in the cervical and thoracic segments of the spinal cord; the axons of these cells innervate the diaphragm and the anterior abdominal muscles. A *vomiting center* has been located in the reticular formation of the medulla; it is in the vicinity of the dorsal motor nucleus of the vagus nerve and close to the respiratory center (Kuntz, 1953; Borison and Wang, 1953). Some of the descending (reticulospinal) fibers from the vomiting center terminate in the intermediate gray columns of the lower thoracic segments; impulses traversing these fibers are relayed to the stomach by way of the splanchnic nerves, celiac ganglion and celiac plexus. Connections from the vomiting center to the dorsal motor nucleus of the vagus nerve account for vagal impulses to the stomach. Contraction of the pyloric sphincter and antrum of the stomach are produced by the vagal (parasympathetic) impulses and inhibition of the cardiac sphincter and fundus by the splanchnic (sympathetic) impulses (Kuntz, 1953).

The **cough reflex** traverses an arc which is very similar to that for the vomiting reflex. Peripheral processes of nodose ganglion cells are distributed to receptors in the mucosa of the larynx by way of the superior laryngeal nerve. Irritation of the mucosa gives origin to nerve impulses which reach the nucleus solitarius and are then relayed to anterior gray column cells through the medium of reticular cells and reticulospinal fibers. The diaphragm and abdominal muscles are thus activated. The closure of the glottis and inhibition of respiration which immediately precede the explosive phase of the reflex are no doubt effected by indirect connections from the nucleus solitarius to the nucleus ambiguus and respiratory center. The simultaneous closure of the glottis and contraction of the abdominal muscles produce the explosive pressure within the bronchial tree which is released in the form of a cough.

BIBLIOGRAPHY

ARIEFF, A. J. and PYZIK, S. W., 1953: The ciliospinal reflex in injuries of the cervical spinal cord in man. A.M.A. Arch. Neurol. Psychiat., *70*, 621-629.

BAKER, A. B., MATZKE, H. A. and BROWN, J. R., 1950: Poliomyelitis III. Bulbar poliomyelitis: a study of medullary function. A.M.A. Arch. Neurol. Psychiat., *63*, 257-281.

BORISON, H. L. and WANG, S. C., 1953: Physiology and pharmacology of vomiting. Pharmacol. Rev., *5*, 193-230.

BOUCKAERT, J. J. and HEYMANS, C., 1933: Carotid sinus reflexes: influence of central blood pressure and blood supply on respiratory and vasomotor centers. J. Physiol., *79*, 49-66.

HARRIS, A. J., HODES, M. C. R. and MAGOUN, H. W., 1944: The afferent path of the pupillodilator reflex in the cat. J. Neurophysiol., *7*, 231-243.

KUNTZ, A., 1953: *The Autonomic Nervous System*, 4th Ed., Lea & Febiger, Philadelphia.

LANGWORTHY, O. R., 1943: General principles of autonomic innervation. A.M.A. Arch. Neurol. Psychiat., *50*, 590-602.

LARSELL, O. and DOW, R. S., 1933: The innervation of the human lung. Am. J. Anat., *52*, 125-146.

MATZKE, H. A. and BAKER, A. B., 1952: Poliomyelitis. V. The pons. A.M.A. Arch. Neurol. Psychiat., *68*, 1-15.

MERRITT, H. H. and MOORE, M., 1933: The Argyll Robertson pupil; an anatomic physiologic explanation of the phenomenon, with a survey of its occurrence in neurosyphilis. A.M.A. Arch. Neurol. Psychiat., *30*, 357-373.

METTLER, F. A., 1935: Corticifugal fiber connections of the cortex of *Macaca mulatta*: the frontal region. J. Comp. Neurol., *61*, 509-542.

PITTS, R. F., MAGOUN, H. W. and RANSON, S. W., 1939a: Localization of the medullary respiratory centers in the cat. Am. J. Physiol., *126*, 673-688.

——— 1939b: The origin of respiratory rhythmicity. Am. J. Physiol., *127*, 654-670.

RAY, B. S. and STEWART, H. J., 1948: Role of glossopharyngeal nerve in the carotid sinus reflex in man, relief of carotid sinus syndrome by intracranial section of the glossopharyngeal nerve. Surgery, *23*, 411-424.

TANG, P. C., 1953: Localization of the pneumotaxic center in the cat. Am. J. Physiol., *172*, 645-652.

WILSON, W. C., 1952: Analysis of cerebral control of reflex pupillary dilation in cat and monkey. A.M.A. Arch. Neurol. Psychiat., *68*, 393-397.

WOLDRING, S. and DIRKEN, M. N. J., 1951: Site and extension of bulbar respiratory centre. J. Neurophysiol., *14*, 227-241

Chapter 23

The Rhinencephalon

THE rhinencephalon (nose brain) includes, in addition to the pathways and cortical areas directly related to the sense of smell, many centers and projection pathways to other telencephalic areas that are necessary for visceral and somatic responses to smell but are not primarily concerned with olfaction. Thus, the components of the rhinencephalon can be will be evident from the discussion which follows.

A. Primary olfactory components
   olfactory nerve
   olfactory bulb
   olfactory tract
   lateral olfactory stria and gyrus
   anterior part of parahippocampal gyrus (hippocampal gyrus)

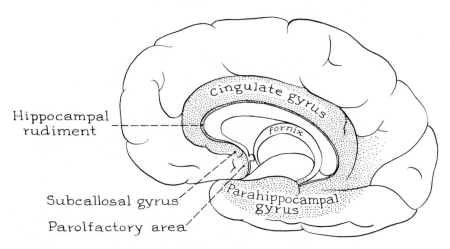

FIG. 192. Schematic drawing of the medial surface of the cerebral hemisphere to illustrate the limbic lobe cortex (stippled areas).

arbitrarily grouped in two major divisions. One includes the rostral parts related to primary reception of olfactory stimuli. The other includes a medial complex of cortex, subcortical nuclei and fiber tracts which developed phylogenetically along with the strictly olfactory system and are known as the *limbic lobe or limbic system* (Fig. 192) (Broca, 1878; MacLean, 1958). The intimate structural and functional interrelations of parts in these two divisions which are listed below

amygdaloid nucleus (corticomedial portion)

B. Limbic components
   1. Cortical areas
      medial olfactory area (septal area)
      hippocampal rudiment (induseum griseum)
      fornicate gyrus
         cingulate gyrus
         isthmus
      parahippocampal gyrus

(273)

hippocampus
amygdala
posterior orbital and insular
    cortex

2. Pathways
fornix
mammillothalamic tract
stria medullaris
stria terminalis
medial forebrain bundle
cingulum

the rhinencephalon is *allocortex* or *heterogenetic cortex* which implies that it does not show 6 layers at some stage of ontogenetic development as is characteristic of neocortex which is homogenetic. *Mesopallium* or *mesocortex* is a term commonly used for the ring of cortex which is roughly equivalent to gyrus fornicatus (Fig. 192). Kaada *et al.* (1949) have shown that visceral responses may be elicited by stimulating

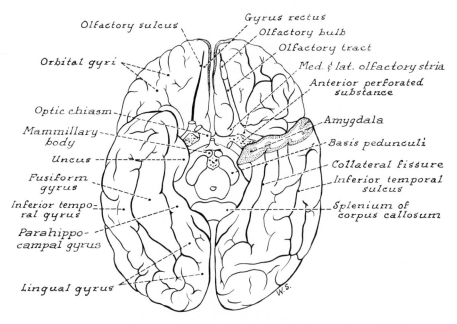

FIG. 193. The inferior surface of the cerebrum (after Toldt). The anterior part of the left temporal lobe, the brain stem caudal to the mesencephalic level, the right olfactory tract and bulb and the left half of the optic chiasm have been removed.

With respect to the phylogenetic and ontogenetic development of the cerebral cortex, the rhinencephalic components are more primitive. Accordingly, the terms *archipallium* (hippocampus and hippocampal rudiment) and *paleopallium* (for the rostral part of the parahippocampal gyrus) are often applied to these older parts as opposed to the *neopallium* which comprises the major part of the cerebral cortex in man. An additional term applicable to the cortex of

electrically along the entire ring of cortex.

The **septal** or **medial olfactory area** refers to the basal olfactory centers in the region of the olfactory trigone and anterior perforated substance (Figs. 192, 193 and 199). The area includes the subcallosal gyrus, parolfactory area and septal nuclei which are in relation to the septum pellucidum and anterior commissure. Also included is the *hippocampal rudiment (induseum griseum)* which extends from the region of the medial olfactory stria to the hippocampus and encircles the corpus callosum (Figs. 192 and 196); it contains the medial and lateral longitudinal striae. Olfactory fibers to the medial olfactory area course in the medial olfactory stria.

The **parahippocampal gyrus,** on the medial surface of the temporal lobe of the cerebral hemisphere, lies between the hippocampal and collateral fissures (Figs. 192 and 193). The *uncus* encircles the anterior end of the hippocampal fissure (Fig. 208). The lateral olfactory stria, which contain axons of mitral cells in the olfactory bulb (Fig. 96), course posterolaterally from the olfactory tract and terminate in the lateral olfactory gyrus, rostral part of parahippocampal gyrus, uncus and underlying amygdala (Figs. 193 and 199). These areas comprise the *pyriform lobe.* The lateral olfac-

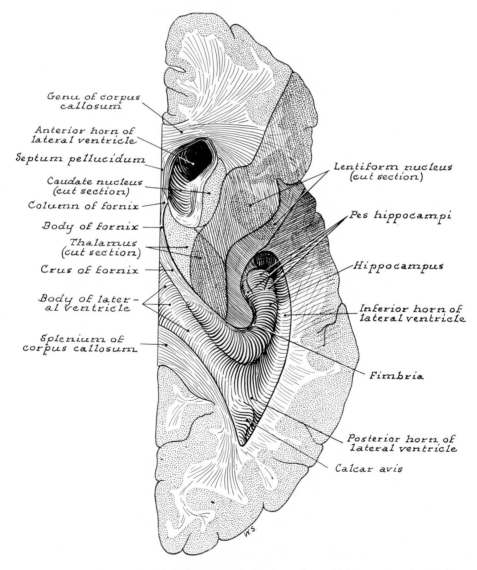

Genu of corpus callosum

Anterior horn of lateral ventricle

Septum pellucidum

Caudate nucleus (cut section)

Column of fornix

Body of fornix

Thalamus (cut section)

Crus of fornix

Body of lateral ventricle

Splenium of corpus callosum

Lentiform nucleus (cut section)

Pes hippocampi

Hippocampus

Inferior horn of lateral ventricle

Fimbria

Posterior horn of lateral ventricle

Calcar avis

FIG. 194.   The floor of the inferior horn of the lateral ventricle as seen from above.

tory gyrus is often called the prepyriform area and the posterior part of the pyriform lobe is the entorhinal cortex, area 28 of Brodmann (Fig. 133). The latter does not receive direct fibers from the olfactory tract.

The *hippocampus* probably receives some olfactory impulses from the uncus and the hippocampal gyrus by way of association neurons. The hippocampus forms a long, curved elevation in the floor of the inferior horn of the lateral ventricle (Fig. 194). The presence of

cortical gray matter in this location, as previously stated, results, in part, from outgrowth of the medial aspect of the temporal lobe of the brain on either side of the hippocampal fissure and, in part, from ingrowth or invagination of the cortex which originally lined the fissure. In spite of convincing evidence that the hippocampus is not primarily an olfactory center (Allen, 1940), it is probable that it does function as an association center for olfactory *and other* impulses. Its relation to the hypothalamus was con-

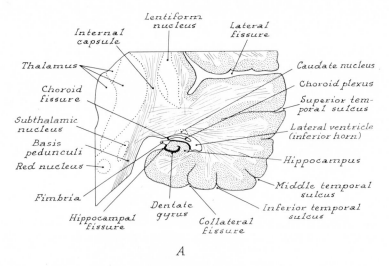

A

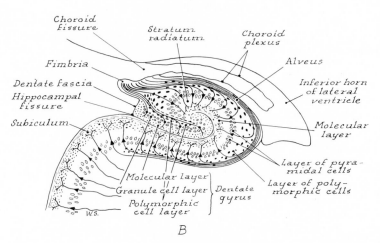

B

Fig. 195. *A,* Frontal section through the temporal lobe and adjacent areas of the right half of the brain to show the structure and relations of the hippocampus. *B,* Diagrammatic representation of the histologic structure of the hippocampus.

sidered earlier (Chapter 20). The definitive morphologic and gross anatomical features of the hippocampus are considered under the heading of "Rhinencephalon" partly because of its associative olfactory function and mainly because its inclusion there-under has become a matter of custom throughout neurological literature.

The structure and position of the hippocampus are best shown in frontal sections through appropriate segments of the temporal lobe of the cerebrum (Fig. 195). The temporal cortex immediately above the hippocampal fissure is designated as the *dentate fascia* because its medial border presents numerous serrations. The dentate fascia is continuous with the *dentate gyrus* of the hippocampus, and the dentate gyrus, in turn, is almost completely surrounded by that part of the hippocampal gray matter which developed from the inferior boundary of the hippocampal fissure. The arrangement of the gray matter of the hippocampus indicates that the ingrowth of cortex from the inferior boundary of the hippocampal fissure is more extensive than that from its upper boundary. The appearance of the hippocampus in cross-section (Fig. 195, *B*) is responsible for its being called the *cornu ammonis* (ram's horn).

The **dentate fascia** and **gyrus,** when examined microscopically, are found to consist of three layers (Fig. 195, *B*): an outer *molecular layer,* an intermediate *granule cell layer* containing small ovoid or fusiform cells and an inner *layer of polymorphic cells.*

The *outer part of the hippocampus* or that part continuous with the lower boundary of the hippocampal fissure, is similarly stratified (Fig. 195, *B*) but its intermediate layer contains medium-sized pyramidal cells and is, therefore, referred to as the *layer of pyramidal cells.* The apical dendrites of the pyramidal cells, as they course outward toward the molecular layer, form the *stratum radiatum.* The cortex of the hippocampal gyrus adjacent to, and continuous with the outer part of the hippocampus is known as the *subiculum* (Fig. 195).

A thin layer of white matter, known as the *alveus,* covers the ventricular surface of the hippocampus (Fig. 195). The alveus consists of axons of neurons in the hippocampus which enter the fimbria and then continue through the crus, body, and anterior column of the fornix to their termination in the mammillary body (Fig. 196) and of commissural axons from the hippocampus of the opposite side. The hippocampal commissure, through which the two hippocampi are connected, consists of a band of transversely coursing fibers between the right and left crura of the fornix (Fig. 197). The *fimbria* of the hippocampus is located on its medial side (Fig. 195) and is directly continuous with the crus of the fornix (Fig. 197).

The *fornix* consists of a body, two crura and two anterior columns (Fig. 197). The right and left crura, after arching upward and forward around the posterior limits of the thalami, unite to form the body. The columns of the fornix arch downward and backward from the body and enter the mamillary bodies (Fig. 196). The body and crura of the fornix are attached to and intimately associated with the under surface of the corpus callosum; the columns diverge from the corpus callosum but are attached to its body, genu and rostrum by the septum pellucidum. Several investigators have suggested that the fornix contains fibers coursing in both directions between septal area and hippocampus, and Votaw and Lauer (1963) have confirmed the presence of a hippocampal afferent system of fibers in the fornix of the monkey which arise from anterior olfactory areas. Those fibers

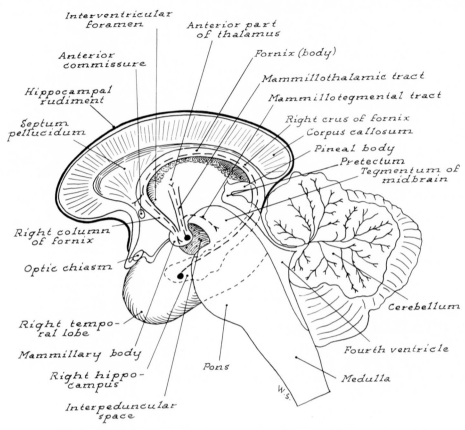

FIG. 196. Diagram to show the origin, relations and termination of the fornix.

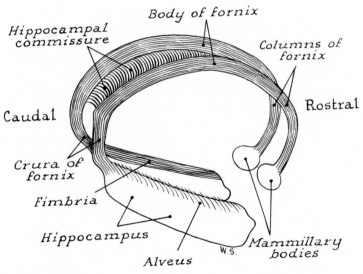

FIG. 197. Diagram of the fornix, hippocampi, mammillary bodies and hippocampal commissure.

from the septal region to the hippocampus have been said to constitute the *dorsal fornix*. These two-way connections have been studied by Green and Shimamoto (1953) who also reviewed the other connections of the hippocampus (with midbrain tegmentum, mammillary bodies and other hypothalamic areas and with other parts of the cerebrum). They found that weak electrical or mechanical stimulation of the fimbria induced motor fits and cortical electrical discharges similar to those of psychomotor epilepsy, and attributed the responses to connections through the hippocampal commissure to the opposite temporal lobe and other parts of the cerebrum because they could still be elicited after removal of hypothalamus and thalamus on the side of stimulation. Hunter (1950) and Kaada *et al.* (1953) have also seen manifestations, in cats, of what would be classified as psychomotor epilepsy as it occurs in man, when they stimulated the hippocampus. The behavior, as described by Kaada *et al.* consisted of quick glancing or searching movements to the contralateral side and a facial expression indicating "attention" associated with surprise, bewilderment and anxiety; reaction to real external stimuli was decreased with fixation of attention on "something" in the environment; some cats showed fear, anger and fury. The initial searching to one side indicated to these investigators that there was an initial discharge in the opposite hemisphere as postulated by Green and Shimamoto.

The **mammillothalamic tract (bundle of Vicq d'Azyr)** (Fig. 196) is a prominent bundle of fibers, demonstrable by gross dissection, which carries impulses (from the mammillary body) to the anterior nuclei of the thalamus. It may include some thalamomammillary fibers. The anterior nuclei of the thalamus projects mainly to areas 23 and 24 of the cingulate gyrus, as previously described

(Chapter 20). Fibers which arise from the mammillary body in common with the mammillothalamic tract and are shunted to the tegmental nuclei of the midbrain comprise the *mammillotegmental tract*.

The **stria medullaris thalami,** originating in the medial olfactory area, provides a pathway through which impulses from the olfactory cortex may be projected downward through the central nervous system; it arches upward anterior to the thalamus and then courses posteriorly along the dorsomedial border of the thalamus (Figs. 198 and 199). The stria ends in the *habenular nucleus* which is located in the epithalamus. The *epithalamus,* consisting of pineal body and habenular trigone, is located between the pretectum of the mesencephalon and the tela choroidea of the third ventricle. The *habenular trigone* contains the right and left habenular nuclei, the habenular commissure and the posterior commissure. Bürgi (1954) traced fibers of the stria medullaris through the habenular commissure and forward in the contralateral stria; these forward-coursing fibers appeared to end in the supraoptic nucleus and, possibly, in the amygdaloid nucleus. Termination in the former nucleus suggested, in Bürgi's opinion, that the stria has a "neurovegetative function."

Efferent impulses from the medial olfactory area upon reaching the habenular nucleus by way of the stria medullaris thalami (Figs. 198 and 199) may be relayed to the interpeduncular nucleus through the *habenulopeduncular tract (fasciculus retroflexus of Meynert)*. The *interpeduncular nucleus,* as its name implies, is located between the cerebral peduncles. Fibers from the interpeduncular nucleus course to the tegmental nuclei of the midbrain which, in turn, are connected with lower motor neurons through the medium of the dorsal longitudinal fasciculus and, according to

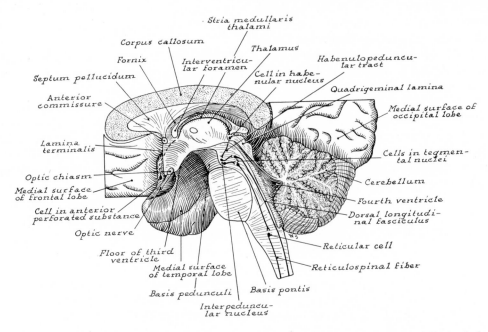

FIG. 198. Diagram of the olfactory projection pathway through the stria medullaris thalami, habenular nucleus and interpeduncular nucleus.

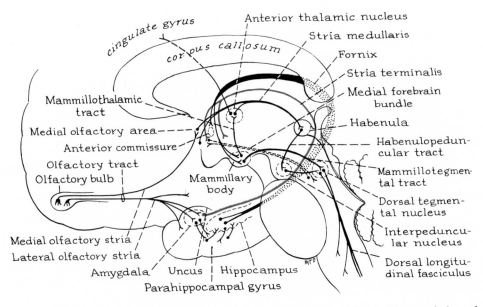

FIG. 199. Composite diagram to illustrate the major components of the rhinencephalon, their relations and connections.

Woodburne *et al.* (1946), through the rubrospinal tract.

The projection via the *stria terminalis,* of the amygdaloid nucleus upon the preoptic region and hypothalamus appears to complete another complex pathway from olfactory cortex to the hypothalamus (Fig. 199). Stimulation of the phylogenetically old corticomedial part of the amygdaloid nucleus, in cats, elicited controversive movements, tonic and clonic movements of the extremities, licking, sniffing, chewing and inhibition of respiratory and other spontaneous somatomotor activities, pupillary dilatation, salivation, micturition, defecation and pilo-erection, while stimulation of the phylogenetically younger basolateral division produced behavior changes consisting of searching movements to the opposite side, associated with bewilderment and anxiety and sometimes fear, anger and fury (Kaada *et al.*, 1954). The admixture of visceral with somatic responses, resulting from stimulation of the amygdaloid nucleus seems to indicate a close relationship with the hypothalamus. The similarity between responses from amygdaloid nucleus and hippocampus (Kaada *et al.,* 1953) indicates parallel circuits between each of them and the hypothalamus and between them and multiple cerebral cortical areas.

Many olfactory projection pathways have been described but, since the sense of smell does not play as important a part in the activities of man as it does in many of the other mammals, it is unnecessary to consider all their complex ramifications. It is of more significance that phylogenetic, cyto-architectural, physiologic and psychological investigations, some of which have been described above, indicate that the rhinencephalic mechanisms represent an early neural development involved in affectively determined behavior (MacLean and Delgado, 1953).

Significantly, Papez (1937) proposed that the rhinencephalic structures, interconnected as they are with the hypothalamus and thalamus, provide an anatomical substrate for emotional responses. As suggested above, a number of stimulation and ablation experiments have provided support for this concept and it is appropriate to mention a few of these studies. Klüver and Bucy (1937, 1938, 1939) produced pronounced behavioral disturbances in monkeys by bitemporal lobectomies. These included visual agnosia, a compulsiveness to contact and examine objects, a strong oral tendency, an apparent loss of fear and a marked increase in sexual behavior. Schreiner and Kling (1953, 1954, 1956) produced essentially these same behavioral disturbances in cats and monkeys by removal of the amygdalar nuclei and adjacent cortex. Apparent contradictory results were obtained by Bard and Mountcastle (1948) who observed that cats subjected to ablations of the amygdala, anterior hippocampus and surrounding neocortex evidenced rage reactions. In their analysis these authors found that these reactions did not ensue from neocortical removal unless the underlying nuclei were involved. Green *et al.* (1957) found that in cats hypersexuality ensued after lesions which were restricted to the pyriform cortex overlying the amygdaloid nucleus. The more recent experiments of Summers and Kaelber (1962) suggest that savage behavior or rage reactions do not follow bilateral removal of the amygdala and adjacent pyriform cortex unless there is damage to the hypothalamus. Additional support for the role of rhinencephalic structures in emotional responses emerges from the results of implanting electrodes in the septal region and other parts of the limbic system of rats (Olds, 1954, 1956, 1958). Following appropriate placement, the animals will stimulate themselves repeatedly, which suggests that the stimulation is related to motivation.

Another functional parameter of the rhinencephalon is suggested by the evidence that the hippocampus is concerned with or related in some way to recent memory mechanisms (Penfield and Milner, 1958). Additionally, it has been

a dreamy state of unreality and there may be associated sensations of taste. Motor phenomena, such as champing of the jaws and smacking of the lips may appear. The stimulation experiments, involving hippocampus and amygdaloid nucleus suggest that they may be concerned in the phenomena which constitute uncinate fits.

The neurons in the hippocampus (cornu ammonis) are likely to be the first and, frequently, the only neurons in

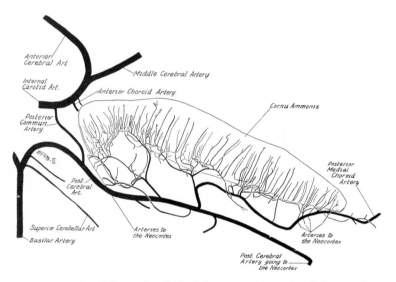

Fig. 200.   Arterial supply of the left cornu ammonis of the monkey
(Nilges, courtesy of J. Comp. Neurol.).

shown that the limbic cortex has important relationships with the reticular formation of the brain stem and probably plays a role in the alerting process (Green, 1958; Adey, 1958). A relationship of the limbic system to the pituitary-adrenocortical system has also been suggested (Mason, 1957).

Uncinate fits result from lesions of the temporal lobe which impinge upon the uncus or the anterior part of the hippocampal gyrus. They are characterized by olfactory hallucinations which usually consist of sensations of disagreeable odors. The attacks may be followed by

the brain to suffer from infectious, degenerative or toxic processes. A marked loss of cells in the hippocampus is usually evident in the brains of individuals who die from carbon monoxide poisoning. A similar loss of cells is characteristic of the hippocampi in brains from neurosyphilitic and epileptic patients. This selective vulnerability of the hippocampus is probably due to peculiarities of its vascularization. It has been suggested that the rake-like pattern of the branches of the posterior cerebral artery which supply the hippocampus (Fig. 200) may be a factor in the inadequate supply of blood to rather extensive areas of the hippocampus in cases of circulatory crises such as occur in epilepsy and carbon monoxide poisoning (Scharrer, 1940; Nilges, 1944).

BIBLIOGRAPHY

ADEY, W. R., 1958: Organization of the rhinencephalon. In *Reticular Formation of the Brain*. H. H. JASPER, *et al.* eds., Henry Ford Hosp. Intern. Symposium, Little, Brown & Co., Boston, pp. 621-644.

ALLEN, W. F., 1940: Effect of ablating the frontal lobes, hippocampi and occipito-parieto-temporal (excepting pyriform areas) lobes on positive and negative olfactory conditioned reflexes. Am. J. Physiol., *128*, 754-771.

BARD, P. and MOUNTCASTLE, V. B., 1948: Some forebrain mechanisms involved in expression of rage with special reference to suppression of angry behavior. Assoc. Res. Nerv. Ment. Dis., *27*, 362-404.

BROCA, P., 1878: Anatomie comparée des circonvolutions cérébrales. Le grand lobe limbique et la scissure limbique dans le série des mammiferes. Rev. Anthropol., *1*, 385-498.

BÜRGI, S., 1954: Über zwei Anteile der Stria medullaris und die Frage eines besonderen neuro-vegetativen Mechanismus. Arch. Psychiat. Z. Neurol., *192*, 301-310.

GREEN, J. D., 1957: The rhinencephalon: aspects of its relation to behavior and the reticular activating system. In *Reticular Formation of the Brain*. H. H. JASPER *et al.* eds. Henry Ford Hosp. Intern. Symposium, Little, Brown & Co., Boston, pp. 607-619.

GREEN, J. D. and SHIMAMOTO, T., 1953: Hippocampal seizures and their propagation. A.M.A. Arch. Neurol. Psychiat., *70*, 687-702.

GREEN, J. D., CLEMENTE, C. D. and DE GROOT, J., 1957: Rhinencephalic lesions and behavior in cats. J. Comp. Neurol., *108*, 505-545.

HUNTER, J., 1950: Further observations on subcortically induced epileptic attacks in unanesthetized animals. Electroencephalo. Clin. Neurophysiol., *2*, 193-201.

KAADA, B. R., PRIBRAM, K. H. and EPSTEIN, J. A., 1949: Respiratory and vascular responses in monkeys from temporal pole, insula, orbital surface and cingulate gyrus. J. Neurophysiol., *12*, 347-356.

KAADA, B. R., JANSEN, J. JR. and ANDERSEN, P., 1953: Stimulation of the hippocampus and medial cortical areas in unanesthetized cats. Neurology, *3*, 844-857.

KAADA, B. R., ANDERSEN, P. and JANSEN, J. JR., 1954: Stimulation of the amygdaloid nuclear complex in unanesthetized cats. Neurology, *4*, 48-64.

KLÜVER, H. and BUCY, P. C., 1937: "Psychic blindness" and other symptoms following bilateral temporal lobectomy in rhesus monkeys. Am. J. Physiol., *119*, 352-353.

———— 1938: An analysis of certain effects of bilateral temporal lobectomy in the rhesus monkey with special reference to "psychic blindness." J. Psychol., *5*, 33-54.

———— 1939: Preliminary analysis of functions of the temporal lobes in monkeys. A.M.A. Arch. Neurol. Psychiat., *42*, 979-1000.

MACLEAN, P. D. and DELGADO, J. M. R., 1953: Electrical and chemical stimulation of frontotemporal portions of limbic system in the waking animal. Electroencephalo. Clin. Neurophysiol., *5*, 91-100.

MACLEAN, P. D., 1958: The limbic system with respect to self-preservation and the preservation of the species. J. Nerv. Ment. Dis., *127*, 1-11.

MASON, J. W., 1958: The central nervous system regulation of ACTH secretion. In *Reticular Formation of the Brain*, H. H. JASPER, *et al.*, eds., Henry Ford Hosp. Intern. Symposium, Little, Brown & Co., Boston, pp. 645-662.

NILGES, R. G., 1944: Arteries of mammalian cornu ammonis. J. Comp. Neurol., *80*, 177-190.

OLDS, J., 1956: A preliminary mapping of electrical reinforcing effects in the rat brain. J. Comp. Physiol. Psychol., *49*, 281-285.

———— 1958: Satiation effects in self-stimulation of the brain. J. Comp. Physiol. Psychol., *51*, 675-678.

OLDS, J. and MILNER, P., 1954: Positive reinforcement produced by electrical stimulation of septal and other regions of the rat brain. J. Comp. Physiol. Psychol., *47*, 419-427.

PAPEZ, J. W., 1937: A proposed mechanism of emotion. A.M.A. Arch. Neurol. Psychiat., *38*, 725-743.

PENFIELD, W. and MILNER, B., 1958: Memory deficit produced by bilateral lesions in the hippocampal zone. A.M.A. Arch. Neurol. Psychiat., *79*, 475-497.

SCHARRER, E., 1940: Vascularization and vulnerability of the cornu ammonis in the oppossum. A.M.A. Arch. Neurol. Psychiat., *44*, 483-506.

SCHREINER, L. and KLING, A., 1953: Behavioral changes following rhinencephalic injury in cat. J. Neurophysiol., *16*, 643-659.

———— 1954: Effects of castration on hypersexual behavior induced by rhinencephalic injury in cat. A.M.A. Arch. Neurol. Psychiat., *72*, 180-186.

———— 1956: Rhinencephalon and behavior. Am. J. Physiol., *184*, 486-490.

SUMMERS, T. B. and KAELBER, W. W., 1962: Amygdalectomy: effects in cats and a survey of its present status. Am. J. Physiol., *203*, 1117-1119.

VOTAW, C. L. and LAUER, E., 1963: An afferent hippocampal fiber system in the fornix of the monkey. J. Comp. Neurol., *121*, 195-206.

WOODBURNE, R. T., CROSBY, E. C. and McCOTTER, R. E., 1946: The mammalian midbrain and isthmus regions. Part II. The fiber connections. A. The relations of the tegmentum of the midbrain with the basal ganglia in Macaca mulatta. J. Comp. Neurol., *85*, 67-92.

Chapter 24

The Ventricles of the Brain

THE ventricular system of the brain includes two lateral ventricles, the third ventricle, the cerebral aqueduct and the fourth ventricle (Fig. 201). The lateral ventricles communicate with the third ventricle through the interventricular foramina. The cerebral aqueduct connects the third ventricle with the fourth; corpus callosum, inferiorly by the thalamus and caudate nucleus and medially by the fornix. The corpus callosum and caudate nucleus approximate one another to form a narrow lateral boundary (Fig. 203). The shallow longitudinal groove between the dorsal convex surface of the caudate nucleus and that of the thalamus,

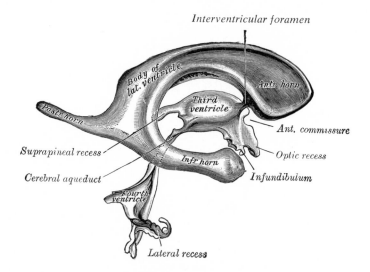

Interventricular foramen

Body of lat. ventricle

Ant. horn

Third ventricle

Post. horn

Ant. commissure

Suprapineal recess

Optic recess

Cerebral aqueduct

Infr. horn

Infundibulum

Fourth ventricle

Lateral recess

FIG. 201. Drawing of a cast of the ventricular system of the brain as seen from the side (Retzius in Gray's Anatomy).

the fourth ventricle communicates with the subarachnoid space through the median foramen of Magendie and the lateral paired foramina of Luschka. The ventricular system is lined by a layer of ependymal cells.

The **lateral ventricles** are within the cerebral hemispheres; each consists of a body and anterior, posterior and inferior horns (Fig. 202). The **body of the lateral ventricle** is bounded superiorly by the in the floor of the body of the lateral ventricle, contains the stria and vena terminalis. The choroid plexus of the body of the lateral ventricle is developed by evagination, through the choroid fissure, of the pia mater lining of the cerebral fissure (Fig. 203). That portion of the ependymal lining of the ventricle which was originally reflected from the fornix to the dorsal surface of the thalamus, across the choroid fissure, is carried into

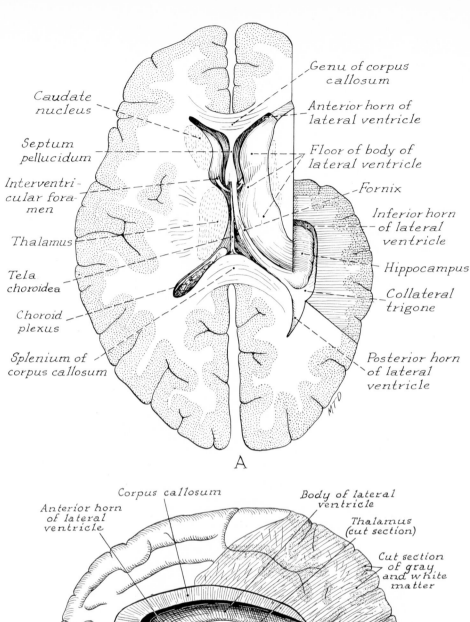

Caudate nucleus

Septum pellucidum

Interventricular foramen

Thalamus

Tela choroidea

Choroid plexus

Splenium of corpus callosum

Genu of corpus callosum

Anterior horn of lateral ventricle

Floor of body of lateral ventricle

Fornix

Inferior horn of lateral ventricle

Hippocampus

Collateral trigone

Posterior horn of lateral ventricle

A

Corpus callosum

Anterior horn of lateral ventricle

Body of lateral ventricle

Thalamus (cut section)

Cut section of gray and white matter

Anterior commissure

Lamina terminalis

Optic nerve

Temporal pole

Optic chiasm

Uncus

Inferior horn of lateral ventricle

Posterior horn of lateral ventricle

B

FIG. 202. *A*, Drawing to show the right lateral ventricle as seen from above. Note in the midline the tela choroidea of the third ventricle, and on the left the choroid plexus of the lateral ventricle. *B*, The right lateral ventricle exposed from its medial side.

the ventricle with the choroid plexus and thus comes to form its ependymal covering.

The **anterior horn of the lateral ventricle** extends forward and downward into the frontal lobe of the cerebral hemisphere. Its slanting floor is formed by the head of the caudate nucleus and its roof by the corpus callosum (Figs. 202 and 204). The anterior horn is limited anteriorly by the genu and rostrum of the corpus callosum; it is limited medially by the septum pellucidum which also serves to separate it from its fellow of

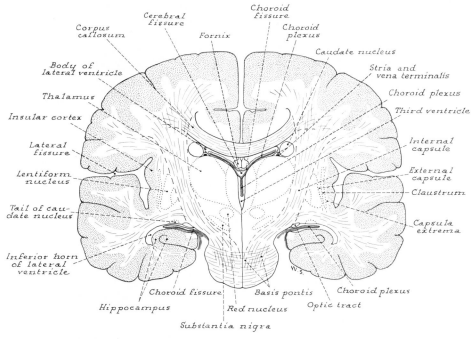

FIG. 203.   Frontal section of the brain through the bodies of the lateral ventricles to show the relations of the cerebral fissure, choroid fissures and ventricles to one another.

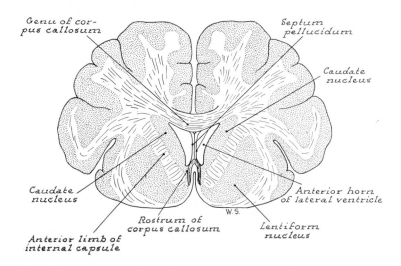

FIG. 204.   Frontal section through the anterior horns of the lateral ventricles.

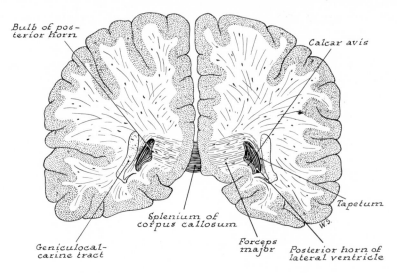

FIG. 205.   Frontal section through the posterior horns of the lateral ventricles.

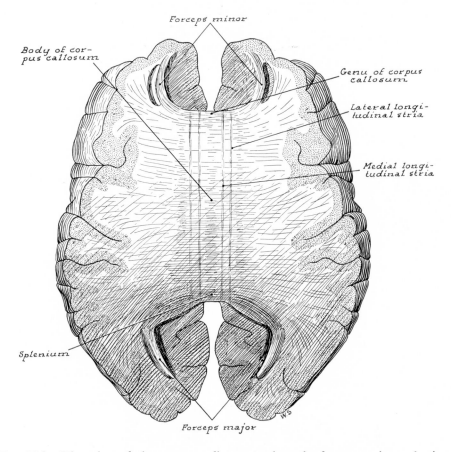

FIG. 206.   Dissection of the corpus callosum to show the forceps major and minor.

the opposite side. The *septum pellucidum* is a double-layered structure extending from the corpus callosum to the columns of the fornix (Figs. 196 and 204). A cavity, developed between the two layers of the septum and known as the *cavum pellucidum* is sometimes referred to as the fifth ventricle although it has no connection with the ventricular system. Fluid sometimes accumulates in the cavum pellucidum and results in marked dilatation which may lead to severe pressure symptoms and require surgical interven-

tion. The choroid plexus does not extend into the anterior horn of the lateral ventricle.

The **posterior horn of the lateral ventricle** extends into the central white matter of the occipital lobe (Figs. 202 and 205). Its roof, lateral wall, and a considerable part of its medial wall are formed by radiations of the corpus callosum. The callosal fibers in its roof and lateral wall are distributed to the cortex of the temporal lobe; they constitute what has been termed the *tapetum* of the corpus callo-

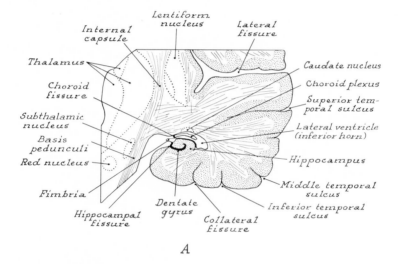

A

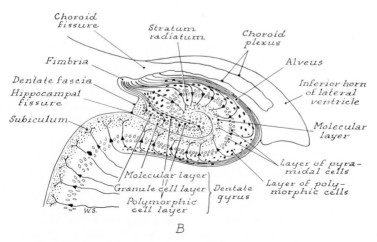

B

Fig. 207.   *A*, Frontal section through the temporal lobe of the brain to show the conformation of the inferior horn of the lateral ventricle as it appears in cross-section. *B*, Enlarged drawing of the inferior horn and the microscopic structure of the hippocampus.

sum. The callosal fibers in the medial wall of the posterior horn contribute to the formation of the *forceps major* which connects the right and left occipital lobes (Fig. 206). The forceps major accounts for a longitudinal prominence in the medial wall of each posterior horn known as the *bulb of the posterior horn* (Fig. 205). A second longitudinal prominence immediately inferior to the bulb, is pro-

floor of the inferior horn. The *hippocampus,* which has been described (Chapter 23), forms a prominent elevation in the medial part of the floor; it terminates rostrally in three or more digitations which are responsible for the designation of *pes hippocampi* for this part of the hippocampus. The fimbria of the hippocampus lies along its medial side and, as has been noted, is continuous with the

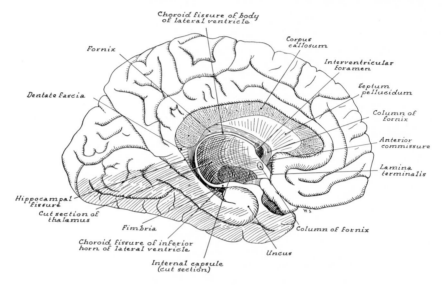

FIG. 208.   Medial view of the left half of the brain showing the continuity of the choroid fissure of the body of the lateral ventricle with that of its inferior horn.

duced by the rostral part of the calcarine fissure and is called the *calcar avis.* The choroid plexus does not extend into the posterior horn.

The **inferior horn of the lateral ventricle** begins at the junction of the body and posterior horn and curves ventrally and rostrally into the temporal lobe (Fig. 202). The triangular area developed between the diverging inferior and posterior horns is named the *collateral trigone.* The *collateral eminence,* formed by ingrowth of the collateral fissure from the medial surface of the temporal lobe, begins at the collateral trigone and continues forward in the lateral part of the

crus of the fornix. The roof of the inferior horn is formed by the central white matter of the temporal lobe (Fig. 207). The *stria terminalis* and the tail of the caudate nucleus are found in the medial part of the roof. The former arises from and the latter ends at the amygdaloid nucleus. The amygdaloid nucleus is responsible for a slight bulge in the rostral part of the roof of the inferior horn known as the *amygdaloid tubercle.* The choroid plexus and the choroid fissure of the inferior horn are continuous with those of the body of the lateral ventricle (Fig. 208). The choroid fissure of the inferior horn is between the fimbria of the hippocampus and the basis cerebri. The plexus is developed through ingrowth of pia mater through the fissure; it acquires an ependymal covering in the same manner as was described for the choroid plexus of the body of the ventricle.

The **interventricular foramen (of Monro)** is located between the column of the fornix and the anterior limit of the thalamus (Fig. 208). The column of the fornix, immediately below the point at which it forms the anterior boundary of the interventricular foramen, enters the substance of the hypothalamus through which it courses to the mammillary body. The choroid fissure of the lateral ventricle terminates anteriorly at the interventricular foramen while the

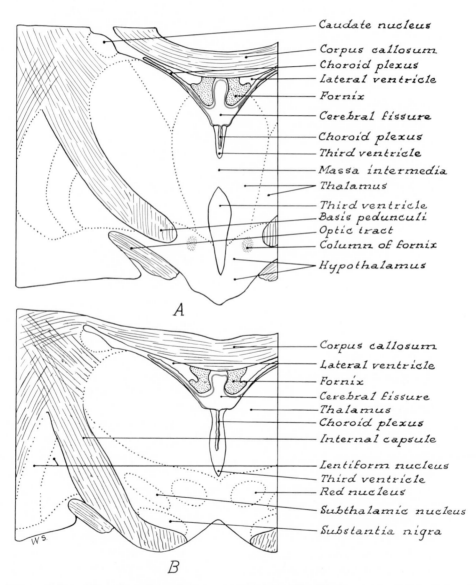

FIG. 209.   *A*, Frontal section through the middle third of the third ventricle. *B*, Frontal section through the caudal part of the third ventricle.

choroid plexus is continuous through the foramen with the choroid plexus of the third ventricle.

The **third ventricle,** situated between the right and left thalami, is a narrow cavity whose floor is formed by the hypothalamus and, near its caudal limit, by the subthalamus (Fig. 209). The anterior boundary of the third ventricle is

Vascular folds from the tela choroidea invaginate into the ventricle and form its choroid plexus. The ependymal membrane of the plexus is invaginated ahead of the vascular folds in the same manner as previously described in connection with the development of the choroid plexuses of the lateral ventricles. The tela choroidea, as such, ends posteriorly at

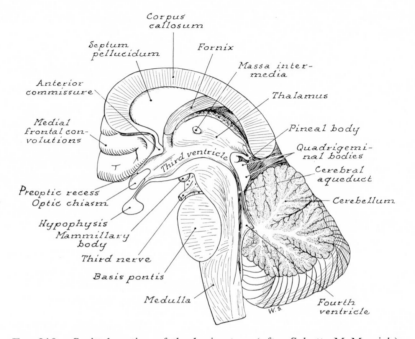

FIG. 210.   Sagittal section of the brain stem (after Sobotta-McMurrich).

formed by the anterior commissure and the lamina terminalis (Fig. 198). The *lamina terminalis* extends from the anterior commissure to the optic chiasm. The *preoptic recess* of the third ventricle is in the angle formed between the lamina terminalis and optic chiasm (Fig. 210).

The ependymal roof of the third ventricle stretches between the dorsomedial borders of the thalami (Fig. 209). It is covered by a layer of pia mater known as the *tela choroidea.* The tela choroidea of the third ventricle is continuous with the pia mater lining the cerebral fissure.

the habenular trigone where it is continuous with the pia mater covering that structure.

The **cerebral aqueduct** begins at the caudal limit of the third ventricle. It passes caudally through the midbrain, where it is surrounded by the central gray matter (aqueductal gray), and opens into the rostral end of the fourth ventricle (Fig. 210).

The **fourth ventricle** is bounded ventrally by the pons and medulla and dorsally by the cerebellum (Fig. 210). It is continuous caudally with the central canal of the spinal cord. The rostrolateral walls of the ventricle are formed by the superior and inferior cerebellar peduncles (Fig. 211). Caudally, the lateral boundaries consist of the clavae, cuneate tubercles and restiform bodies. The restiform bodies contribute to the caudal and lateral boundaries before they turn up-

tween the two clavae. The lateral angles are immediately caudal to the dorsally directed segments of the restiform bodies. The cavity of the fourth ventricle extends outward over the dorsal surfaces of the intramedullary portions of the restiform bodies to form the *lateral recesses* of the ventricle.

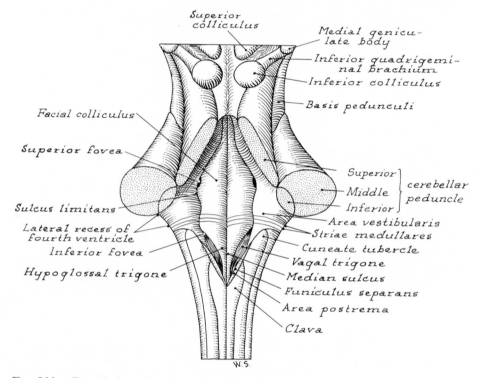

FIG. 211.   Dorsal view of a portion of the brain stem to show the boundaries and floor of the fourth ventricle.

ward to the cerebellum and to the rostrolateral boundaries as they course from the medulla to the cerebellum. The floor of the fourth ventricle, or *rhomboid fossa,* extends from the rostral limit of the pons to the junction of the open and closed portions of the medulla (Fig. 211). The rostral angle of the rhomboid fossa is between the right and left brachia conjunctiva; its caudal angle, also known as the *calamus scriptorius,* is found be-

The **rhomboid fossa** is divided into right and left halves by the median sulcus which extends from its rostral to its caudal angle. Each lateral half of the rhomboid fossa is subdivided into medial and lateral portions by the *sulcus limitans.* The area lateral to the sulcus limitans overlies the vestibular nuclei and is called the *area vestibularis.* The region medial to the sulcus, in the rostral half of the rhomboid fossa, overlies the abducens

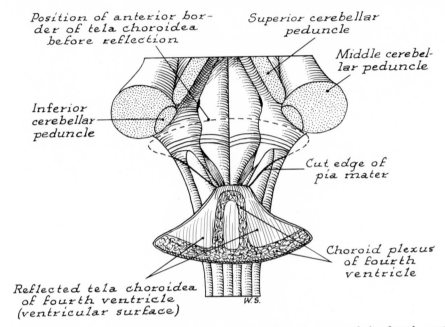

*Position of anterior bor-
der of tela choroidea
before reflection*

*Superior cerebellar
peduncle*

*Middle cerebel-
lar peduncle*

*Inferior
cerebellar
peduncle*

*Cut edge of
pia mater*

*Choroid plexus
of fourth
ventricle*

*Reflected tela choroidea
of fourth ventricle
(ventricular surface)*

W.S.

FIG. 212.   Diagram to show the conformation of the choroid plexus of the fourth ventricle.

nucleus and the internal genu of the facial nerve; it is called *facial colliculus.* The medial area of the caudal half of the rhomboid fossa (medial to the sulcus limitans) is divided into a medial *hypoglossal trigone* and a lateral *vagal trigone* by a sulcus which begins at the inferior fovea and extends medially and caudally to terminate at the median sulcus. The trigones overlie the hypoglossal nucleus and the dorsal motor nucleus of the vagus nerve. The vagal trigone, because of its blue-gray color, is also referred to as the *ala cinerea.* The *inferior fovea* is a depression in the sulcus limitans near the junction of the rostral and caudal halves of the rhomboid fossa. The *funiculus separans* is an obliquely placed ridge at the caudal limit of the vagal trigone. The narrow area between the funiculus separans and the clava is termed the *area postrema.* Several narrow transverse ridges at the junction of the rostral and caudal halves of the rhomboid fossa are

known as the *striae medullares;* the ridges are produced by transversely coursing fibers. The origin and termination of the striae medullares have not been definitely established but there is considerable evidence that they originate in the arcuate nuclei and terminate in the cerebellum (Mettler, 1942; Rasmussen and Peyton, 1946). A depression in the rostral part of the sulcus limitans is designated as the *superior fovea.* A shallow groove extends rostrally and medially from the superior fovea; it is bluish in color and is called the *locus caeruleus.*

The **roof of the fourth ventricle** is formed by the anterior medullary velum, the central white matter of the cerebellum and the tela choroidea of the fourth ventricle (Fig. 210). The anterior medullary velum has been described; it stretches between the superior borders of the superior cerebellar peduncles. The tela choroidea, like that of the third ventricle, invaginates into the ventricle to form its choroid plexus. The choroid plexus of the fourth ventricle develops along a transverse and two longitudinal lines (Fig. 212) so that its ultimate configuration is that of the letter "T." The transverse bar of the "T" extends from the lateral recess of one side to that of the other. A posterior median aperture in the tela choroidea is called the *foramen of Magendie*. The *foramina of Luschka* are continuous with the lateral recesses of the ventricle. All three foramina serve to connect the fourth ventricle with the subarachnoid space.

BIBLIOGRAPHY

METTLER, F. A., 1942: *Neuroanatomy*, C. V. Mosby Company, St. Louis.

RASMUSSEN, A. T. and PEYTON, W. T., 1946: Origin of the ventral external arcuate fibers and their continuity with the striae medullares of the fourth ventricle of man. J. Comp. Neurol., *84*, 325-337.

Chapter 25

The Cerebrospinal Fluid

THE **cerebrospinal fluid** is produced chiefly by filtration from the blood through the semipermeable membranes of the choroid plexuses. Like the aqueous humor of the eye and the glomerular fluid in the kidney it is practically free of proteins and has a high chloride content which keeps it in osmotic equilibrium with the blood plasma (Bailey, 1948; Davson, 1956). Sodium probably reaches the cerebrospinal fluid by way of the choroid plexuses. The mode of penetration has been assumed to consist of entrance of the molecules into the secretory cells of the plexuses, from which they are ejected in the primary secretion; there is, in addition, a direct diffusion from brain parenchyma and pial vessels (Davson, 1956).

The pressure at which the fluid is filtered through the capillaries of the plexuses is equal to the pressure in the capillaries minus the osmotic pressure of the nonpermeable constituents of the plasma. The actual pressure in the ventricles is always lower because of continuous absorption. In accordance with these facts the rate of formation and pressure of the cerebrospinal fluid may be increased by decreasing the osmotic pressure of the plasma or by increasing the pressure in the capillaries. The former may be done by intravenous injection of distilled water and the latter by occlusion of the great cerebral vein. Conversely, by injection of hypertonic solutions into the venous system the pressure of the cerebrospinal fluid may be made to fall rapidly to zero, or its flow through the choroid

plexuses may actually be reversed (Bailey, 1948).

Most of the fluid is formed in the lateral ventricles and passes from there through the interventricular foramina to the third ventricle; some contribution is made by the choroid plexus of the third ventricle and the fluid then passes through the cerebral aqueduct into the fourth ventricle where fluid is again added by the choroid plexus of that ventricle. From the fourth ventricle the cerebrospinal fluid passes through the lateral foramina (of Luschka) into the subarachnoid space around the medulla; from here some of the fluid reaches the cisterna magna, but the greater part passes forward to the cisternae pontis and basalis. Whether there is any flow from the fourth ventricle to the cisterna magna by way of the foramen of Magendie has been controversial. Schaltenbrand and Putnam (1927) definitely stated that there is none and even denied the presence of the foramen but Davson (1956) has agreed with Barr (1948) that the foramen "does indeed, exist" and that there is a direct flow of fluid from the fourth ventricle to the cisterna magna through it.

The **cisterns** are expansions of the subarachnoid space. The *cisterna magna* is in the angle formed between the posterior inferior surface of the cerebellum and the tela choroidea of the fourth ventricle (Fig. 213). The pia mater is closely applied to the inferior surface of the cerebellum, as it is to all the surfaces of the central nervous system, while the arachnoid mater is reflected from the pos-

(296)

terior border of the cerebellum to the dorsal surface of the closed portion of the medulla. The *cisterna pontis* is situated about the pons, especially in its basilar sulcus and in the transverse sulci at its rostral and caudal borders. It is continuous caudally with the subarachnoid cavity around the medulla and rostrally with the cisterna basalis. The *cisterna basalis* consists chiefly of the wide

ular foramen causes distention only of the corresponding lateral ventricle; if the choroid plexus of this ventricle is previously removed no distention results (Dandy, 1919).

It has been shown that the fluid passes mainly upward around the brain from the cisternae magna and basalis and that it is absorbed into the venous system through the *arachnoidal granulations.*

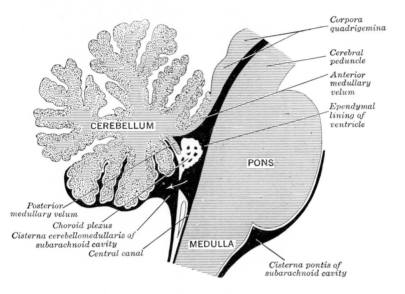

FIG. 213. Median sagittal section of the cerebellum and a portion of the brain stem to show the locations of the cisterna magna and cisterna pontis. The former is designated as the "cisterna cerebellomedullaris." (Gray's Anatomy.)

interval developed between the pia mater lining the interpeduncular space and the arachnoid mater ventral to the space.

The flow of fluid from the fourth ventricle into the subarachnoid space has not been observed directly, but it is inferred from both clinical and experimental evidence which shows that obstruction of the foramina causes a hydrocephalus which involves the entire ventricular system, while an occlusion of the cerebral aqueduct causes dilatation only of the third and lateral ventricles. Further forward in the ventricular system, an obstruction of one interventric-

These granulations are most abundant along the superior longitudinal sinus; if they are occluded an external hydrocephalus develops and if dense adhesions are formed around the brain stem the same result follows. In its passage upward from the cisterna basalis the cerebrospinal fluid mainly traverses the lateral or Sylvian fissure.

The total effective force which determines *absorption of cerebrospinal fluid* into the venous sinuses by way of the arachnoidal granulations appears to be "compounded normally of the hydrostatic pressure (subarachnoid pressure minus cerebral venous pressure) and of the colloid osmotic pressure of the blood" (Weed, 1935). Weed's experiments on quadrupeds have indicated that the hydrostatic element is relatively insignificant since the pressure of the cerebrospinal fluid customarily exceeds the sagittal venous pressure by only 15 to 35 mm. of saline and occasionally the latter exceeds the former. The major effective force, therefore, is the osmotic pressure of the colloids of the blood, and since the cerebrospinal fluid is almost totally lacking in proteins, this osmotic pull is in the neighborhood of 250 to 300 mm. of saline. It must be noted, however, that Davson (1956) tended to discount the importance of osmotic pressure in the outflow of cerebrospinal fluid from the subarachnoid space. He concluded as follows: "Until more is known about the permeability of arachnoid villi to colloidal matter we must suspend judgment as to the nature of the forces . . . ; there is every reason to believe that the difference in hydrostatic pressure in the cerebrospinal fluid and dural venous sinuses is an important factor, but whether it is the only one remains to be decided."

The probability that the osmotic force, even in quadrupeds, is relatively greater than the hydrostatic force, would make it appear that the assumption of the erect posture would have little effect upon the rate of absorption of cerebrospinal fluid into the sagittal sinus. Weed has hypothesized, however, on the basis of Ayer's finding (1926) of a small negative pressure on cisternal puncture in man in the sitting position, and Walter's deduction (1929) that in erect man, the point at which cerebrospinal fluid pressure equals atmospheric pressure is in the mid-thoracic region, that in the erect position man has a negative cerebrospinal fluid pressure of not less than 400 millimeters of saline at the calvarium. "If, under such circumstances the pressure in man's sagittal sinus be still positive (and on this score we have no information), the hydrostatic element (subarachnoid pressure minus sagittal pressure) would be negative by 350 to 400 mm. This negative pressure would be sufficient to overcome the osmotic pressure of the colloids of the blood and no absorption of cerebrospinal fluid could take place in the sagittal sinus. In the more dependent parts of the nervous system absorption could still proceed. But this is speculation and rests too largely on supposition of pressures rather than upon actual determinations."

The choroid plexuses apparently are not the only sources of the cerebrospinal fluid nor are the arachnoidal granulations the only sites of its absorption. If the spinal canal is blocked and the fluid removed from below the obstruction, it is replaced and, at least in certain animals, if the arachnoidal granulations are separated from the dura mater the fluid is still absorbed. It is probable that the fluid may be formed by direct transudation through the walls of the capillaries in the pia-arachnoid membrane and that it may be reabsorbed by the same capillaries, especially over the sulci and gyri of the cerebral hemispheres. It also appears that part of the fluid is absorbed along the cranial and spinal nerves.

The **normal pressure of the cerebrospinal fluid,** with the subject in the horizontal position, varies from 70 to 180 mm. of water. The actual pressure is the same all along the subarachnoid space, and when the pressure is increased at any point it is instantaneously increased in all parts of the space. With the subject in the sitting posture the pressure of the fluid in the lumbar region is increased by 100 to 300 mm., and there is a negative pressure in the lateral ventricles (Merritt and Fremont-Smith, 1937). The pressure of the fluid is influenced, aside from the osmotic pressure of the blood, by both the arterial and venous pressure, but follows the latter more closely (Bailey, 1948). It is usually slightly higher than the venous pressure. Davson (1956) concluded that the effects upon cerebrospinal fluid pressure of postural changes are due to altered gravitational pull on the fluid and to the relative levels of the venous pressure in the cerebral and lumbar regions; the effectiveness of the gravitational pull on the venous blood depends on the pre-existing venous pressure in both regions, the amount of blood that flows from one region to the other during the postural change, and the associated reflex vascular adjustments. Since the pressure follows closely the intracranial venous pressure it is very easy to raise the pressure of the cerebrospinal fluid by obstructing the internal jugular veins in the neck; this results in intracranial venous congestion. When a tumor or other disease process has obstructed the subarachnoid space at some level above the level of spinal puncture (spinal block), the pressure in the cul-de-sac may rise very slowly or not at all when the jugular veins are compressed, thus confirming the presence of obstruction (Queckenstedt's test). When lateral sinus thrombosis is suspected, the response to jugular compression on the two sides should be compared. If thrombosis is present, increase in pressure is absent or delayed on the affected side (Adams, 1942).

The **volume and rate of the vascular circulation through the brain** depend upon the caliber of the intracranial arterioles and capillaries and the difference between the arterial and venous blood pressures. The caliber of the intracranial arterioles is influenced by chemical substances in the blood stream, by vasomotor nerves, by variations of the venous pressure and by *variations in the pressure of the cerebrospinal fluid*. The difference between the arterial and venous pressures is influenced by obstruction to the venous outflow from the cranial cavity, by variations of the systemic arterial pressure, and by *variations in pressure of the spinal fluid*. Any increase in the pressure of the cerebrospinal fluid is immediately transmitted to the thin-walled veins, so that the pressure of the venous blood and of the cerebrospinal fluid becomes almost identical (Wolff and Blumgart, 1929). The veins of the eyeball drain into the cranial cavity and because of this a general increase of intracranial pressure will interfere with their circulation. The result may be seen in the retina by examination with the ophthalmoscope. The veins become engorged and tortuous and the papilla of the optic nerve is edematous and swollen. The optic disc is said to be "choked." If the obstruction continues, hemorrhages occur and, finally, atrophy of the optic nerve fibers.

The removal of cerebrospinal fluid from the dural cul-de-sac, caudal to the lower limit of the spinal cord, has been discussed. *Cisternal puncture* constitutes another method of withdrawal of cerebrospinal fluid. In carrying out the procedure a long needle is introduced into the cisterna magna. The needle penetrates the posterior midline structures of the neck and the atlanto-occipital membrane between the atlas and occipital bone. It enters the cranial cavity through the posterior limit of the foramen magnum and enters the cistern by piercing the arachnoid mater overlying it.

Withdrawal of cerebrospinal fluid is associated with a sudden fall in fluid pressure—113 mm. of saline after removing 35 ml. (Masserman, 1934). Some observers (Ayala, 1925) have noted a more marked decrease in pressure after removal of a like amount from a subject in whom a cerebral tumor has impinged upon the subarachnoid space and decreased the total amount of fluid. The difference was attributed to the fact that similar amounts of fluid removed in the tumor cases represented greater proportions of the total. The injection of saline or cerebrospinal fluid into the dural sac is accompanied by a steep rise in pressure which is followed by a rapid return to normal as the fluid is removed from the subarachnoid space (Davson, 1956).

BIBLIOGRAPHY

ADAMS, F. D., 1942: Cabot and Adams' *Physical Diagnosis*. 13th Ed., Williams & Wilkins Co., Baltimore.

AYALA, G., 1925: Die Physiopathologie der Mechanik des Liquor cerebrospinalis und der Rachidial-quotient. Monatsschr. Psychiat. Neurol., *58*, 65-101.

AYER, J. B., 1926: Cerebrospinal fluid pressure from the clinical point of view. Assoc. Res. Nerv. Ment. Dis., *4*, 159-171.

BAILEY, P., 1948: *Intracranial Tumors*, Charles C Thomas, Springfield.

BARR, M. L., 1948: Observations on the foramen of Magendie in a series of human brains. Brain, *71*, 281-289.

DANDY, W. E., 1919: Experimental hydrocephalus. Ann. Surg., *70*, 129-142.

DAVSON, H., 1956: *Physiology of the Ocular and Cerebrospinal Fluids*, Little, Brown & Co., Boston.

MASSERMAN, J. H., 1934: Cerebrospinal hydrodynamics. IV. Clinical experimental studies. A.M.A. Arch. Neurol. Psychiat., *32*, 523-553.

MERRITT, H. H. and FREMONT-SMITH, F., 1937: *The Cerebrospinal Fluid*, W. B. Saunders Co., Philadelphia.

SCHALTENBRAND, G. and PUTNAM, T. J., 1927: Untersuchungen zum Kreislauf des Liquor cerebrospinalis mit Hilfe intravenöser Fluorescineinspritzungen. Deutsche Ztschr. f. Nervenh., *96*, 123-132.

WALTER, F. K., 1929: *Die Blut-Liquorschranke: eine physiologische und klinische Studie*. G. Thieme, Leipzig.

WEED, L. H., 1935: Certain anatomical and physiological aspects of the meninges and cerebrospinal fluid. Brain, *58*, 383-397.

WOLFF, H. G. and BLUMGART, H. L., 1929: The cerebral circulation: VI. The effect of normal and of increased intracranial cerebrospinal fluid pressure on the velocity of intracranial blood flow. A.M.A. Arch. Neurol. Psychiat., *21*, 795-804.

Chapter 26

The Blood Supply of the Central Nervous System

THE brain derives its blood supply from the internal carotid and vertebral arteries. The former is a terminal branch of the common carotid and the latter is a branch of the subclavian artery. The internal carotid enters the cranial cavity through the carotid canal in the petrosa of the temporal bone. The vertebral artery, after coursing upward through the successive transverse foramina of the upper six cervical vertebrae, enters the cranial cavity through the foramen magnum.

The **internal carotid artery** courses forward through the cavernous sinus where it gives off small branches to the *semilunar ganglion, pituitary body,* and the *tuberal area of the hypothalamus.* It turns upward and backward at the anterior limit of the cavernous sinus to the medial aspect of the anterior clinoid process, perforates the dura of the sinus roof and then gives off the ophthalmic, posterior communicating and anterior choroidal arteries. The internal carotid ends below the anterior perforated space by dividing into the anterior and middle cerebral arteries (Fig. 214). The **ophthalmic branch** enters the orbit through the optic foramen and is distributed to the structures therein, including the bulbus oculi.

The **posterior communicating artery**

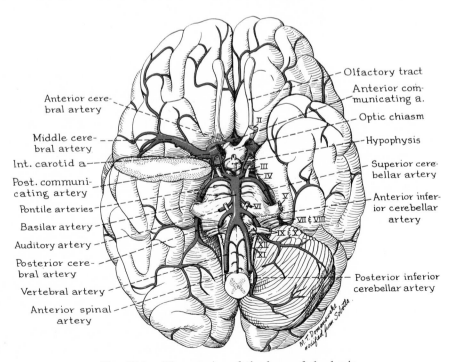

Anterior cerebral artery
Middle cerebral artery
Int. carotid a
Post. communicating artery
Pontile arteries
Basilar artery
Auditory artery
Posterior cerebral artery
Vertebral artery
Anterior spinal artery

Olfactory tract
Anterior communicating a.
Optic chiasm
Hypophysis
Superior cerebellar artery
Anterior inferior cerebellar artery
Posterior inferior cerebellar artery

II
III
IV
V
VI
VII & VIII
IX & X
XII
XI

FIG. 214.   The arteries of the base of the brain.

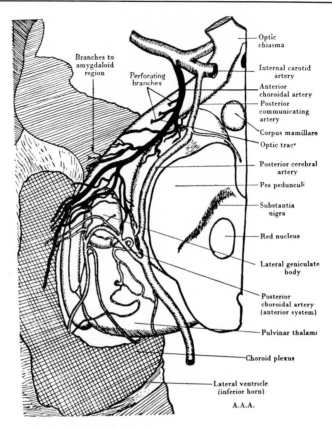

FIG. 215.   Dissection to show the general course and relations of the anterior choroidal artery
(A. A. Abbie, courtesy of Brain).

usually originates from the internal carotid (Fig. 215), but it may arise from the
middle cerebral artery; it courses backward over the optic tract and basis pedunculi, alongside the hippocampal gyrus,
and joins the posterior cerebral which is
a terminal branch of the basilar artery.
It gives off a *middle thalamic branch,* a
branch to the *hippocampal gyrus,* and—
particularly if the anterior choroidal artery is small—branches to the *optic tract.*
The posterior communicating artery has
also been found to distribute branches to
the *lateral tuberal* and *lateral mammillary
areas of the hypothalamus* and to the
genu of the internal capsule (Rubinstein,
1944). In about 8 per cent of cases in
which the posterior cerebral artery is a
branch of the internal carotid, the poste-

rior communicating artery connects the
posterior cerebral and basilar arteries
(Kuhlenbeck, 1954).

The **anterior choroidal artery** also
passes backward on the optic tract and
basis pedunculi (Fig. 215)); it enters
the inferior horn of the lateral ventricle
through the choroid fissure, supplies
branches to the *hippocampus* and its
fimbria, and ends in the *choroid plexus.*
Branches are also distributed to the
*globus pallidus, optic tract, amygdaloid
nucleus, tail of the caudate nucleus, uncus,* ventral part of the *posterior limb of
the internal capsule, sublentiform part of
the internal capsule,* and the anterior part
of the *lateral geniculate body* (Alexander,
1942). Abbie (1934) traced branches
of the anterior choroidal artery to the

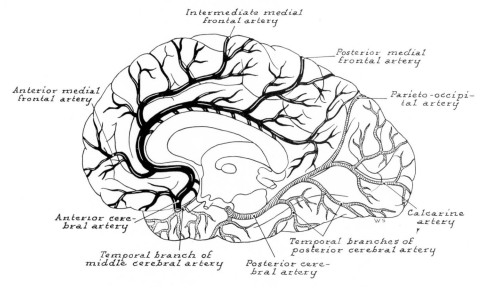

Intermediate medial
frontal artery

Posterior medial
frontal artery

Anterior medial
frontal artery

Parieto-occipi-
tal artery

Anterior cere-
bral artery

Calcarine
artery

Temporal branch of
middle cerebral artery

Temporal branches of
posterior cerebral artery

Posterior cere-
bral artery

FIG. 216.   Distribution of cerebral arteries on the medial and tentorial surfaces of the right cerebral hemisphere (Redrawn from Gray's Anatomy).

middle third of the *cerebral peduncle, red nucleus, lateral ventral nucleus of the thalamus* and the *subthalamic nucleus.*

The **anterior cerebral artery** passes anteriorly and medially across the anterior perforated substance between the olfactory and optic nerves (Fig. 214). It enters the sagittal fissure between the frontal lobes of the brain and communicates with the corresponding artery of the opposite side through the anterior communicating artery. From this point it courses anteriorly and superiorly around the genu of the corpus callosum and then posteriorly along the upper surface of that commissural structure (Fig. 216). It gives off large branches to the cortex of the *medial surfaces of the frontal and parietal lobes,* branches to the *genu, body and splenium* of the *corpus callosum,* and eventually terminates by anastomosing with the posterior cerebral artery. The cortical branches terminate by crossing the superior border of the hemisphere and anastomosing with the cortical branches of the middle cerebral artery on the dorsolateral surface (Fig. 218).

Branches of the anterior cerebral artery are also distributed to the olfactory bulb and to the medial part of the orbital surface of the frontal lobe (Abbie, 1934).

A few small branches of the anterior cerebral artery are distributed to the basal ganglia through the anterior perforated substance; they are called *anterior striate branches* and they end in the anterior limit of the *head of the caudate nucleus,* in the same area of the *putamen,* and in the *medio-ventral part of the anterior limb of the internal capsule* (Alexander, 1942). The so-called *central branches* of the anterior cerebral are given off in front of the optic chiasm and are distributed to the *supraoptic region of the hypothalamus, columns of the fornix, rostrum of the corpus callosum, lamina terminalis,* and *septum pellucidum.* The *recurrent artery (of Heubner)* arises from the anterior cerebral in the region of the anterior communicating artery (Fig. 217). It divides into several branches which are distributed to the *external capsule,* antero-lateral aspect of the *lentiform nucleus,* head of the *caudate nucleus*

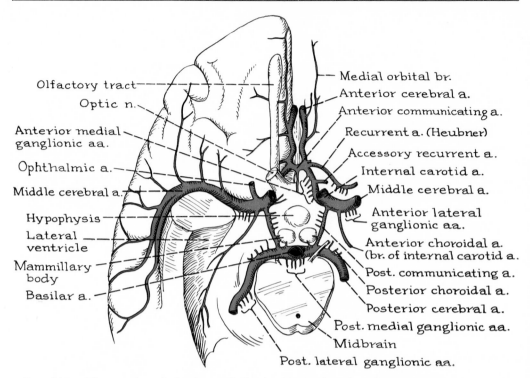

Olfactory tract
Optic n.
Anterior medial ganglionic aa.
Ophthalmic a.
Middle cerebral a.
Hypophysis
Lateral ventricle
Mammillary body
Basilar a.

Medial orbital br.
Anterior cerebral a.
Anterior communicating a.
Recurrent a. (Heubner)
Accessory recurrent a.
Internal carotid a.
Middle cerebral a.
Anterior lateral ganglionic aa.
Anterior choroidal a. (br. of internal carotid a.
Post. communicating a.
Posterior choroidal a.
Posterior cerebral a.
Post. medial ganglionic aa.
Midbrain
Post. lateral ganglionic aa.

Fig. 217.   The arteries of the base of the brain showing the origin of the recurrent artery (after Rubenstein, 1944).

and *anterior limb of the internal capsule.* Two or three small branches of this artery penetrate the lentiform nucleus and continue to the *genu of the internal capsule;* the most posterior of these branches may extend into the anterior part of the posterior limb of the internal capsule (Rubinstein, 1944). Kuhlenbeck (1954) noted that the recurrent artery is also called *medial striate* and indicated that it distributes mainly to the head of the caudate nucleus and the adjacent part of the internal capsule.

The **middle cerebral artery** is the larger of the two terminal branches of the internal carotid (Fig. 214). It passes obliquely upward and laterally into the lateral (Sylvian) fissure; opposite the insula it divides into several *cortical branches* which are distributed to the *dorsolateral surfaces of the frontal, parietal,* and *temporal lobes* of the hemis-phere (Fig. 218). The cortical branches anastomose inferiorly and posteriorly with those of the posterior cerebral and superiorly with those of the anterior cerebral artery. The *central (striate) branches* of the middle cerebral enter the brain through the anterior perforated substance (Fig. 219); they are distributed to the *putamen* and *caudate nucleus* and to those parts of the *internal capsule* which are adjacent to these structures, *i.e.,* the *anterior limb,* the *dorsolateral portion of the genu,* and the *dorsal area of the posterior limb.* Injection studies have shown that the *external capsule* and the *claustrum* are also supplied by these branches (Alexander, 1942). "Ganglionic twigs" from the middle cerebral artery are also distributed to the more lateral areas of the hypothalamus (Rubinstein, 1944). Abbie (1934) has observed, in a comparative study, that the more laterally

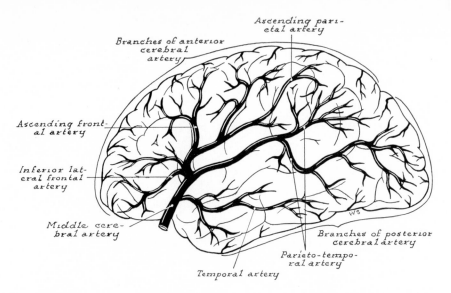

FIG. 218. Distribution of cerebral arteries on the dorsolateral surface of the cerebral hemisphere (Redrawn from Gray's Anatomy).

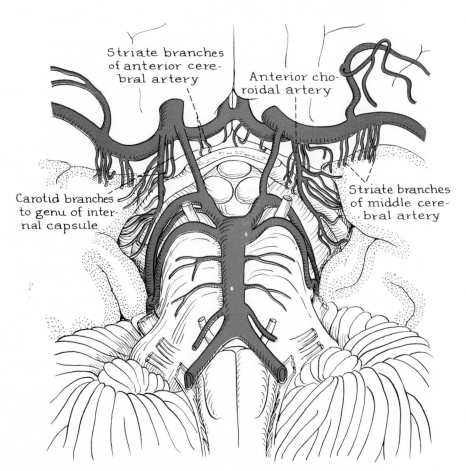

FIG. 219. The striopallidal arterial blood vessels at the base of the brain (after Alexander, 1942).

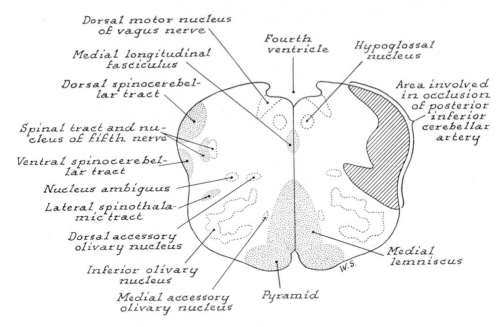

Fig. 220. Diagram to show the structures in the medulla that are damaged as the result of thrombosis of the posterior inferior cerebellar artery.

placed of the striate branches of the middle cerebral artery (lateral striate arteries) in man tend to be considerably larger than the medial ones. On the basis of his observations, Abbie made the following statements: "The concentration of a great number of arteries at the base of the external capsule—a greater number than in any other part of the brain—explains why Charcot called this the site of election for cerebral hemorrhage. The chances of arterial rupture here are at least twice as great as anywhere else." Kuhlenbeck (1954) has called attention to "one or two larger" lenticulostriate arteries which are in close relation to the internal capsule, corresponding in position to Charcot's "artery or arteries of cerebral hemorrhage."

The **intracranial portion of the vertebral artery** extend forward from the foramen magnum to the lower border of the pons where it unites with its fellow to form the basilar artery (Fig. 214). Its branches are: meningeal, posterior spinal, posterior inferior cerebellar, anterior spinal, and medullary. The *meningeal branch* is given off at the level of the foramen magnum; it ramifies between the bone and dura mater in the posterior cranial fossa and supplies the *falx cerebelli*. The *posterior spinal artery* arises alongside the medulla and passes caudally into the spinal canal where it is in relation to the posterior roots of the spinal nerves.

The **posterior inferior cerebellar artery** is the largest branch of the vertebral. It is given off near the rostral limit of the medulla and winds dorsally around the medulla between the filaments of the hypoglossal nerve and then between those of the vagus and spinal accessory to be distributed to the posterior part of the *inferior surface of the cerebellum* (Fig. 214). It anastomoses with branches of the anterior inferior and superior cerebellar arteries and sends branches to the *choroid plexus of the fourth ventricle*. In its course over the medulla it distributes important *medullary branches* to the lateral areas of the medulla; these branches supply blood to the *lateral spinothalamic tract, nucleus ambiguus, spinal tract and nucleus of the fifth nerve,* and to the *ventral and dorsal spinocerebellar tracts.* Thrombosis of the posterior inferior cerebellar artery, which not infrequently occurs, results in symptoms referable to interference with the blood supply to these structures.

The **posterior inferior cerebellar artery syndrome** (of Wallenberg), due to thrombosis (Fig. 220), is characterized by loss of pain and thermal sensibility from the neck down on the side opposite the lesion (lateral spinothalamic tract), loss of pain and thermal sensibility in the ipsilateral half of the face (spinal nucleus and tract of the trigeminal), ipsilateral paralysis of the soft palate, larynx, and pharynx (nucleus ambiguus), and ipsilateral ataxia (spinocerebellar tracts and cerebellum).

The **anterior spinal artery** arises from the vertebral near the point at which it joins its fellow to form the basilar artery (Fig. 214). It courses obliquely downward and inward and joins the corresponding artery of the opposite side. The combined vessel lies in the ventromedian fissure of the medulla and spinal cord and supplies branches to the ventral areas of each.

The **medullary branches** arise from the vertebral artery and its branches, and are distributed to the medulla. Those from the posterior inferior cerebellar branch, referred to above, are the most important.

The **basilar artery** is a single trunk formed by the junction of the two vertebral arteries; it extends from the lower to the upper border of the pons, lying in its median sulcus, and terminates by dividing into right and left posterior cerebral arteries (Fig. 214). As previously noted, the posterior cerebral artery may be a branch of the internal carotid in which case its position is taken by the posterior communicating artery. (The posterior cerebral artery develops as a branch of the internal carotid.) In addition to its terminal branches the basilar artery gives off the following branches on each side: pontile, internal auditory, anterior inferior cerebellar, and superior cerebellar.

The **pontile arteries** pass transversely outward and curve around the lateral surfaces of the pons. They supply the *pons,* the *middle cerebellar peduncle* and the *roots of the trigeminal nerve.*

The **internal auditory artery** traverses the internal auditory canal and is distributed to the *internal ear.*

The **anterior inferior cerebellar arteries** are given off about midway in the course of the basilar. They course dorsally to be distributed to the inferior surface of the cerebellum where they anastomose with the posterior inferior cerebellar arteries.

The **superior cerebellar arteries** arise from the basilar artery near its termination. Each passes laterally around the basis pedunculi and reaches the tentorial surface of the cerebellum. A medial branch is distributed to the *superior vermis* and *anterior medullary velum*; a lateral branch supplies the superior surface of the cerebellar hemisphere and anastomoses posteriorly with the posterior inferior cerebellar artery.

The **posterior cerebral arteries** (Fig. 214), terminal divisions of the basilar, are separated from the superior cerebellar arteries by the third and fourth nerves. Each arches upward and backward between the basis pedunculi and the uncus and is distributed to the *medial and inferior surfaces of the temporal and occipital lobes* and to the *lateral surface of the occipital lobe* (Figs. 214, 216 and 218). Anastomoses with the middle and anterior cerebral arteries have been mentioned in connection with those vessels. The *cortical branches* include *anterior* *and posterior temporal, calcarine, and parieto-occipital.* The last two course along the fissures of the same name; the calcarine artery is of particular significance since it supplies the visual cortex. The *central branches* include three groups: posteromedial, posterolateral, and posterior choroid. The *posteromedial branches* enter the brain through the posterior perforated substance in the roof of the interpeduncular space; they supply the *mammillary bodies,* the *medial part of the thalamus* and the *tegmentum and central gray matter of the midbrain.* The *posterolateral branches* are distributed to the *posterior part of the thalamus,* the *cerebral peduncles,* the *corpora quadrigemina,* the *geniculate bodies* and, according to Rubinstein (1944), to the *posterior limb* and the *retro- and sublentiform* components of the *internal capsule.* Abbie (1934) also included a small part of the *tail of the caudate nucleus* in the list of structures supplied by these branches. The *posterior choroid branches* course forward through the transverse cerebral fissure and are distributed to the *telae choroideae* and *choroid plexuses* of the third and lateral ventricles and to the *body* and *crura* of the *fornix.*

The **circle of Willis** is formed by the proximal portions of the two posterior cerebral arteries, the paired posterior communicating arteries, the internal carotids, the anterior cerebrals, and the anterior communicating artery. Free anastomosis between the two internal carotid and the two vertebral arteries through the circle of Willis serves to equalize the flow of blood to the various parts of the brain. If one carotid or one vertebral is obstructed, the parts of the brain normally supplied by the vessel can still receive their blood supply through the remaining patent vessels by way of the circle of Willis. There is evidence from animal experiments to indicate that one vertebral artery is sufficient for the blood supply of the brain when there is a well-developed arterial circle. Failure of development of certain portions of the arterial circle no doubt accounts for the hemiplegia that occasionally results from unilateral ligation of either the internal or the common carotid artery.

The cortical branches of the cerebral arteries ramify and anastomose in the pia mater, giving off branches to the cortical substance; some of the branches extend through the cortex into the underlying white substance. The anastomosis between the various cortical arteries is not sufficient to provide adequate circulation in case a large branch is occluded. The central branches of the cerebral arteries, which ramify within the substance of the brain, are probably not end arteries as stated by Abbie (1934) and others. Campbell (1938) has shown, in the brain of the cat, that there are anastomoses between the penetrating arteries, but such anastomoses ordinarily do not occur until the arteries reach precapillary size. Even in the basal ganglia and white matter, where anastomoses are least common, Campbell found small anastomosing branches between arterioles measuring seventy microns in diameter. The central anastomoses that have been demonstrated in mammalian brains are probably of considerable importance in preventing permanent damage to the brain from occlusion of small vessels, but they are not of sufficient caliber to assure an adequate blood supply to a given area when the main artery to that area has been occluded. Anatomically, then, the central arteries are not end arteries; functionally, however, the larger branches of the cortical arteries may be so considered.

The nervous mechanisms involved in the functioning of cerebral blood vessels have been studied in cat, monkey and man by Christensen *et al.* (1953). They summarized their findings in the monkey as follows: Most nerves are found along

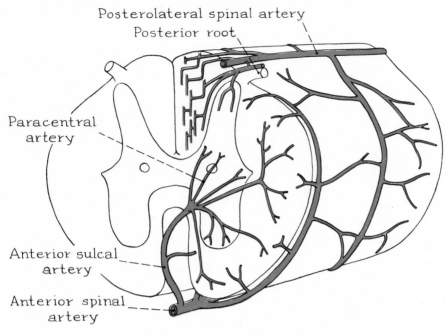

Posterolateral spinal artery

Posterior root

Paracentral artery

Anterior sulcal artery

Anterior spinal artery

FIG. 221.   Diagram of the arterial supply of the human spinal cord
(after Herren and Alexander, 1939).

the arteries; they contain mostly small, unmyelinated axons; from nerve bundles found consistently along the larger pial arteries, nerve fibers are distributed less consistently to the smaller pial arteries and to arterioles in both pia and cortex; some cerebral arteries were observed to have a fine network of nervous tissue with a fibrillar or syncitial appearance and with nuclei typical of sheath cells; neurofibrils were seen to leave plexuses in the walls of small pial arteries and, after passing along the artery for a short distance, to gradually disappear; the syncytial tissue was sometimes present along arterioles as they entered the cerebral cortex. The probable functions of the two types of nervous tissue around the pial and cerebral vessels were not elaborated upon but it seems, in the light of such studies, that cerebral vasospasm may play an important role in the phenomenon of thrombosis as it relates to apoplexy and that blocking the stellate ganglion in thrombotic

apoplexy may be a justifiable procedure. This hypothesis assumes that the nervous tissue around pial and cerebral vessels is an extension of the internal carotid plexus which originates from the superior cervical sympathetic ganglion and enters the cranial cavity with the internal carotid artery.

The **blood supply of the spinal cord** comes from the anterior and posterior spinal arteries and from the spinal branches of the vertebral, intercostal, lumbar, and sacral arteries. The *anterior* and *posterior spinal arteries* originate from the vertebral arteries as they course on the anterolateral aspect of the medulla. The two anterior spinal branches unite anterior to the pyramid to form a single vessel (Fig. 214). As the spinal arteries course downward in the spinal canal they receive reinforcing branches from the segmental arteries. The posterior spinal arteries, as such, may terminate at any level of the cord by joining the anterior spinals. The three sets of arteries form an extensive *extramedullary plexus* around the spinal cord from which the intramedullary branches originate (Fig. 221).

A number of *anterior sulcal arteries* arise from the anterior spinal artery and enter the anterior median fissure of the cord (Fig. 221). These supply the *anterior* and *lateral horns,* the *central gray, part of the posterior horn* and the *anterior and lateral funiculi.* Penetrating branches from the *posterior* (posterolateral) *spinal artery* supply the *posterior gray column* and the *posterior white column* (Fig. 221). The *peripheral arteries* from the extramedullary plexus penetrate the *ventral, lateral* and *dorsal white columns*; their distribution is almost entirely limited to the white matter (Fig. 221).

The **venous return from the brain** is facilitated by numerous veins, all of which are direct or indirect tributaries of the dural sinuses (Fig. 222, *A*). The *superior* and *inferior sagittal sinuses* are found in the superior and inferior borders of the falx cerebri; the former drains into either right or left lateral sinus and the latter into the straight sinus. The *lateral sinuses* begin at the internal occipital protuberance and empty into the internal jugular veins; they consist of transverse portions within the posterior or attached border of the tentorium cerebelli and sigmoid portions which course downward in the angles formed between the petrous and mastoid parts of the temporal bones. The *straight sinus* is located at the junction of falx cerebri and tentorium cerebelli; it empties into either right or left lateral sinus. The *cavernous sinuses* are found on either side of the body of the sphenoid; they receive the venous drainage from the eyes by way of the ophthalmic veins and empty into the superior and inferior petrosal sinuses. The *superior petrosal sinus* courses laterally along the superior border of the petrosa and empties into the lateral sinus. The *inferior petrosal sinus* is directed downward and backward from the cavernous sinus, along the lateral margin of the basilar process of the occipital bone; it empties into the internal jugular vein. The *occipital sinus* is in the attached border of the falx cerebelli; it empties into one or the other of the lateral sinuses.

The **superior cerebral veins,** eight to twelve in number, drain the *dorsolateral and medial surfaces of the cerebrum* (Fig. 222, *B*). Those from the dorsolateral surface are joined by those from the medial surface at the superior border of the hemisphere and the combined vessels enter the superior sagittal sinus.

The **inferior cerebral veins** drain the blood from the *inferior surface of the cerebrum* and, to some extent, from the inferior part of the dorsolateral surface (Fig. 224, *A*). Those from the inferior surfaces of the frontal lobes drain partly into the inferior sagittal sinus and partly into the cavernous sinuses. Those from the inferior surfaces of the temporal lobes drain into the superior petrosal and transverse sinuses. A large vein from the occipital lobe empties into the great cerebral vein just before the latter enters the straight sinus.

The paired **internal cerebral veins,** formed in the transverse cerebral fissure, unite between the splenium of the corpus callosum and the tectum of the midbrain to form the great cerebral vein (Fig. 223). The main tributaries of each internal cerebral vein are the vena terminalis and the choroid vein, but they also receive direct tributaries from the *thalamus, corpus callosum, pineal body, corpora quadrigemina, cerebellum, occipital lobe* of the cerebrum, and the *choroid plexus* of the third ventricle.

The **vena terminalis,** formed by veins from the *thalamus* and *basal ganglia,* courses forward in the sulcus between

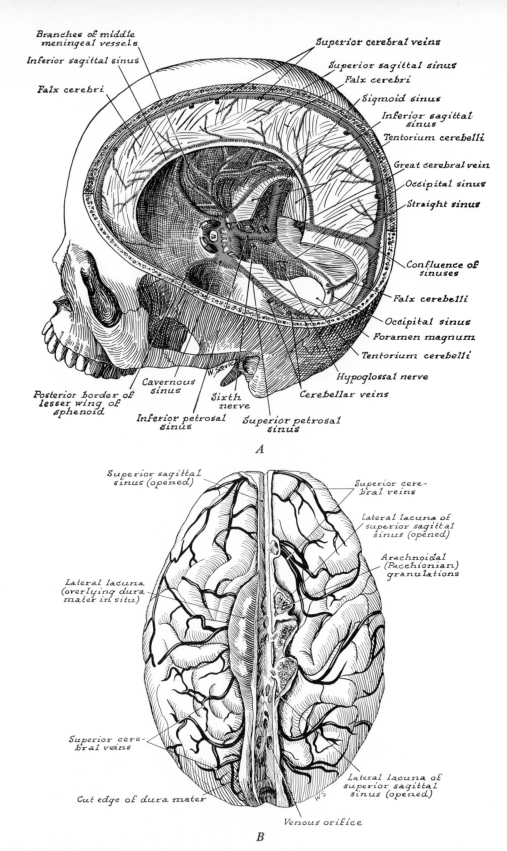

Branches of middle meningeal vessels

Inferior sagittal sinus

Falx cerebri

Superior cerebral veins

Superior sagittal sinus

Falx cerebri

Sigmoid sinus

Inferior sagittal sinus

Tentorium cerebelli

Great cerebral vein

Occipital sinus

Straight sinus

Confluence of sinuses

Falx cerebelli

Occipital sinus

Foramen magnum

Tentorium cerebelli

Hypoglossal nerve

Cerebellar veins

Posterior border of lesser wing of sphenoid

Cavernous sinus

Sixth nerve

Inferior petrosal sinus

Superior petrosal sinus

A

Superior sagittal sinus (opened)

Superior cerebral veins

Lateral lacuna of superior sagittal sinus (opened)

Arachnoidal (Pacchionian) granulations

Lateral lacuna (overlying dura mater in situ)

Superior cerebral veins

Cut edge of dura mater

Lateral lacuna of superior sagittal sinus (opened)

Venous orifice

B

Fig. 222. *A*, The interior of the skull with brain removed and dural reflections shown. The dural sinuses are indicated. (After Sobotta-McMurrich.) *B*, Veins of the dorsolateral surface of the hemisphere (Redrawn from Toldt).

(311)

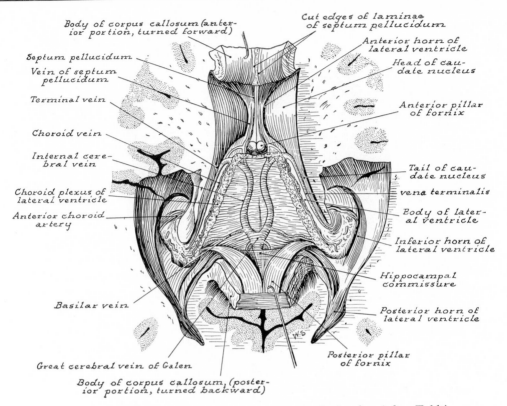

Body of corpus callosum (anterior portion, turned forward)

Cut edges of laminae of septum pellucidum

Septum pellucidum

Anterior horn of lateral ventricle

Vein of septum pellucidum

Head of caudate nucleus

Terminal vein

Anterior pillar of fornix

Choroid vein

Internal cerebral vein

Tail of caudate nucleus

Choroid plexus of lateral ventricle

vena terminalis

Anterior choroid artery

Body of lateral ventricle

Inferior horn of lateral ventricle

Hippocampal commissure

Basilar vein

Posterior horn of lateral ventricle

Great cerebral vein of Galen

Posterior pillar of fornix

Body of corpus callosum, (posterior portion, turned backward)

Fig. 223. The internal cerebral and great cerebral veins (after Toldt).

the caudate nucleus and thalamus and joins the choroid vein in the region of the interventricular foramen. In addition to tributaries from the thalamus and basal ganglia, the vena terminalis receives others from the *fornix* and *septum pellucidum.*

The **choroid vein** begins in the inferior horn of the lateral ventricle and ascends along the choroid plexus to the interventricular foramen. It receives tributaries from the *hippocampus, corpus callosum,* and *fornix.*

The **basal (basilar) vein** of either side begins in the region of the anterior perforated substance (Fig. 224, *A*) where it is formed by the junction of the deep Sylvian vein (from the insular region) and the anterior vein of the corpus callosum. It passes backward over the optic tract and basis pedunculi, curves dorsally

around the midbrain and empties into the great cerebral vein. The basal vein drains the *olfactory trigone, optic tract, tuber cinereum, mammillary bodies, posterior perforated substance, uncus,* and *cerebral peduncles.*

The **veins from the pons and medulla** terminate in the inferior petrosal and lateral sinuses.

The **superior cerebellar veins** ramify on the superior surface of the cerebellum; some cross the superior vermis and drain into the great cerebral vein and straight sinus; others run laterally to the transverse and superior petrosal sinuses.

The **inferior cerebellar veins** course forward and laterally to the inferior petrosal and transverse sinuses or directly backward to the occipital sinus.

The **venous drainage of the spinal cord** begins with the intramedullary veins

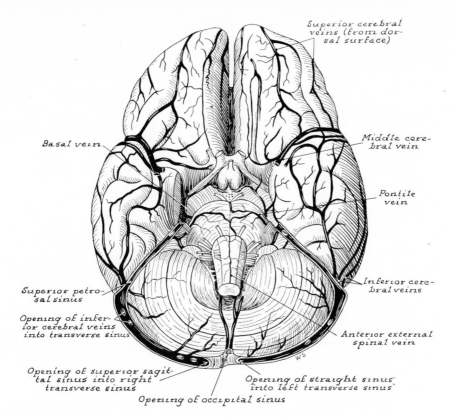

Superior cerebral veins (from dorsal surface)

Middle cerebral vein

Basal vein

Pontile vein

Inferior cerebral veins

Superior petrosal sinus

Opening of inferior cerebral veins into transverse sinus

Anterior external spinal vein

Opening of superior sagittal sinus into right transverse sinus

Opening of straight sinus into left transverse sinus

Opening of occipital sinus

A

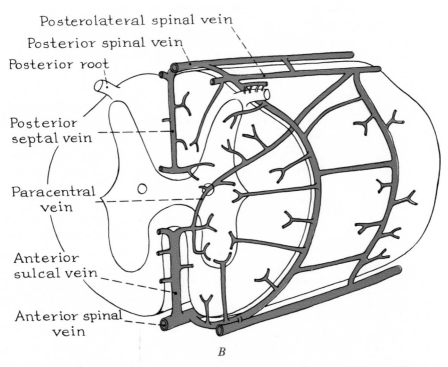

Posterolateral spinal vein

Posterior spinal vein

Posterior root

Posterior septal vein

Paracentral vein

Anterior sulcal vein

Anterior spinal vein

B

FIG. 224. *A*, The veins on the base of the brain (redrawn from Toldt). *B*, Diagram of the veins of the spinal cord (after Herren and Alexander, 1939).

(313)

which emerge from it and empty into ventral and dorsal venous channels. Four longitudinal channels are usually present, the *anterior, anterolateral, posterior* and *posterolateral* (Fig. 224, *B*). The distribution of veins is similar to that of the arteries (Fig. 224, *B*). In the cervical region the venous channels drain into the vertebral vein, in the thoracic region into the intercostal veins, and in the upper lumbar region into the lumbar and sacral veins.

SUMMARY OF THE ARTERIAL DISTRIBUTION TO THE CENTRAL
NERVOUS SYSTEM

I. Cerebral Cortex

    A. Frontal lobe

        Lateral surface—*middle cerebral artery*

        Medial surface—*anterior cerebral artery*

        Inferior surface—*middle cerebral artery* and *anterior cerebral artery*

    B. Parietal lobe

        Lateral surface—*middle cerebral artery*

        Medial surface—*anterior cerebral artery*

    C. Temporal lobe

        Lateral surface—*middle cerebral artery*

        Medial surface—*middle cerebral artery, posterior cerebral artery, anterior choroidal artery* and *posterior communicating artery*

        Inferior surface—*posterior cerebral artery*

    D. Occipital lobe

        Lateral surface—*posterior cerebral artery*

        Medial surface—*posterior cerebral artery*

        Inferior surface—*posterior cerebral artery*

II. Internal Capsule

    A. Anterior limb—*striate branches of middle cerebral artery, striate branches of anterior cerebral artery* and *recurrent branch of anterior cerebral artery*

    B. Genu—*striate branches of middle cerebral artery, recurrent branch of anterior cerebral artery* and *posterior communicating artery*

    C. Posterior limb—*striate branches of middle cerebral artery, anterior choroidal artery* and *posterolateral branches of posterior cerebral artery*

    D. Sublentiform portion—*anterior choroidal artery* and *posterolateral branches of posterior cerebral artery*

    E. Retrolentiform portion—*posterolateral branches of posterior cerebral artery*

III. Corpus Callosum

    A. Rostrum—*central branches of anterior cerebral artery*

    B. Genu, body and splenium—branches from the *cortical trunk of anterior cerebral artery*

IV. **Basal Ganglia**

    A. Caudate nucleus—*striate branches of middle cerebral artery, striate branches of anterior cerebral artery, anterior choroidal artery, recurrent branch of anterior cerebral artery* and *posterolateral branches of posterior cerebral artery*

    B. Putamen—*striate branches of middle cerebral artery, striate branches of anterior cerebral artery* and *recurrent branch of anterior cerebral artery*

    C. Globus pallidus—*anterior choroidal artery*

    D. Amygdaloid nucleus—*anterior choroidal artery*

    E. Claustrum—*striate branches of middle cerebral artery*

V. **Hippocampus**—*anterior choroidal artery* and *posterior choroidal branches of posterior cerebral artery*

VI. **Fornix**

    A. Anterior columns—*central branches of anterior cerebral artery*

    B. Body and crura—*posterior choroidal branches of posterior cerebral artery*

VII. **Thalamus**—*anterior choroidal artery, posteromedial branches of posterior cerebral artery, posterolateral branches of posterior cerebral artery* and *posterior communicating artery*

VIII. **Hypothalamus**

    A. Lateral area—*striate branches of middle cerebral artery*

    B. Supraoptic area—*central branches of anterior cerebral artery*

    C. Tuberal area—branches from *internal carotid artery* and *posterior communicating artery*

    D. Mammillary area (including mammillary bodies)—*posteromedial branches of posterior cerebral artery* and *posterior communicating artery*

IX. **Subthalamus**—*anterior choroidal artery* and *posteromedial branches of posterior cerebral artery*

X. **Optic Tract**—*anterior choroidal artery* and *posterior communicating artery*

XI. **Geniculate Bodies**

    A. Lateral—*anterior choroidal artery* and *posterolateral branches of posterior cerebral artery*

    B. Medial—*posterolateral branches of posterior cerebral artery*

XII. **Olfactory Bulb**—*anterior cerebral artery*

XIII. **Lamina Terminalis**—*central branches of anterior cerebral artery*

XIV. **Septum Pellucidum**—*central branches of anterior cerebral artery*

XV. **External Capsule**—*recurrent branch of anterior cerebral artery* and *striate branches of middle cerebral artery*

XVI. **Pineal Body**—*posterolateral branches of posterior cerebral artery*

XVII. **Choroid Plexuses**

    A. Lateral ventricle—*anterior choroidal artery* and *posterior choroidal branches of posterior cerebral artery*

    B. Third ventricle—*posterior choroidal branches of posterior cerebral artery*

    C. Fourth ventricle—*posterior inferior cerebellar artery*

XVIII. **Mesencephalon**

    A. Basis pedunculi—*posterolateral branches of posterior cerebral artery* and *anterior choroidal artery*

    B. Tegmentum—*posteromedial branches of posterior cerebral artery* and *anterior choroidal artery*

    C. Central gray matter—*posteromedial branches of posterior cerebral artery*

    D. Corpora quadrigemina—*posterolateral branches of posterior cerebral artery*

XIX. **Pons**—*pontile branches of basilar artery*

XX. **Medulla**—*posterior inferior cerebellar artery, medullary branches of vertebral artery* and *anterior spinal artery*

XXI. **Cerebellum and Cerebellar Peduncles**—*posterior inferior cerebellar artery, anterior inferior cerebellar artery, superior cerebellar artery* and *pontile branches of basilar artery*

XXII. **Spinal Cord**—*anterior spinal artery, posterior spinal artery* and *segmental branches of vertebral, intercostal, lumbar* and *sacral arteries*

BIBLIOGRAPHY

ABBIE, A. A., 1934: The morphology of the forebrain arteries, with especial reference to the evolution of the basal ganglia. J. Anat., 68, 433-470.

ALEXANDER, L., 1942: The vascular supply of the striopallidum. In diseases of the basal ganglia. Assoc. Res. Nerv. Ment. Dis., 21, 77-132.

CAMPBELL, A. C. P., 1938: The vascular architecture of the cat's brain. A study by vital injection. Assoc. Res. Nerv. Ment. Dis., 18, 69-93.

CHRISTENSEN, K., LEWIS, E. and STUESSE, T., 1953: Innervation of cerebral blood vessels. XIX Intern. Physiol. Congr., Montreal, pp. 268-269.

HERREN, R. Y. and ALEXANDER, L., 1939: Sulcal and intrinsic blood vessels of human spinal cord. A.M.A. Arch. Neurol. Psychiat., 41, 678-687.

KUHLENBECK, H., 1954: The human diencephalon. A summary of development, structure, function and pathology. Confinia Neurol., 14 (Suppl.), 1-230.

RUBINSTEIN, H. S., 1944: Relation of circulus arteriosus to hypothalamus and internal capsule. A.M.A. Arch. Neurol. Psychiat., 52, 526-530.

Chapter 27

The Interstitial Tissue of the Central Nervous System

THE interstitial tissue of the central nervous system includes all the non-nervous cells except those which make up the cerebral vascular tree and the meninges. The functions of the interstitial cells are secondary to the activities of the nerve cells. They support and apparently nourish the nerve cells; they take part in the repair processes subsequent to destructive lesions and provide cytologic evidence of the pathological influences which may have been operative

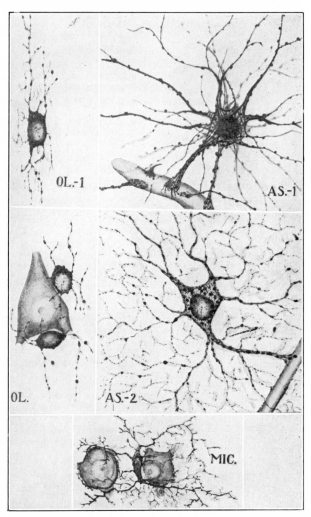

FIG. 225. Interstitial cells of the central nervous system. *AS.-1*, Fibrous astrocyte with perivascular feet on vessel; *AS.-2*, protoplasmic astrocyte; *MIC.*, microglia; *OL.*, oligodendroglia. (Penfield and Cone, in Cowdry's *Special Cytology*, courtesy of Paul B. Hoeber, Inc.).

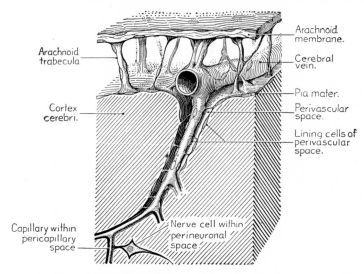

Arachnoid trabecula

Cortex cerebri.

Capillary within pericapillary space

Arachnoid membrane.

Cerebral vein.

Pia mater.

Perivascular space.

Lining cells of perivascular space.

Nerve cell within perineuronal space

Fig. 226. Diagrammatic representation of the arachnoid and pia mater to illustrate the subarachnoid space and perivascular channels (L. H. Weed, courtesy of Am. J. Anat.)

upon the central nervous system (Penfield, 1932).

Ependymal cells, neuroglia, and *microglia* are the main constituents of the interstitial tissue. The ependymal cells line the cavities of the central nervous system and are sometimes included under the heading of neuroglia (Maximow and Bloom, 1952).

Neuroglia cells (Fig. 225), according to Penfield (1932), are of two types: *astrocytes* (astroglia) and *oligodendrocytes* (oligodendroglia). The development of both types of cells from the medullary epithelium of the developing neural tube has been described (Chapter 3).

Astrocytes are of two varieties—*protoplasmic* and *fibrous*. Both have irregularly oval nuclei which are somewhat larger than those of oligodendrocytes and microgliacytes; the chromatin is scattered and small in amount and the absence of nucleoli distinguishes them from the nuclei of nerve cells. The cytoplasm of astrocytes is relatively abundant and granular. *Protoplasmic astrocytes* have numerous rather thick plasmatic expan-

sions which branch freely. *Fibrous astrocytes* are distinguished from the protoplasmic cells by long, relatively thin, smooth, and little branched expansions; associated with the cytoplasm of their bodies and expansions are neuroglial fibers which have been described as intracellular by Maximow and Bloom (1952) and as "primarily extracellular" by Andrew and Ashworth (1944). With few exceptions the astrocytes found in the cellular areas of the normal nervous system (cortex, nuclei, and gray columns of the spinal cord) are of the protoplasmic variety while those in the white substance are fibrous.

The **processes (expansions) of astrocytes** (protoplasmic and fibrous) are attached to blood vessels (Fig. 225) and to pia mater; they form the neuroglial limiting membrane around the vessels and beneath the pia mater. The attachment to blood vessels is effected through the medium of *perivascular feet* which wrap around the walls of capillaries, small veins, and small arteries. The perivascular feet combine with the pia mater which extends into the central nervous system around the larger blood vessels, to form the *pia-glia membrane*. The fibers of the fibrous astrocytes pass into the perivascular feet and over the smaller vessels; they may extend considerably beyond the vessels. The *subpial foot* resembles the perivascular foot in form. Many astrocytes send processes long distances to terminate in relation to the pia mater of cerebrum, cerebellum, and spinal cord. Numerous small astrocytes are closely applied to the under surface of the cerebral pia mater.

The space between the pia-glia membrane and the vascular adventitia has been termed the *Virchow-Robin* or *perivascular space* (Fig. 226). Tissue fluids may pass to the surface along these perivascular spaces and join the cerebrospinal fluid; that there is a flow of fluid *from* the subarachnoid space *into* the perivascular spaces is indicated by the experiments of Rodriguez (1955) who observed, after subarachnoid administration of proflavine, that the nuclei of cells of the central nervous system were stained. Rodriguez also noted that the dye penetrated the endothelium of the intraneural vessels (from the outside in) although intravenous injection of proflavine indicated a failure of it to penetrate the endothelium of intraneural vessels; there is no staining of central nervous tissue after intravenous dye injection which indicates that the endothelium constitutes a blood-brain barrier. The existence of a true perivascular space in relation to capillary or precapillary portions of intraneural blood vessels has been disproven by electron microscopic observations (Wyckoff and Young, 1954 and 1956; Dempsey and Wislocki, 1955). It has been found that glial elements fill all intervening spaces between the neurons and the vascular elements of nervous tissues and that the plasma membranes of all cellular components are in intimate contact with themselves and with the basal membrane of the capillaries. A distance of 120 to 250 Ångstroms can be observed between adjacent membranes and this is seen to be filled by a material of definite electron density (De Robertis *et al.*, 1958a).

Oligodendrocytes differ morphologically from astrocytes in a number of respects; these include the absence of perivascular feet, the absence of fibers, the smaller, more delicate processes, and the smaller cell bodies (Fig. 225). Their nuclei are also rounder and smaller than those of astrocytes. Oligodendrocytes show very little variation in form, regardless of where they are situated in the nervous system. Their appearance in the various layers of the cerebellum and cerebrum, in the optic tracts, optic nerves, and spinal cord is approximately the same.

Many oligodendrocytes are arranged as satellites of nerve cells and their processes (Fig. 225). In fact, most *perineuronal satellites* are oligodendrocytes, but a few microglia cells are similarly located. The oligodendroglia cells of the central nervous system are analogous with the subcapsular cells of peripheral ganglia and the sheath of Schwann cells of peripheral nerves. They are often seen in the little hollows between adjacent processes of a nerve cell. The anterior gray column cells in the spinal cord and the Betz cells in Area 4 of the cerebral cortex are not as closely surrounded by satellite cells as other cells in the central nervous system.

Oligodendroglia cells also appear throughout both gray and white matter in the form of *perivascular satellites*. Their cell bodies are closely applied to capillaries and their processes are directed away from them. Under pathological conditions these cells may be considerably increased in number and they must be distinguished from perivascular leucocytes (Penfield, 1932). *Interfascicular oligodendrocytes* are found in rows between myelinated nerve fibers. There may be twenty to forty cells in such a row (Fig. 227). The longer processes course upward and downward upon the nerve fibers and the shorter processes wrap around them. The myelinated fibers are thus more or less enclosed in a loosely woven net of such processes. The rela-

tionship of the oligodendroglia to nerve fibers in the central nervous system resembles that of the sheath of Schwann cells to peripheral nerve fibers.

The **functions attributed to neuroglia cells** are many. *Astrocytes* have long been considered the *supporting structure* of the nervous system and it seems logical

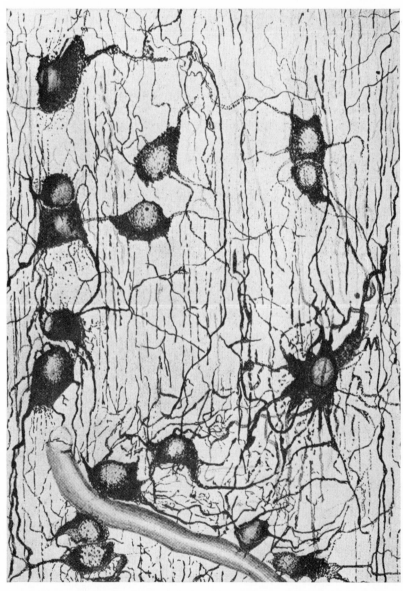

FIG. 227. Interfascicular oligodendroglia in the cerebellar white matter of a cat. The larger expansions generally parallel the nerve fibers. Cell "*m*" is not a typical oligodendroglia cell but has characteristics of both oligodendroglia and astroglia. (Penfield, courtesy of Brain.)

to assume that the fibrous astrocytes have a function similar to that subserved by connective tissue in other organs. Andrew and Ashworth (1944) have accepted neuroglia fibers as "homologous with those of other connective tissues" and have stressed the role of individual cells, of ectodermal origin, in the production of the fibers. It has also been suggested that the astrocytes may serve the neurons in a *nutritive* and *insulating* capacity. Gerschenfeld *et al.* (1959), on the basis of morphologic and experimental evidence, concluded that astroglia function as a water-ion compartment, in the central nervous system, which is involved in the selective transport of fluids and metabolites between the vascular system and neurons. This water-ion compartment, in the central nervous system, replaces, functionally, the extracellular space and intercellular ground substance found in other body tissues. After incubation of brain slices in an isotonic solu-

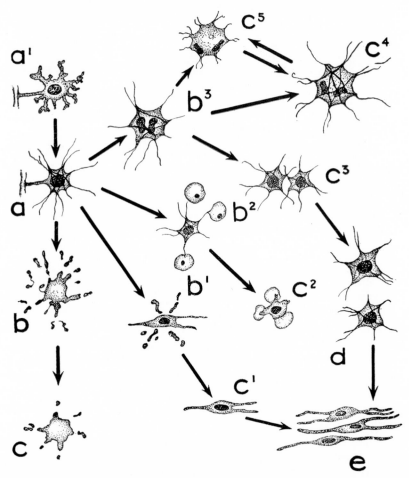

FIG. 228.   Pathologic changes in astrocytes. *a,* normal fibrous astrocyte; *a¹,* normal protoplasmic astrocyte which may become transformed into fibrous variety after destructive lesions of the gray matter; *a* to *c,* acute regressive change; *b¹* and *c¹,* changes leading to possible formation of piloidal astrocyte, *e; b²* and *c²,* dendrophagocytosis; *b³* and *c³,* gliosis leading to formation of piloidal astrocytes under certain circumstances; *c⁴,* monster glia; *c⁵,* hyalinized, swollen astrocyte. (C. B. Courville, courtesy of Pacific Press Publ. Assn.)

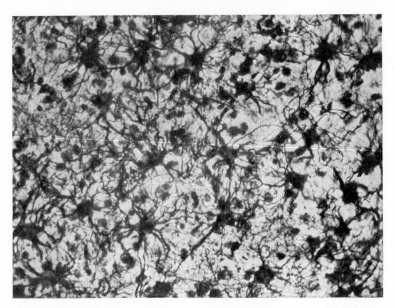

FIG. 229. Localized gliosis about the wall of an abscess of the brain. (C. B. Courville, courtesy of Pacific Press Publ. Assn.)

tion, a considerable increase in water content of the slices was found to be due, not to increase in, or formation of, an extracellular space, but to a considerable swelling of the astrocytes.

Oligodendrocytes are believed to have an important role in the *formation* and *maintenance of myelin*; evidence in favor of this supposition, according to Penfield (1932) is as follows: Oligodendrocytes first appear in the fiber tracts in large numbers at the time of myelination; they are not seen before myelination begins; at this period the protoplasmic granules in the oligodendrocytes are unusually large and numerous indicating, presumably, an increased functional activity; the position of the cells is in rows between the nerve fibers, resembling the arrangement of sheath of Schwann cells; the perineuronal cells resemble the subcapsular cells of the spinal ganglia in their relation to the neuron; the processes are always protoplasmic and wrap around the "nerve tubes"; oligodendrocytes follow the nerve tubes right up to the cell body and are especially likely to be placed on the sides of the axon hillock. Recent electron microscopic observations of the ultrastructure of oligodendroglial cells have demonstrated, beyond doubt, the role of these cells in central myelination (De Robertis *et al.*, 1958b and 1958c).

Gliosis may result from *trauma* to the central nervous system, from *inflammatory processes*, or from *interference with the blood supply* to a given area; it involves an increase in number and size of astrocytes together with increase in size and number of fibers associated with fibrous astrocytes (Fig. 228). Protoplasmic astrocytes are transformed into the fibrous type. In gliosis associated with brain injuries the astrocytes which are in or near the actual wound undergo clasmatodendrosis (disintegration of processes) and disappear. Outside this area, where the blood supply is disturbed but not completely interrupted the astrocytes and their processes are at first irregularly swollen. Later they begin to increase in number through amitotic division. After the stages of swelling and multiplication, fibrils begin to be laid down and the newly formed cells become true fibrous neuroglia. The end result is likely to be a dense fibrous scar (Fig. 229). The presence of injured cerebral tissue appears to stimulate gliosis since, in cleanly excised operative wounds, the glial proliferation is much less pronounced. There may be a chemical substance elaborated by focal or widespread death of cerebral tissue which produces gliosis of those astrocytes capable of survival (Penfield, 1932). In some pathological conditions the barrier membrane may disappear and connective tissue from the pia and arachnoid may invade the central nervous system. In the cicatrix developed during the healing process following traumatic injury of the brain, collagen and neuroglia fibers are often intermingled like the strands of a rope.

Oligodendrocytosis, or increase in perineuronal satellites, is associated with abnormality of the nerve cells such as is present in various inflammatory processes. In cases where the nerve cells are progressively disappearing the oligodendroglia satellites remain and replace (in position) the vanishing nerve cells. Oligodendrocytosis occurs in the white matter of the central nervous system as well as in the gray matter; interfascicular cells may increase greatly in number. In general, the oligodendrocytes are capable of less positive reaction to pathological conditions than either astrocytes or microglia, but observations by several investigators have indicated that cells generally conceded to belong in the class of oligodendroglia carry out neuronophagia, active cytolysis, and ingestion of the material of the nerve cell body (Andrew and Ashworth, 1945).

The **microglia cells** differ from neuroglia cells in their origin as well as in morphologic and physiologic characteristics (Fig. 225). They have long been believed to have a mesodermal rather than an ectodermal origin and this has been conclusively demonstrated by Dougherty (1944). Microglia cells migrate into the central nervous system from the pia mater at a stage in embryologic development when the neuroglia cells are already present and well developed. The nuclei of the microgliacytes are polymorphic; they may be round, oval, bacillar, triangular, or they may be twisted and resemble the letter "S." Their chromatin contents are abundant which makes them almost identical with the nuclei of lymphocytes. Microglia cells have only a small amount of perinuclear protoplasm. The processes vary in length and thickness and the number of their secondary branches is variable; they are, however, characteristically broad at their points of origin from the cell body and they gradually become thinner toward their distal ends. All the processes, including secondary and tertiary branches, are covered with spine-like projections (Fig. 229). Most microgliacytes are multipolar but bipolar and monopolar cells are found in small numbers. Bipolar cells are particularly evident in the stratum radiatum of the hippocampus where they tend to parallel the dendrites of the pyramidal cells.

Microglia cells are found in all regions of the central nervous system but are more abundant in the gray than in the white matter. In the gray regions of the cerebrum, cerebellum, and spinal cord they account for a small proportion of the perineuronal satellites. The microglia-vascular relations differ from those that exist between astrocytes and blood vessels in that there are no implantation feet. In most instances the microgliacytes in contact with vessels are multipolar and their processes extend in both directions along the vessel.

Microglia cells are markedly reactive to pathologic processes. In the presence of a destructive process the cells closest to the area of the injury are the first to intervene; soon more distant microgliacytes begin to move toward the lesion. Migration is effected through ameboid and stereotropic movements along the nervous network (Penfield, 1932). Morphologic transformations of the microglia also occur in and around pathologic processes. The cell processes are affected first; they become thicker and shorter. This is followed by an increase in the volume of the cell body and still later the retraction of the processes is almost complete and the cell is round and lobulated. Finally the processes completely disappear and the cells assume a spherical corpuscular form with vacuolar and reticulated protoplasm; at this stage they are commonly referred to as *compound granular corpuscles* or *gitter cells* (Fig. 230). The morphologic changes appear to be associated with an active phagocytic function of the cells. They phagocytose neuron débris, erythrocytes, and leucocytes. The substances taken up by them are broken down within the cell into lipids, hemosiderin, etc. It is possible that the compound granular corpuscles carry all or a part of their load to blood vessels where it may be taken up by the endothelial cells. Because of their phagocytic properties and their origin from the mesoderm, microglia cells are considered by many investigators to belong to the reticulo-endothelial system. Convincing evidence in support of this concept has been presented by Dougherty (1944)

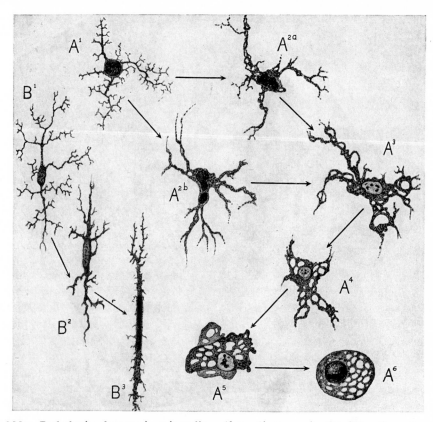

FIG. 230. Pathologic changes in microglia. A^1 to A^6, stages in the formation of compound granular corpuscle (glitter cell); B^1 to B^3, stages in the formation of rod cell. (C. B. Courville, courtesy of Pacific Press Publ. Assn.)

who found that the microglia cells are capable of ingesting lipids, India ink and trypan blue, and that the cells which migrate into the brains of newborn animals as progenitors of the sessile microglia are histiocytes. He also observed that the microglia take up particulate matter and colloidal dye when the blood-brain barrier is broken down and that the macrophages derived from microglia (gitter cells) are morphologically identical with the histiocytes (microglioblasts) which form microglia, the histiocytes arising from lymphocytes, and with the histiocytes found in inflammations generally.

Rod cells (stäbchenzellen) represent another common type of transformation occurring in microgliacytes (Fig. 230). Such cells tend to appear in pathologic processes of long standing such as general paralysis (neurosyphilis). The typical rod cells have long straight or curved nuclei and scanty perinuclear protoplasm; the latter is continued into two broad processes which have numerous filiform or sparsely branched collaterals. Fat droplets or small vacuoles may be present in the protoplasm. In general, paralysis rod cells are found in the various layers of the cerebral cortex where they tend to be oriented in a plane at right angles to the surface.

Tumors of the central nervous system commonly arise from and are made up of glial elements. Included in this group of tumors are *spongioblastomas* (which arise from primitive spongioblasts), *astroblastomas, oligodendroblastomas, astrocytomas,* and *oligodendrocytomas.* All such tumors, whether they result from proliferation of one or another glial element, come under the general heading of *gliomata.*

BIBLIOGRAPHY

ANDREW, W. and ASHWORTH, C. T., 1944: Morphological similarity of neuroglia fibers to fibers of other connective tissues. Am. J. Anat., *75,* 329-367.

———— 1945: The adendroglia. A new concept of the morphology and reactions of the smaller neuroglial cells. J. Comp. Neurol., *82,* 101-127.

DEMPSEY, E. W. and WISLOCKI, G. B., 1955: An electron microscopic study of blood-brain barrier in rat, employing silver nitrate as vital stain. J. Biophysic. Biochem. Cytol., *1,* 245-256.

DEROBERTIS, E. D. P., GERSCHENFELD, H. M. and WALD, F., 1958a: Some aspects of glial function as revealed by electron microscopy. Proc. 4th Intern. Congr. Electron Microscopy, Berlin.

———— 1958b: Submicroscopic analysis of myelination in the central nervous system. Anat. Rec., *130,* 292.

———— 1958c: Cellular mechanism of myelination in the central nervous system. J. Biophysic. Biochem. Cytol., *4,* 651-662.

DOUGHERTY, T. F., 1944: Studies on the cytogenesis of microglia and their relation to cells of the reticulo-endothelial system. Am. J. Anat., *74,* 61-95.

GERSCHENFELD, H. M., WALD, F., ZADUNAISKY J. A. and DEROBERTIS, E. D. P., 1959: Function of an astroglia in the water-ion metabolism of the central nervous system. Neurology, *9,* 412-425.

MAXIMOW, A. A. and BLOOM, W., 1952: *A Textbook of Histology,* 6th Ed., W. B. Saunders Co., Philadelphia.

PENFIELD, W., 1932: *Cytology and Cellular Pathology of the Nervous System.* Paul B. Hoeber, Inc., New York.

PENFIELD, W. and CONE, W., 1932. In *Cowdry's Special Cytology,* Paul B. Hoeber, Inc., New York, p. 1449.

RODRIGUEZ, L. A., 1955: Experiments on the histologic locus of the hemato-encephalic barrier. J. Comp. Neurol., *102,* 27-45.

WYCKOFF, R. W. G. and YOUNG, J. Z., 1954: The nerve cell surface. J. Anat., *88,* 568.

———— 1956: The motor-neuron surface. Proc. Roy. Soc., Lond. B, *144,* 440-450.

Atlas of Brain Stem
and Adjacent Structures

(See index on page 403)

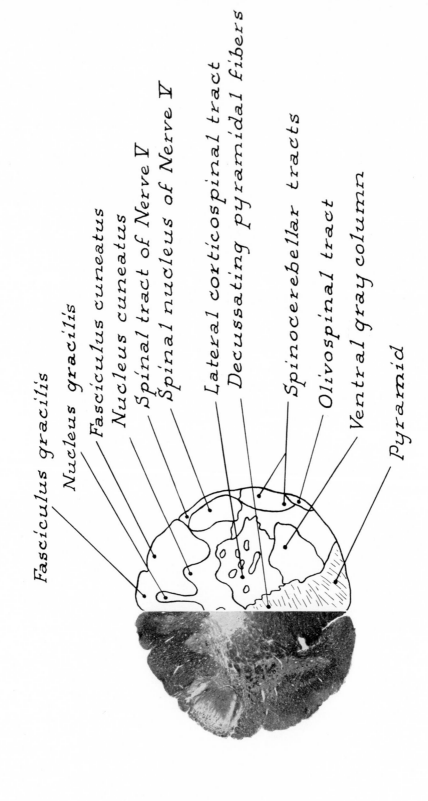

Fasciculus gracilis

Nucleus gracilis

Fasciculus cuneatus

Nucleus cuneatus

Spinal tract of Nerve V

Spinal nucleus of Nerve V

Lateral corticospinal tract

Decussating pyramidal fibers

Spinocerebellar tracts

Olivospinal tract

Ventral gray column

Pyramid

FIG. 231

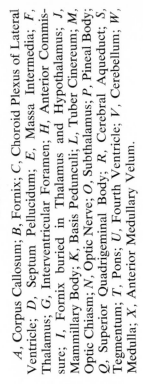

Fig. 231

Section through the closed medulla at the level of the pyramidal decussation. The nucleus gracilis, nucleus cuneatus, and the spinal nucleus of the trigeminal nerve are clearly evident as is the ventral gray column which has been separated from the remainder of the gray matter by the decussating pyramidal fibers. The lateral corticospinal tracts, as contributed to by the pyramidal fibers, appear in the interval between the ventral gray column and the remainder of the gray matter. At this particular level pyramidal fibers are crossing from the right pyramid to the left lateral corticospinal tract.

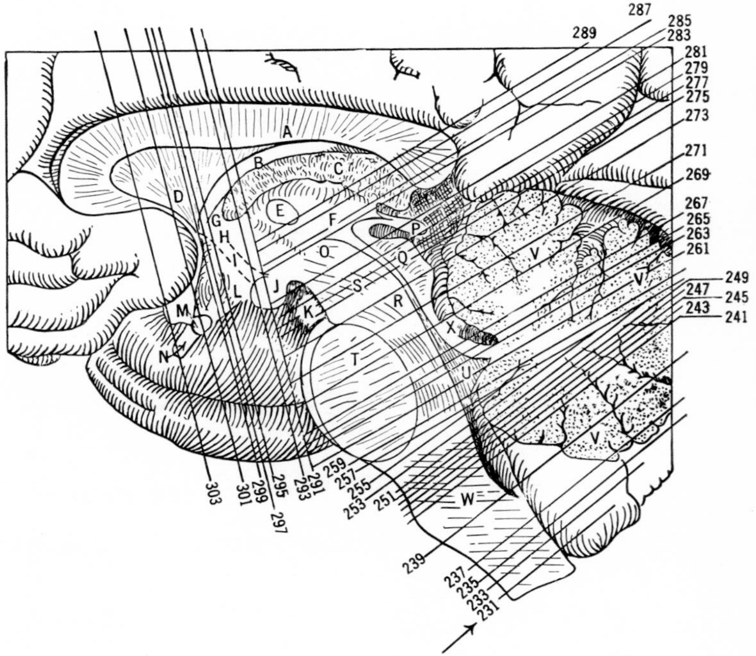

Fig. 232

A, Corpus Callosum; *B*, Fornix; *C*, Choroid Plexus of Lateral Ventricle; *D*, Septum Pellucidum; *E*, Massa Intermedia; *F*, Thalamus; *G*, Interventricular Foramen; *H*, Anterior Commissure; *I*, Fornix buried in Thalamus and Hypothalamus; *J*, Mammillary Body; *K*, Basis Pedunculi; *L*, Tuber Cinereum; *M*, Optic Chiasm; *N*, Optic Nerve; *O*, Subthalamus; *P*, Pineal Body; *Q*, Superior Quadrigeminal Body; *R*, Cerebral Aqueduct; *S*, Tegmentum; *T*, Pons; *U*, Fourth Ventricle; *V*, Cerebellum; *W*, Medulla; *X*, Anterior Medullary Velum.

(329)

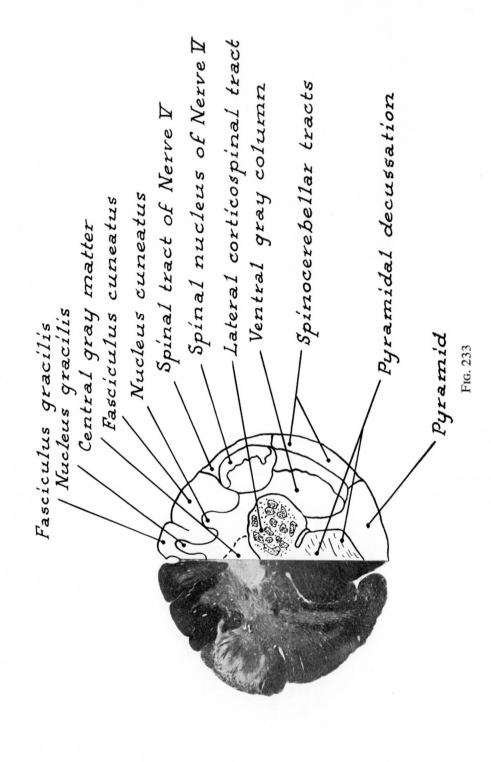

Fasciculus gracilis
Nucleus gracilis
Central gray matter
Fasciculus cuneatus
Nucleus cuneatus
Spinal tract of Nerve V
Spinal nucleus of Nerve V
Lateral corticospinal tract
Ventral gray column
Spinocerebellar tracts
Pyramidal decussation
Pyramid

Fig. 233

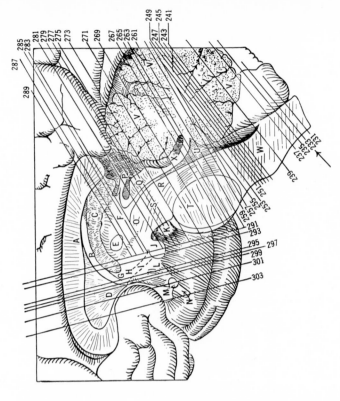

FIG. 233

Section through closed medulla at the level of the pyramidal (motor) decussation. The lateral corticospinal tracts are becoming evident ventrolateral to the central gray matter, on either side, where they are being formed by decussating corticospinal fibers. Immediately dorsolateral to the pyramid are the ventral and dorsal spinocerebellar tracts; dorsal to the latter tract is the spinal tract of the trigeminal nerve which overlies the trigeminal spinal nucleus. The nucleus cuneatus and nucleus gracilis are dorsal and lateral to the central gray matter and are covered by their respective spinal fasciculi. The proximity of this level to the upper cervical spinal cord is indicated by the ventral gray column which has been essentially isolated from the remainder of the gray matter by the decussating corticospinal fibers.

FIG. 234

A, Corpus Callosum; *B*, Fornix; *C*, Choroid Plexus of Lateral Ventricle; *D*, Septum Pellucidum; *E*, Massa Intermedia; *F*, Thalamus; *G*, Interventricular Foramen; *H*, Anterior Commissure; *I*, Fornix buried in Thalamus and Hypothalamus; *J*, Mammillary Body; *K*, Basis Pedunculi; *L*, Tuber Cinereum; *M*, Optic Chiasm; *N*, Optic Nerve; *O*, Subthalamus; *P*, Pineal Body; *Q*, Superior Quadrigeminal Body; *R*, Cerebral Aqueduct; *S*, Tegmentum; *T*, Pons; *U*, Fourth Ventricle; *V*, Cerebellum; *W*, Medulla; *X*, Anterior Medullary Velum.

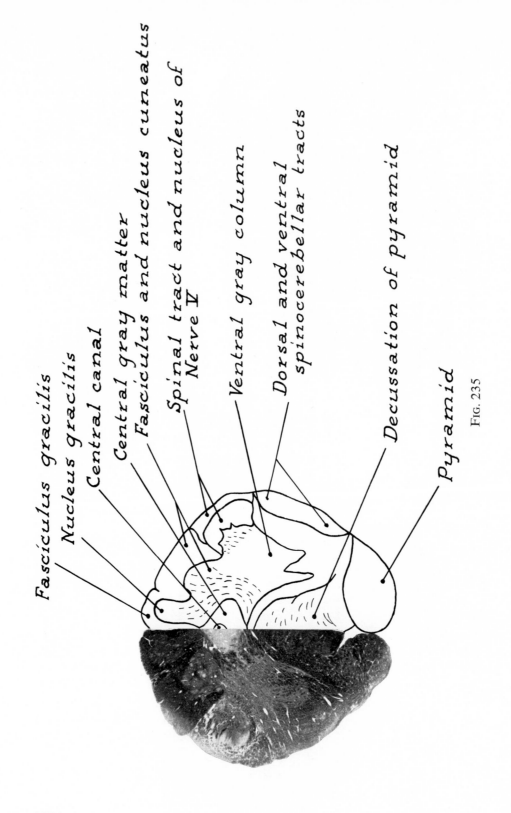

Fasciculus gracilis

Nucleus gracilis

Central canal

Central gray matter

Fasciculus and nucleus cuneatus

Spinal tract and nucleus of Nerve V

Ventral gray column

Dorsal and ventral spinocerebellar tracts

Decussation of pyramid

Pyramid

Fig. 235

Fig. 235

Section through the caudal part of the closed medulla which shows the decussation of the corticospinal fibers from pyramids to lateral corticospinal tracts. The nucleus gracilis, nucleus cuneatus, and spinal nucleus of the trigeminal nerve appear in that order lateral to the posteromedian septum. The nuclei gracilis and cuneatus are covered by the fasciculi of the same name and the spinal nucleus of the trigeminal nerve is separated from the periphery by the spinal tract. The dorsal and ventral spinocerebellar tracts lie at the periphery and immediately ventral to the spinal tract of the trigeminal nerve. A few internal arcuate fibers from the nuclei gracilis and cuneatus are seen coursing ventrally and medially around the central gray matter.

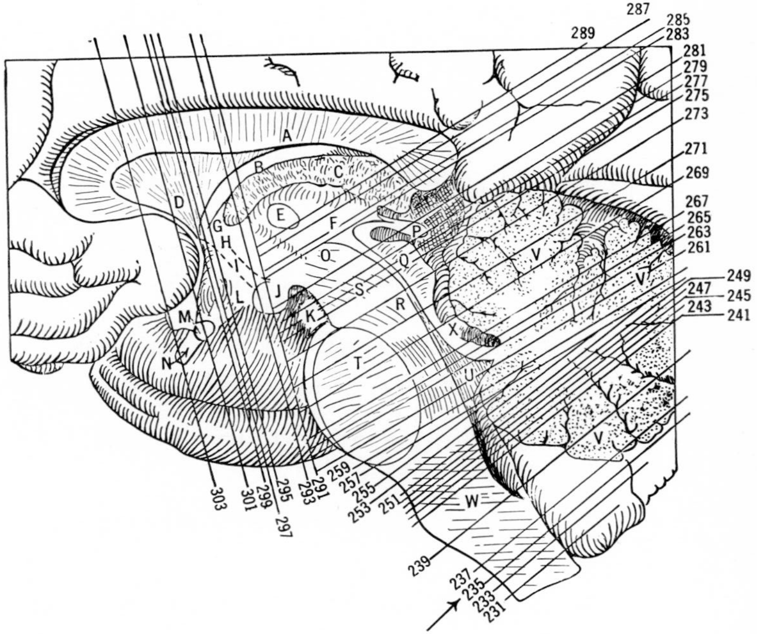

Fig. 236

A, Corpus Callosum; B, Fornix; C, Choroid Plexus of Lateral Ventricle; D, Septum Pellucidum; E, Massa Intermedia; F, Thalamus; G, Interventricular Foramen; H, Anterior Commissure; I, Fornix buried in Thalamus and Hypothalamus; J, Mammillary Body; K, Basis Pedunculi; L, Tuber Cinereum; M, Optic Chiasm; N, Optic Nerve; O, Subthalamus; P, Pineal Body; Q, Superior Quadrigeminal Body; R, Cerebral Aqueduct; S, Tegmentum; T, Pons; U, Fourth Ventricle; V, Cerebellum; W, Medulla; X, Anterior Medullary Velum.

(333)

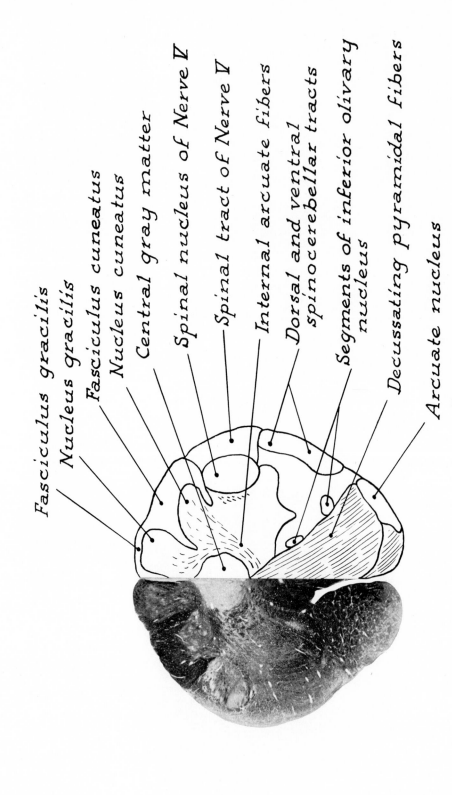

Fasciculus gracilis

Nucleus gracilis

Fasciculus cuneatus

Nucleus cuneatus

Central gray matter

Spinal nucleus of Nerve V

Spinal tract of Nerve V

Internal arcuate fibers

Dorsal and ventral
spinocerebellar tracts

Segments of inferior olivary
nucleus

Decussating pyramidal fibers

Arcuate nucleus

Fig. 237

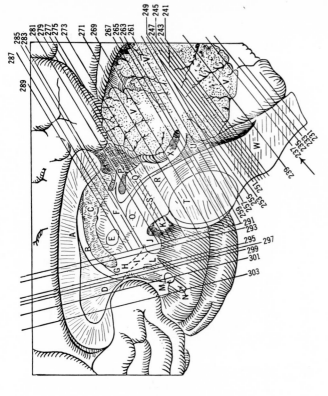

Fig. 237

Section through the closed part of the medulla at a level which demonstrates the overlapping of the motor and sensory decussations. Pyramidal fibers, on the right, are seen crossing the midline toward the left lateral corticospinal tract. Internal arcuate fibers from the gracile and cuneate nuclei encircle the central gray matter and, after crossing the midline, contribute to the formation of the medial lemniscus. The relationships of the nucleus gracilis, nucleus cuneatus, and spinal nucleus of the trigeminal nerve are essentially unchanged from those observed in more caudal levels except that the first two nuclei are becoming more prominent at the expense of the fasciculi which terminate in them. The spinal tract of the trigeminal nerve overlies the spinal nucleus and the spinocerebellar tracts lie between it and the arcuate nucleus which is placed somewhat lateral as well as ventral to the pyramid.

Fig. 238

A, Corpus Callosum; *B,* Fornix; *C,* Choroid Plexus of Lateral Ventricle; *D,* Septum Pellucidum; *E,* Massa Intermedia; *F,* Thalamus; *G,* Interventricular Foramen; *H,* Anterior Commissure; *I,* Fornix buried in Thalamus and Hypothalamus; *J,* Mammillary Body; *K,* Basis Pedunculi; *L,* Tuber Cinereum; *M,* Optic Chiasm; *N,* Optic Nerve; *O,* Subthalamus; *P,* Pineal Body; *Q,* Superior Quadrigeminal Body; *R,* Cerebral Aqueduct; *S,* Tegmentum; *T,* Pons; *U,* Fourth Ventricle; *V,* Cerebellum; *W,* Medulla; *X,* Anterior Medullary Velum.

(335)

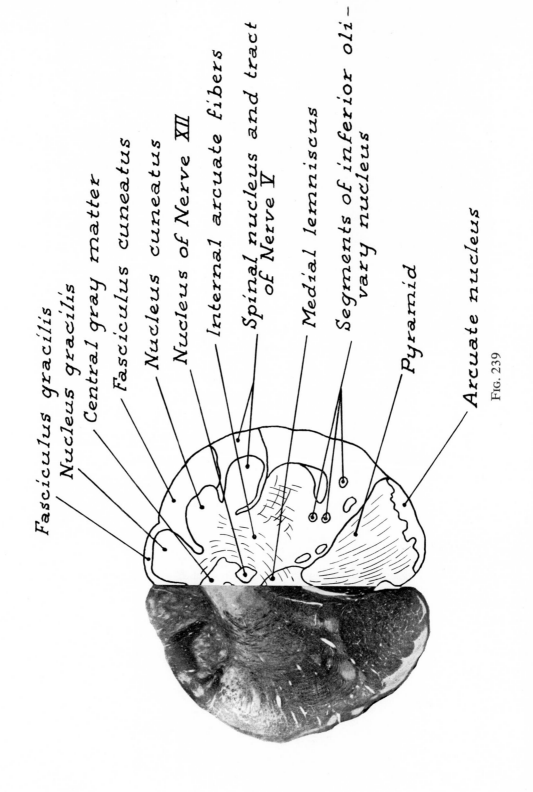

Fasciculus gracilis

Nucleus gracilis

Central gray matter

Fasciculus cuneatus

Nucleus cuneatus

Nucleus of Nerve XII

Internal arcuate fibers

Spinal nucleus and tract of Nerve V

Medial lemniscus

Segments of inferior oli‐vary nucleus

Pyramid

Arcuate nucleus

FIG. 239

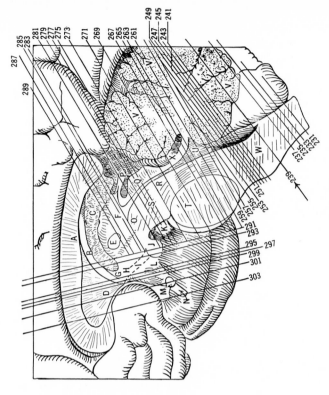

Fig. 239

Fig. 240

A, Corpus Callosum; B, Fornix; C, Choroid Plexus of Lateral Ventricle; D, Septum Pellucidum; E, Massa Intermedia; F, Thalamus; G, Interventricular Foramen; H, Anterior Commissure; I, Fornix buried in Thalamus and Hypothalamus; J, Mammillary Body; K, Basis Pedunculi; L, Tuber Cinereum; M, Optic Chiasm; N, Optic Nerve; O, Subthalamus; P, Pineal Body; Q, Superior Quadrigeminal Body; R, Cerebral Aqueduct; S, Tegmentum; T, Pons; U, Fourth Ventricle; V, Cerebellum; W, Medulla; X, Anterior Medullary Velum.

Section through the closed part of the medulla at the level of the sensory decussation and immediately rostral to the pyramidal or motor decussation. The nuclei gracilis lie on either side of the posteromedian septum; the nucleus cuneatus and the spinal nucleus of the trigeminal nerve appear in that order, lateral to the nucleus gracilis. The fasciculus gracilis, at this level, is not very much in evidence because most of its component fibers have terminated in the nucleus. The fasciculus cuneatus is considerably more in evidence and overlies its nucleus. The spinal nucleus of the trigeminal nerve is separated from the periphery by its tract. The central gray matter is encircled by internal arcuate fibers which have their origin in the nuclei gracilis and cuneatus and which enter the contralateral medial lemniscus. The hypoglossal nuclei, within the central gray matter, are ventrolateral to the central canal on either side. The medial lemnisci are rather indistinctly seen on either side of the median raphe and immediately dorsal to the pyramids. The most caudal segments of the inferior olivary nuclei appear as isolated islands of gray matter in the reticular formation dorsolateral to the pyramids. The arcuate nuclei are applied to the ventral aspects of the pyramids.

(337)

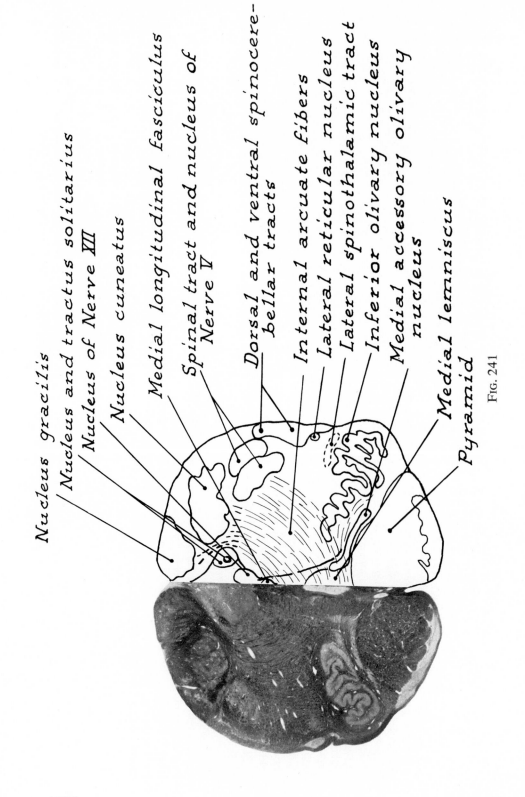

Nucleus gracilis

Nucleus and tractus solitarius

Nucleus of Nerve XII

Nucleus cuneatus

Medial longitudinal fasciculus

Spinal tract and nucleus of Nerve V

Dorsal and ventral spinocerebellar tracts

Internal arcuate fibers

Lateral reticular nucleus

Lateral spinothalamic tract

Inferior olivary nucleus

Medial accessory olivary nucleus

Medial lemniscus

Pyramid

Fig. 241

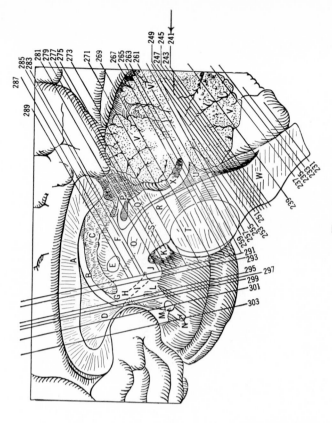

FIG. 241

FIG. 242

Section through the closed part of the medulla oblongata. The central canal is surrounded by the central gray matter within which are seen the nuclei of the hypoglossal nerves and the nuclei solitarii. The nucleus solitarius, on either side, surrounds the tractus solitarius. The nucleus gracilis and nucleus cuneatus are dorsal and lateral to the central gray matter and the spinal tract and nucleus of the trigeminal nerve are ventral to the nucleus cuneatus. Internal arcuate fibers from the nuclei gracilis and cuneatus encircle the central gray matter to enter the contralateral medial lemniscus. More laterally-placed arcuate fibers originate in the spinal nucleus of the trigeminal nerve; these contribute to the formation of the contralateral ventral trigeminal lemniscus which is associated with the lateral spinothalamic tract in the area dorsolateral to the inferior olivary nucleus. The position of the lateral spinothalamic tract is indicated on the right. The median raphe is flanked, on either side, by the medial longitudinal fasciculi, tectospinal fibers (not labelled), medial lemnisci, and pyramids in that order dorsoventrally. The dorsal and ventral spinocerebellar tracts lie between the olivary eminence and the spinal tract and nucleus of the trigeminal nerve. The arcuate nuclei are prominently displayed on the ventral sides of the pyramids.

A, Corpus Callosum; B, Fornix; C, Choroid Plexus of Lateral Ventricle; D, Septum Pellucidum; E, Massa Intermedia; F, Thalamus; G, Interventricular Foramen; H, Anterior Commissure; I, Fornix buried in Thalamus and Hypothalamus; J, Mammillary Body; K, Basis Pedunculi; L, Tuber Cinereum; M, Optic Chiasm; N, Optic Nerve; O, Subthalamus; P, Pineal Body; Q, Superior Quadrigeminal Body; R, Cerebral Aqueduct; S, Tegmentum; T, Pons; U, Fourth Ventricle; V, Cerebellum; W, Medulla; X, Anterior Medullary Velum.

(339)

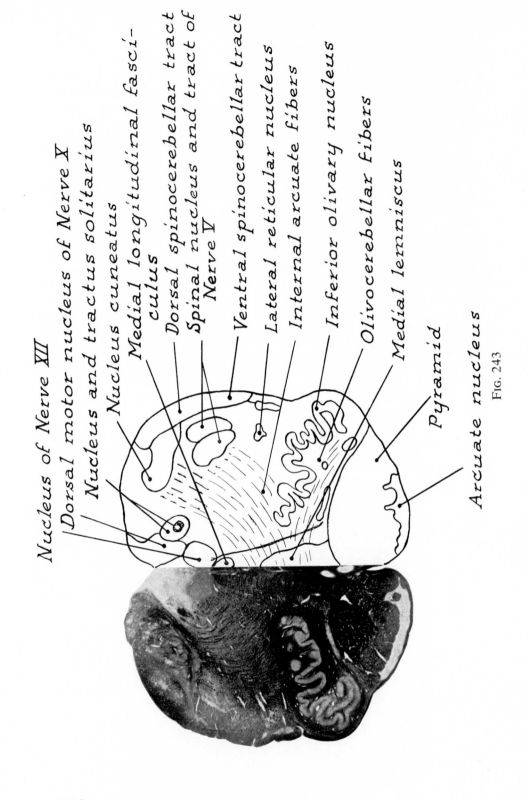

Nucleus of Nerve XII
Dorsal motor nucleus of Nerve X
Nucleus and tractus solitarius
Nucleus cuneatus
Medial longitudinal fasciculus
Dorsal spinocerebellar tract
Spinal nucleus and tract of Nerve V
Ventral spinocerebellar tract
Lateral reticular nucleus
Internal arcuate fibers
Inferior olivary nucleus
Olivocerebellar fibers
Medial lemniscus
Pyramid
Arcuate nucleus

Fig. 243

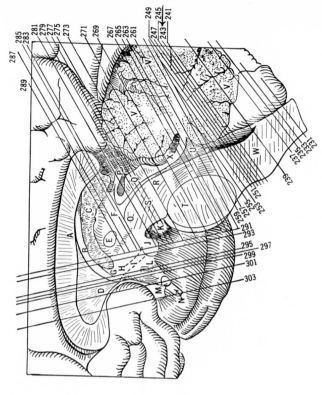

FIG. 243

FIG. 244

A, Corpus Callosum; *B*, Fornix; *C*, Choroid Plexus of Lateral Ventricle; *D*, Septum Pellucidum; *E*, Massa Intermedia; *F*, Thalamus; *G*, Interventricular Foramen; *H*, Anterior Commissure; *I*, Fornix buried in Thalamus and Hypothalamus; *J*, Mammillary Body; *K*, Basis Pedunculi; *L*, Tuber Cinereum; *M*, Optic Chiasm; *N*, Optic Nerve; *O*, Subthalamus; *P*, Pineal Body; *Q*, Superior Quadrigeminal Body; *R*, Cerebral Aqueduct; *S*, Tegmentum; *T*, Pons; *U*, Fourth Ventricle; *V*, Cerebellum; *W*, Medulla; *X*, Anterior Medullary Velum.

Section through the medulla at the junction of its open and closed portions. The central canal is seen opening into the caudal part of the fourth ventricle. In the gray matter ventral to the floor of the fourth ventricle the nucleus and tractus solitarius are clearly visible. The hypoglossal nucleus, on either side, lies ventromedial to the nucleus solitarius; the hypoglossal nerve fibers emerge from it to course ventrally along-side the medial longitudinal fasciculus, medial lemniscus, and pyramid. The rostral part of the nucleus cuneatus is lateral to the nucleus solitarius and is separated from the periphery by the dorsal spinocerebellar tract. The spinal nucleus and tract of the trigeminal nerve are ventral to the nucleus cuneatus. Internal arcuate fibers can be seen emerging from the nucleus cuneatus and spinal nucleus of the trigeminal nerve; the majority of them enter the contralateral medial lemniscus but those from the latter nucleus contribute to the ventral trigeminal lemniscus which is dorsal to the inferior olivary nucleus. Practically all trigeminothalamic fibers in the ventral trigeminal lemniscus are crossed fibers. The medial longitudinal fasciculus, on either side, is intimately related to the hypoglossal nucleus and is separated from the medial lemniscus by the interval which is occupied by tectospinal fibers. The pyramids lie on either side of the ventromedian fissure, immediately ventral to the medial lemnisci. The arcuate nuclei which are caudal prolongations of the pontile nuclei, appear on the ventral sides of the pyramids.

(341)

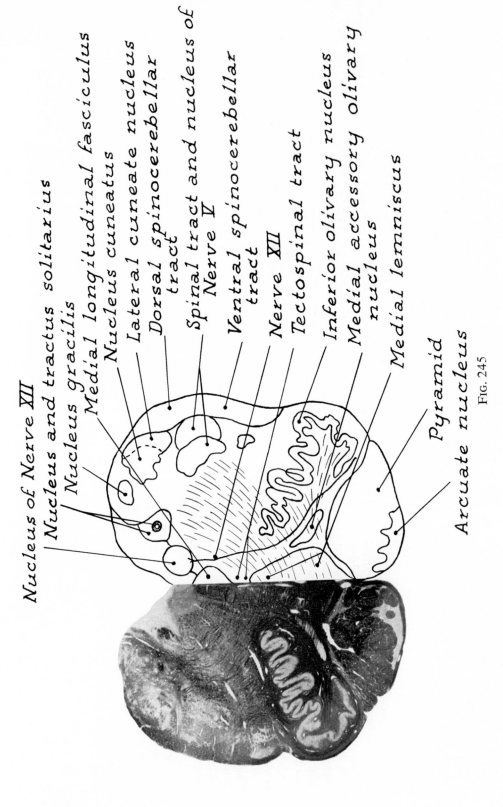

Nucleus of Nerve XII
Nucleus and tractus solitarius
Nucleus gracilis
Medial longitudinal fasciculus
Nucleus cuneatus
Lateral cuneate nucleus
Dorsal spinocerebellar tract
Spinal tract and nucleus of Nerve V
Ventral spinocerebellar tract
Nerve XII
Tectospinal tract
Inferior olivary nucleus
Medial accessory olivary nucleus
Medial lemniscus
Pyramid
Arcuate nucleus

Fig. 245

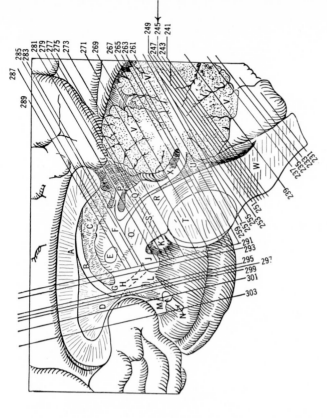

FIG. 245

Section through the open portion of the medulla near the caudal end of the fourth ventricle. The V-shaped floor of the ventricle is flanked, on either side, by gray matter within which are seen the hypoglossal and solitary nuclei; the gray matter of the latter nucleus surrounds the deeply-stained tractus solitarius. The rostral portions of the gracile and cuneate nuclei and the lateral cuneate nucleus are lateral to the nucleus solitarius. The spinal tract and nucleus of the trigeminal nerve are ventral to the cuneate and lateral cuneate nuclei. The median raphe is flanked by the medial longitudinal fasciculi, tectospinal tracts, medial lemnisci, and pyramids dorso-ventrally. The arcuate nuclei, which are caudal extensions of the pontile nuclei, are seen on the ventromedial sides of the pyramids and in relationship to the ventromedian fissure. The olivary eminence is seen as a prominent bulge immediately dorsal to the pyramid and contains the inferior olivary nucleus. The ventral and dorsal spinocerebellar tracts are seen to have migrated dorsally; the former will eventually comprise a major part of the restiform body. Hypoglossal nerve fibers can be traced from the hypoglossal nuclei to the periphery of the medulla where they emerge through the sulcus between the pyramid and olivary eminence; in their course ventrally they lie along-side the medial longitudinal fasciculus, tectospinal tract, medial lemniscus, and pyramid.

FIG. 246

A, Corpus Callosum; B, Fornix; C, Choroid Plexus of Lateral Ventricle; D, Septum Pellucidum; E, Massa Intermedia; F, Thalamus; G, Interventricular Foramen; H, Anterior Commissure; I, Fornix buried in Thalamus and Hypothalamus; J, Mammillary Body; K, Basis Pedunculi; L, Tuber Cinereum; M, Optic Chiasm; N, Optic Nerve; O, Subthalamus; P, Pineal Body; Q, Superior Quadrigeminal Body; R, Cerebral Aqueduct; S, Tegmentum; T, Pons; U, Fourth Ventricle; V, Cerebellum; W, Medulla; X, Anterior Medullary Velum.

(343)

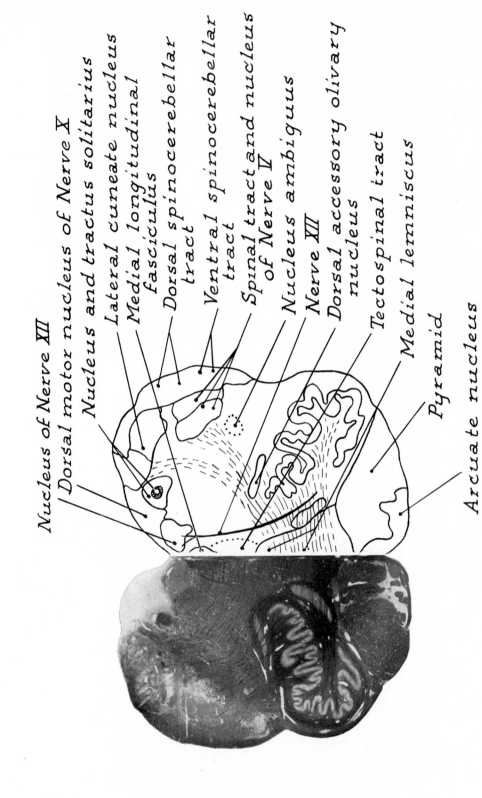

Nucleus of Nerve XII

Dorsal motor nucleus of Nerve X

Nucleus and tractus solitarius

Lateral cuneate nucleus

Medial longitudinal fasciculus

Dorsal spinocerebellar tract

Ventral spinocerebellar tract

Spinal tract and nucleus of Nerve V

Nucleus ambiguus

Nerve XII

Dorsal accessory olivary nucleus

Tectospinal tract

Medial lemniscus

Pyramid

Arcuate nucleus

Fig. 247

(344)

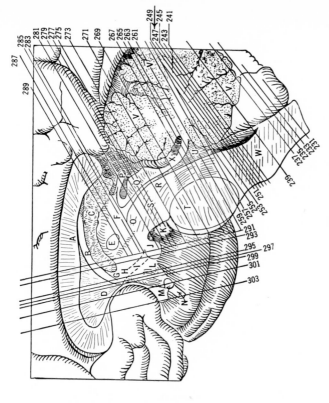

FIG. 247

FIG. 248

A, Corpus Callosum; B, Fornix; C, Choroid Plexus of Lateral Ventricle; D, Septum Pellucidum; E, Massa Intermedia; F, Thalamus; G, Interventricular Foramen; H, Anterior Commissure; I, Fornix buried in Thalamus and Hypothalamus; J, Mammillary Body; K, Basis Pedunculi; L, Tuber Cinereum; M, Optic Chiasm; N, Optic Nerve; O, Subthalamus; P, Pineal Body; Q, Superior Quadrigeminal Body; R, Cerebral Aqueduct; S, Tegmentum; T, Pons; U, Fourth Ventricle; V, Cerebellum; W, Medulla; X, Anterior Medullary Velum.

Section through the open portion of the medulla. The fourth ventricle may be observed to have widened considerably as compared to more caudal levels and to have become more shallow. The gray matter beneath the floor of the ventricle, on either side, contains the hypoglossal nucleus, dorsal motor nucleus of the vagus nerve, and the nucleus solitarius with its tract. The lateral cuneate nucleus and a part of the main cuneate nucleus (latter not labelled) are seen just lateral to the nucleus solitarius. The dorsal and ventral spinocerebellar tracts are dorsolaterally placed with the spinal nucleus and tract of the trigeminal nerve immediately beneath them. The location of the nucleus ambiguus in the reticular formation just ventral to the spinal nucleus of the trigeminal nerve is indicated. The medial longitudinal fasciculi are ventromedial to the hypoglossal nuclei and are separated from the medial lemnisci by the tectospinal tracts. The pyramids and arcuate nuclei are on either side of the median raphe and ventromedian fissure. Hypoglossal nerve fibers can be followed from their origin in the nuclei toward their point of emergence from the medulla. Secondary trigeminal fibers can be traced from the spinal nucleus ventromedially across the median raphe into the contralateral reticular formation where they contribute to the ventral trigeminal lemniscus; the lemniscus is immediately dorsal to the inferior olivary nucleus. Olivocerebellar fibers can be seen to emerge from the hilus of the inferior olivary nucleus, on either side; at somewhat more rostral levels these fibers will be traced into the restiform body through which they reach the cerebellum.

(345)

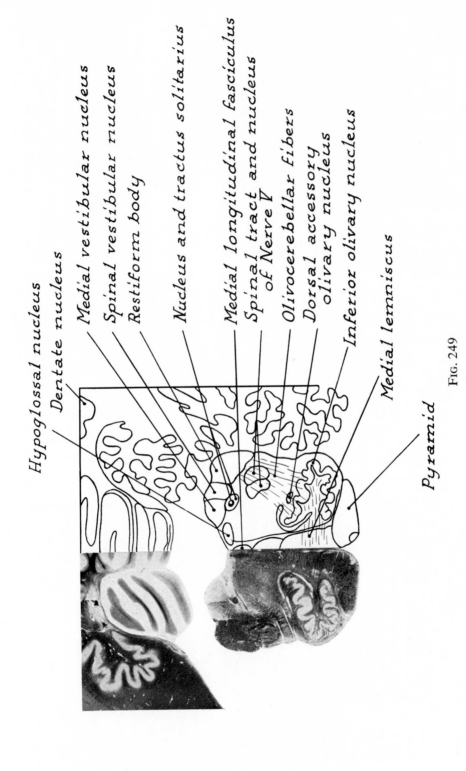

Hypoglossal nucleus

Dentate nucleus

Medial vestibular nucleus

Spinal vestibular nucleus

Restiform body

Nucleus and tractus solitarius

Medial longitudinal fasciculus

Spinal tract and nucleus of Nerve V

Olivocerebellar fibers

Dorsal accessory olivary nucleus

Inferior olivary nucleus

Medial lemniscus

Pyramid

Fig. 249

(346)

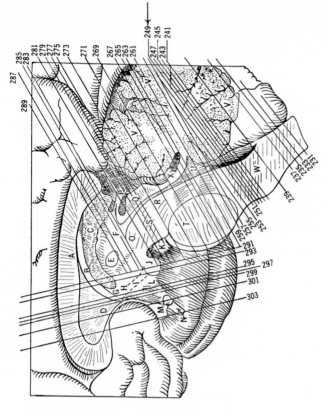

FIG. 249

Section through the open part of the medulla showing the relationship of the cerebellum to it. The restiform body is distinctly seen in the dorsolateral angle of the medulla, with the spinal and medial vestibular nuclei medial to it. The hypoglossal nucleus is between the medial vestibular nucleus and the medial longitudinal fasciculus. Olivocerebellar fibers can be seen entering the restiform body from the contralateral and, to a much lesser extent, from the ipsilateral olivary nuclei. The nucleus and tractus solitarius are ventral to the vestibular nuclei. The relationships of the pyramid, medial lemniscus, tectospinal tract, and inferior olivary nucleus are essentially unchanged from those observed and commented upon at more caudal levels.

FIG. 250

A, Corpus Callosum; B, Fornix; C, Choroid Plexus of Lateral Ventricle; D, Septum Pellucidum; E, Massa Intermedia; F, Thalamus; G, Interventricular Foramen; H, Anterior Commissure; I, Fornix buried in Thalamus and Hypothalamus; J, Mammillary Body; K, Basis Pedunculi; L, Tuber Cinereum; M, Optic Chiasm; N, Optic Nerve; O, Subthalamus; P, Pineal Body; Q, Superior Quadrigeminal Body; R, Cerebral Aqueduct; S, Tegmentum; T, Pons; U, Fourth Ventricle; V, Cerebellum; W, Medulla; X, Anterior Medullary Velum.

(347)

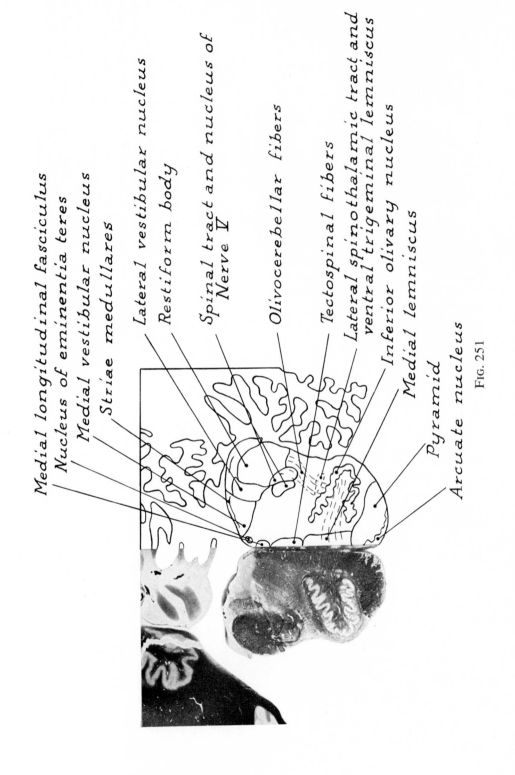

Medial longitudinal fasciculus
Nucleus of eminentia teres
Medial vestibular nucleus
Striae medullares
Lateral vestibular nucleus
Restiform body
Spinal tract and nucleus of Nerve V
Olivocerebellar fibers
Tectospinal fibers
Lateral spinothalamic tract and ventral trigeminal lemniscus
Inferior olivary nucleus
Medial lemniscus
Pyramid
Arcuate nucleus

FIG. 251

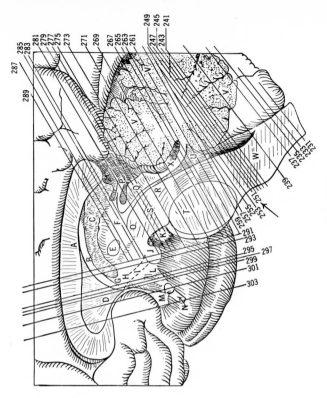

Fig. 251

Section through the upper medulla at a level which shows some of the striae medullares in relation to the dorsal aspects of the medial and lateral vestibular nuclei. The restiform body, on either side, appears in the dorsolateral angle of the section with the spinal tract and nucleus of the trigeminal nerve immediately ventromedial to it. The pyramids and arcuate nuclei appear on either side of the ventromedian fissure. The inferior olivary nucleus is dorsolateral to the pyramid and accounts for the prominent olivary eminence as it appears on the lateral surface of the section. The dark-staining area dorsolateral to the inferior olivary nucleus contains the lateral spinothalamic tract and the ventral trigeminal lemniscus which originates from the contralateral spinal nucleus. The medial lemniscus lies next to the median raphe and immediately dorsal to the pyramid; the tectospinal fibers are dorsal to the lemniscus and the medial longitudinal fasciculus is dorsal to them. The dorsal and lateral aspects of the medulla are more or less covered by the cerebellum. On the left the caudal part of the dentate nucleus is seen to be embedded in the central white matter of the cerebellum.

Fig. 252

A, Corpus Callosum; B, Fornix; C, Choroid Plexus of Lateral Ventricle; D, Septum Pellucidum; E, Massa Intermedia; F, Thalamus; G, Interventricular Foramen; H, Anterior Commissure; I, Fornix buried in Thalamus and Hypothalamus; J, Mammillary Body; K, Basis Pedunculi; L, Tuber Cinereum; M, Optic Chiasm; N, Optic Nerve; O, Subthalamus; P, Pineal Body; Q, Superior Quadrigeminal Body; R, Cerebral Aqueduct; S, Tegmentum; T, Pons; U, Fourth Ventricle; V, Cerebellum; W, Medulla; X, Anterior Medullary Velum.

(349)

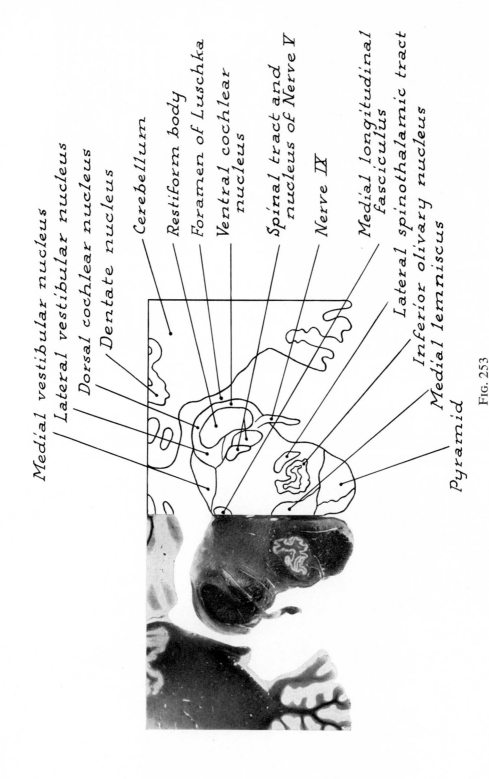

Medial vestibular nucleus

Lateral vestibular nucleus

Dorsal cochlear nucleus

Dentate nucleus

Cerebellum

Restiform body

Foramen of Luschka

Ventral cochlear nucleus

Spinal tract and nucleus of Nerve V

Nerve IX

Medial longitudinal fasciculus

Lateral spinothalamic tract

Inferior olivary nucleus

Medial lemniscus

Pyramid

Fig. 253

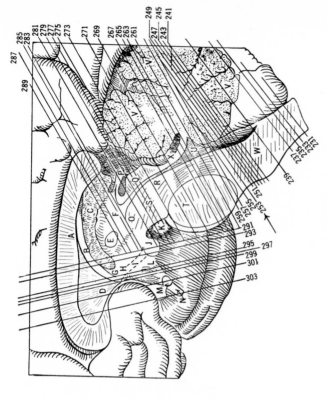

Fig. 253

Fig. 254

A, Corpus Callosum; *B*, Fornix; *C*, Choroid Plexus of Lateral Ventricle; *D*, Septum Pellucidum; *E*, Massa Intermedia; *F*, Thalamus; *G*, Interventricular Foramen; *H*, Anterior Commissure; *I*, Fornix buried in Thalamus and Hypothalamus; *J*, Mammillary Body; *K*, Basis Pedunculi; *L*, Tuber Cinereum; *M*, Optic Chiasm; *N*, Optic Nerve; *O*, Subthalamus; *P*, Pineal Body; *Q*, Superior Quadrigeminal Body; *R*, Cerebral Aqueduct; *S*, Tegmentum; *T*, Pons; *U*, Fourth Ventricle; *V*, Cerebellum; *W*, Medulla; *X*, Anterior Medullary Velum.

Section through the rostral part of the medulla which shows the fourth ventricle roofed over by the vermis of the cerebellum and also shows the communication between the fourth ventricle and subarachnoid space through the foramina of Luschka. At this level the dorsolateral angle of the medulla presents the prominent restiform body which is covered, at this level, by the gray matter comprising the dorsal and ventral cochlear nuclei within which the auditory fibers of the eighth nerve terminate. The spinal tract and nucleus of the trigeminal nerve are medial to the restiform body; the lateral vestibular nucleus is dorsal to them. The medial longitudinal fasciculus is immediately ventral to the floor of the fourth ventricle and adjacent to the median raphe; the medial and lateral vestibular nuclei are lateral to it. Fibers of the glossopharyngeal nerve can be seen entering and leaving the medulla just ventral to the restiform body. The lateral spinothalamic tract and the inferior olivary nucleus are in the ventrolateral area of the reticular formation, just dorsal to the pyramid and lateral to the medial lemniscus. The arcuate nuclei appear on either side of the ventromedian fissure in relation to the pyramid.

(351)

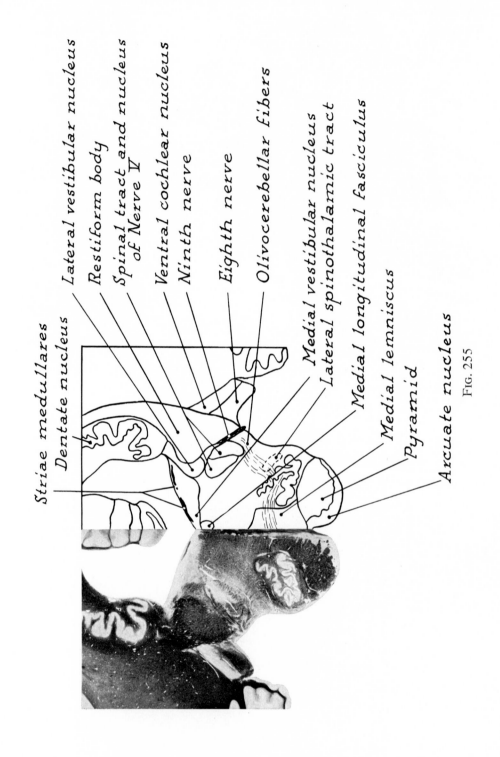

Striae medullares

Dentate nucleus

Lateral vestibular nucleus

Restiform body

Spinal tract and nucleus
of Nerve V

Ventral cochlear nucleus

Ninth nerve

Eighth nerve

Olivocerebellar fibers

Medial vestibular nucleus

Lateral spinothalamic tract

Medial longitudinal fasciculus

Medial lemniscus

Pyramid

Arcuate nucleus

Fig. 255

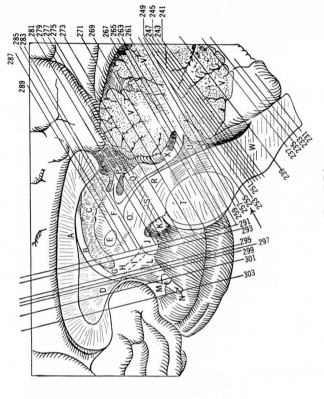

Fig. 255

Fig. 256

A, Corpus Callosum; *B*, Fornix; *C*, Choroid Plexus of Lateral Ventricle; *D*, Septum Pellucidum; *E*, Massa Intermedia; *F*, Thalamus; *G*, Interventricular Foramen; *H*, Anterior Commissure; *I*, Fornix buried in Thalamus and Hypothalamus; *J*, Mammillary Body; *K*, Basis Pedunculi; *L*, Tuber Cinereum; *M*, Optic Chiasm; *N*, Optic Nerve; *O*, Subthalamus; *P*, Pineal Body; *Q*, Superior Quadrigeminal Body; *R*, Cerebral Aqueduct; *S*, Tegmentum; *T*, Pons; *U*, Fourth Ventricle; *V*, Cerebellum; *W*, Medulla; *X*, Anterior Medullary Velum.

Section through the rostral part of the medulla at the level of the eighth nerve. The fourth ventricle is bounded ventrally by the dorsal surface of the medulla and dorsally by the ventral surface of the cerebellum. The dentate nuclei of the cerebellum are seen on either side of the fourth ventricle; a concentration of nerve fibers in the medially-directed hilus of either nucleus represents the beginning of the brachium conjunctivum (superior cerebellar peduncle) which will be seen, eventually, to terminate in the contralateral red nucleus and thalamus. The restiform body, on either side, can be traced dorsally into the cerebellum where it lies upon the lateral aspect of the dentate nucleus. The auditory and vestibular fibers of the eighth nerve are in the angle formed by the cerebellum and restiform body, on either side; some of the filaments of the ninth (glossopharyngeal) nerve emerge from the medulla ventral to the eight nerve fibers. The lateral and medial vestibular nuclei lie between the floor of the fourth ventricle and the spinal nucleus and tract of the trigeminal nerve. The floor of the fourth ventricle is crossed by striae medullares; these may consist of axons of cells in the contralateral arcuate nucleus. The pyramids, medial lemnisci, inferior olivary nuclei, and lateral spino-thalamic tracts occupy their usual positions as seen in more caudal levels. It should be noted, even though not indicated, that the white matter immediately dorsal to the inferior olivary nucleus contains the ventral trigeminal lemniscus as well as the lateral spinothalamic tract.

(353)

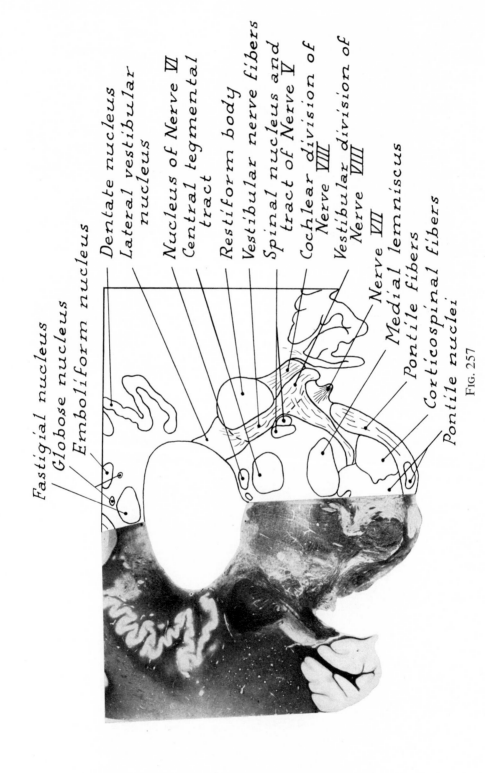

Fastigial nucleus
Globose nucleus
Emboliform nucleus
Dentate nucleus
Lateral vestibular nucleus
Nucleus of Nerve VI
Central tegmental tract
Restiform body
Vestibular nerve fibers
Spinal nucleus and tract of Nerve V
Cochlear division of Nerve VIII
Vestibular division of Nerve VIII
Nerve VII
Medial lemniscus
Pontile fibers
Corticospinal fibers
Pontile nuclei

FIG. 257

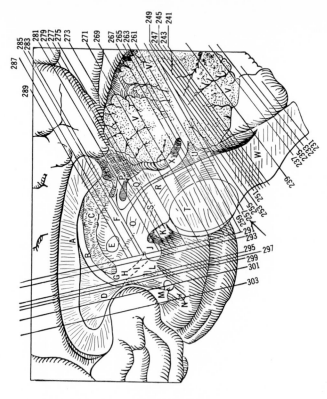

FIG. 257

Section through the brain stem at the level of the eighth nerve. The vestibular and cochlear divisions of the eighth nerve are in the angle formed by the cerebellum and brain stem. Fibers of the facial nerve emerge from the brain just ventral and medial to the eighth nerve. The eighth nerve is closely related to the restiform body. The lateral vestibular nucleus lies medial to the restiform body and vestibular nerve fibers can be seen ending in it. The roof of the fourth ventricle is formed by the vermis of the cerebellum which is seen to contain the fastigial nuclei. The globose and emboliform nuclei and a portion of the dentate nucleus are lateral to the fastigial nucleus on either side. At this level the reticular formation of the medulla becomes continuous with the caudal part of the tegmentum of the pons. The medial lemnisci are beginning to be compressed from the ventral side by the superimposition of the basis pontis. The pyramids are covered by the most ventral and caudal pontile fibers; the arcuate nuclei appear on either side of the midline, in relation to these fibers. The spinal tract and nucleus of the trigeminal nerve lie ventromedial to the restiform body and are separated from it by the vestibular nerve fibers coursing toward the lateral vestibular nucleus.

FIG. 258

A, Corpus Callosum; *B*, Fornix; *C*, Choroid Plexus of Lateral Ventricle; *D*, Septum Pellucidum; *E*, Massa Intermedia; *F*, Thalamus; *G*, Interventricular Foramen; *H*, Anterior Commissure; *I*, Fornix buried in Thalamus and Hypothalamus; *J*, Mammillary Body; *K*, Basis Pedunculi; *L*, Tuber Cinereum; *M*, Optic Chiasm; *N*, Optic Nerve; *O*, Subthalamus; *P*, Pineal Body; *Q*, Superior Quadrigeminal Body; *R*, Cerebral Aqueduct; *S*, Tegmentum; *T*, Pons; *U*, Fourth Ventricle; *V*, Cerebellum; *W*, Medulla; *X*, Anterior Medullary Velum.

(355)

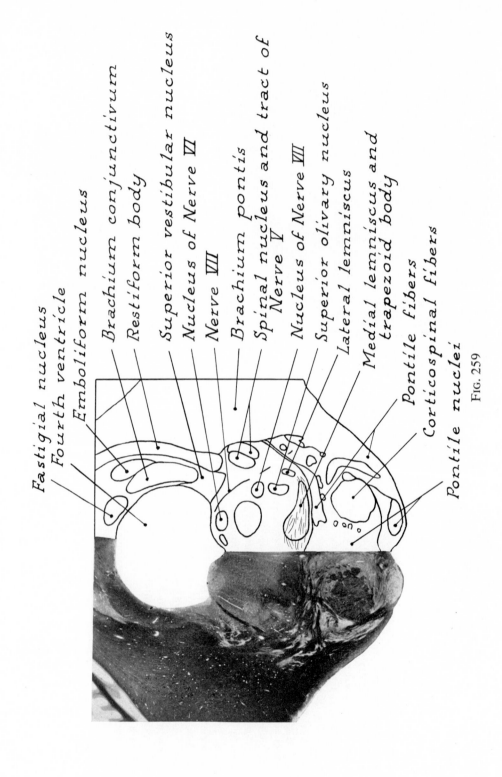

Fastigial nucleus
Fourth ventricle
Emboliform nucleus
Brachium conjunctivum
Restiform body
Superior vestibular nucleus
Nucleus of Nerve VI
Nerve VII
Brachium pontis
Spinal nucleus and tract of Nerve V
Nucleus of Nerve VII
Superior olivary nucleus
Lateral lemniscus
Medial lemniscus and trapezoid body
Pontile fibers
Corticospinal fibers
Pontile nuclei

FIG. 259

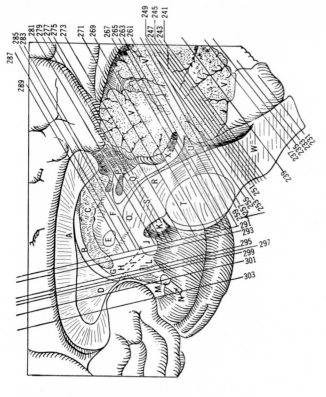

Fig. 259

Fig. 260

Section through the brain stem just rostral to the level of transition from medulla to pons. The transition is indicated by the superimposition upon the pyramids of the most caudal pontile fibers. The continuity of the arcuate nuclei of the medulla with the pontile nuclei is quite apparent at this level. The fourth ventricle is bounded laterally by the brachia conjunctiva and superiorly by the vermis of the cerebellum. The fastigial or roof nuclei of the cerebellum can be seen within that portion of the vermis which bounds the fourth ventricle. The emboliform nucleus is lateral to the fastigial nucleus and is intimately related to the brachium conjunctivum, to which it contributes fibers. The restiform body is seen entering the cerebellum between the brachium conjunctivum and brachium pontis. The nuclei of the abducens nerves are lateral to the medial longitudinal fasciculi and just beneath the floor of the fourth ventricle. The caudalmost fibers of the facial nerve can be followed from the region of the abducens nucleus toward their point of emergence from the brain stem at the junction of pons and medulla. The spinal nucleus and tract of the trigeminal nerve are lateral to the facial nerve fibers and the superior vestibular nucleus is dorsolateral to the trigeminal spinal nucleus. The medial lemniscus, on either side of the median raphe and in the ventral area of the tegmentum, is compressed from the ventral side by the basis pontis so as to result in a shift in its long axis, as seen in cross-section, from vertical to transverse. The transversely-coursing pontile fibers collect laterally to enter and contribute to the brachium pontis.

A, Corpus Callosum; B, Fornix; C, Choroid Plexus of Lateral Ventricle; D, Septum Pellucidum; E, Massa Intermedia; F, Thalamus; G, Interventricular Foramen; H, Anterior Commissure; I, Fornix buried in Thalamus and Hypothalamus; J, Mammillary Body; K, Basis Pedunculi; L, Tuber Cinereum; M, Optic Chiasm; N, Optic Nerve; O, Subthalamus; P, Pineal Body; Q, Superior Quadrigeminal Body; R, Cerebral Aqueduct; S, Tegmentum; T, Pons; U, Fourth Ventricle; V, Cerebellum; W, Medulla; X, Anterior Medullary Velum.

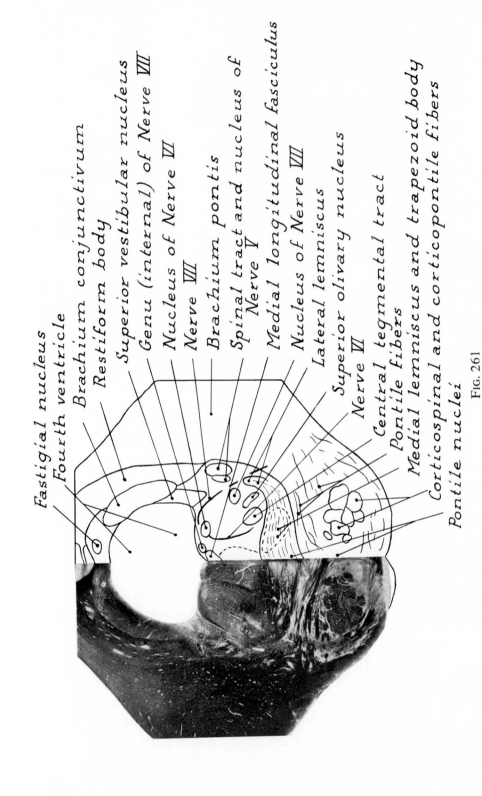

Fastigial nucleus
Fourth ventricle
Brachium conjunctivum
Restiform body
Superior vestibular nucleus
Genu (internal) of Nerve VII
Nucleus of Nerve VI
Nerve VII
Brachium pontis
Spinal tract and nucleus of Nerve V
Medial longitudinal fasciculus
Nucleus of Nerve VII
Lateral lemniscus
Superior olivary nucleus
Nerve VI
Central tegmental tract
Pontile fibers
Medial lemniscus and trapezoid body
Corticospinal and corticopontile fibers
Pontile nuclei

Fig. 261

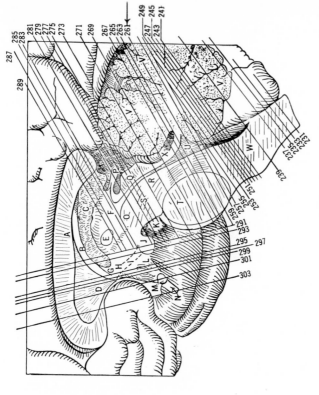

FIG. 261

FIG. 262

Section through the caudal third of the pons showing the nuclei of the abducens nerves and their emerging fibers. The abducens nuclei are located beneath the floor of the fourth ventricle, just lateral to the medial longitudinal fasciculi. The emerging fibers of the facial nerves can be traced from the dorsal aspects of the abducens nuclei ventro-laterally past their own nuclei of origin in the lateral area of the tegmentum and, finally, into the basis pontis which they penetrate to reach the surface. The medial lemnisci, in the ventral areas of the tegmentum, are penetrated by transversely-coursing secondary auditory fibers which comprise the trapezoid body and which enter and form the lateral lemnisci in the ventro-lateral angles of the tegmentum. The superior olivary nucleus, on either side, lies in the angle formed between the medial and lateral lemnisci. The spinal tract and nucleus of the trigeminal nerve are lateral to the facial nerve fibers. The superior vestibular nucleus is in the dorsolateral angle of the tegmentum; the brachium conjunctivum, in the lateral wall of the fourth ventricle, is immediately dorsal to it. The restiform body can be followed dorsally toward the vermis of the cerebellum, lateral to the brachium conjunctivum and medial to the brachium pontis. The basis pontis contains bundles of corticospinal fibers surrounded by pontile fibers; the latter are seen to be contributing to the formation of the brachium pontis. Pontile nuclei are adjacent to the median raphe of the basis, on either side.

A, Corpus Callosum; *B*, Fornix; *C*, Choroid Plexus of Lateral Ventricle; *D*, Septum Pellucidum; *E*, Massa Intermedia; *F*, Thalamus; *G*, Interventricular Foramen; *H*, Anterior Commissure; *I*, Fornix buried in Thalamus and Hypothalamus; *J*, Mammillary Body; *K*, Basis Pedunculi; *L*, Tuber Cinereum; *M*, Optic Chiasm; *N*, Optic Nerve; *O*, Subthalamus; *P*, Pineal Body; *Q*, Superior Quadrigeminal Body; *R*, Cerebral Aqueduct; *S*, Tegmentum; *T*, Pons; *U*, Fourth Ventricle; *V*, Cerebellum; *W*, Medulla; *X*, Anterior Medullary Velum.

(359)

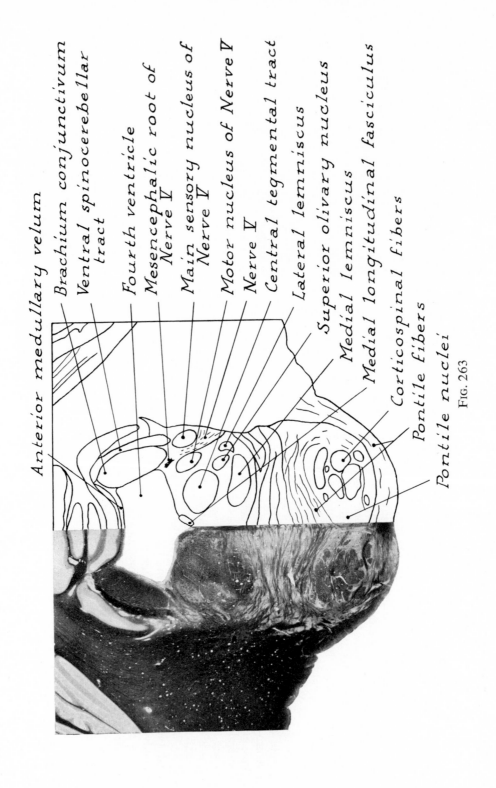

Anterior medullary velum

Brachium conjunctivum

Ventral spinocerebellar tract

Fourth ventricle

Mesencephalic root of Nerve V

Main sensory nucleus of Nerve V

Motor nucleus of Nerve V

Nerve V

Central tegmental tract

Lateral lemniscus

Superior olivary nucleus

Medial lemniscus

Medial longitudinal fasciculus

Corticospinal fibers

Pontile fibers

Pontile nuclei

FIG. 263

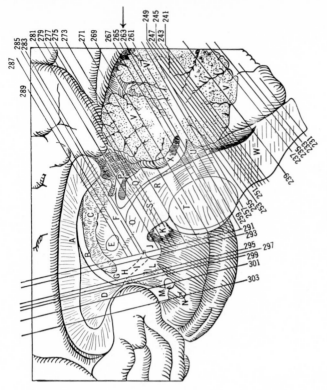

FIG. 263

Section through the pons which shows the motor and main sensory nuclei of the trigeminal nerve. The two nuclei are separated by some of the motor and sensory fibers of the nerve. The mesencephalic root of the trigeminal nerve is seen at the ventrolateral angle of the fourth ventricle where it is between the brachium conjunctivum and the motor nucleus. Other structures, all familiar, within the tegmentum at this level are the medial lemnisci, lateral lemnisci, superior olivary nuclei, medial longitudinal fasciculi, and central tegmental tracts. The fourth ventricle is bounded laterally by the brachia conjunctiva and dorsally by the anterior medullary velum. Corticospinal and corticobulbar fibers in the basis pontis are surrounded by transversely-coursing pontile fibers which are seen to be entering and contributing to the brachia pontis laterally.

FIG. 264

A, Corpus Callosum; *B*, Fornix; *C*, Choroid Plexus of Lateral Ventricle; *D*, Septum Pellucidum; *E*, Massa Intermedia; *F*, Thalamus; *G*, Interventricular Foramen; *H*, Anterior Commissure; *I*, Fornix buried in Thalamus and Hypothalamus; *J*, Mammillary Body; *K*, Basis Pedunculi; *L*, Tuber Cinereum; *M*, Optic Chiasm; *N*, Optic Nerve; *O*, Subthalamus; *P*, Pineal Body; *Q*, Superior Quadrigeminal Body; *R*, Cerebral Aqueduct; *S*, Tegmentum; *T*, Pons; *U*, Fourth Ventricle; *V*, Cerebellum; *W*, Medulla; *X*, Anterior Medullary Velum.

(361)

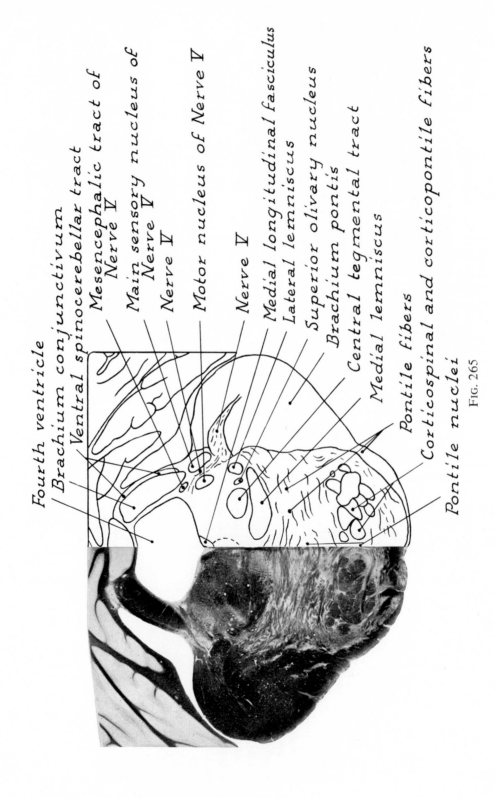

Fourth ventricle

Brachium conjunctivum

Ventral spinocerebellar tract

Mesencephalic tract of Nerve V

Main sensory nucleus of Nerve V

Motor nucleus of Nerve V

Nerve V

Medial longitudinal fasciculus

Lateral lemniscus

Superior olivary nucleus

Brachium pontis

Central tegmental tract

Medial lemniscus

Pontile fibers

Corticospinal and corticopontile fibers

Pontile nuclei

FIG. 265

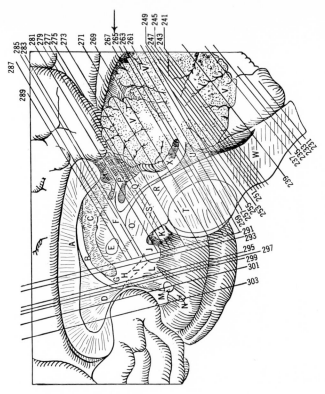

FIG. 265

FIG. 266

Section through the pons which shows the main sensory and motor nuclei of the trigeminal nerve in the lateral area of the tegmentum, on either side. Some of the trigeminal nerve fibers are seen entering and leaving these nuclei. The fourth ventricle is bounded laterally by the brachia conjunctiva and dorsally by the anterior medullary velum which stretches between the brachia. The lateral and dorsal relationship of the cerebellum to the brain stem is indicated. The main sensory nucleus of the trigeminal is immediately ventrolateral to the brachium conjunctivum where it is separated from the more medially-placed motor nucleus by trigeminal nerve fibers. The mesencephalic root of the trigeminal nerve lies in the angle formed by the two trigeminal nuclei and the brachium conjunctivum. The lateral lemniscus is in the ventrolateral angle of the tegmentum and the superior olivary nucleus lies between it and the central tegmental tract. The medial lemniscus is in the ventral area of the tegmentum with the central tegmental tract immediately dorsal to it. The brachium pontis, on either side, is seen to be receiving pontile fibers from the contralateral pontile nuclei. Corticospinal and some corticobulbar fibers are seen in bundles in the center of each half of the basis pontis where they are surrounded by transversely-coursing pontile fibers.

A, Corpus Callosum; B, Fornix; C, Choroid Plexus of Lateral Ventricle; D, Septum Pellucidum; E, Massa Intermedia; F, Thalamus; G, Interventricular Foramen; H, Anterior Commissure; I, Fornix buried in Thalamus and Hypothalamus; J, Mammillary Body; K, Basis Pedunculi; L, Tuber Cinereum; M, Optic Chiasm; N, Optic Nerve; O, Subthalamus; P, Pineal Body; Q, Superior Quadrigeminal Body; R, Cerebral Aqueduct; S, Tegmentum; T, Pons; U, Fourth Ventricle; V, Cerebellum; W, Medulla; X, Anterior Medullary Velum.

(363)

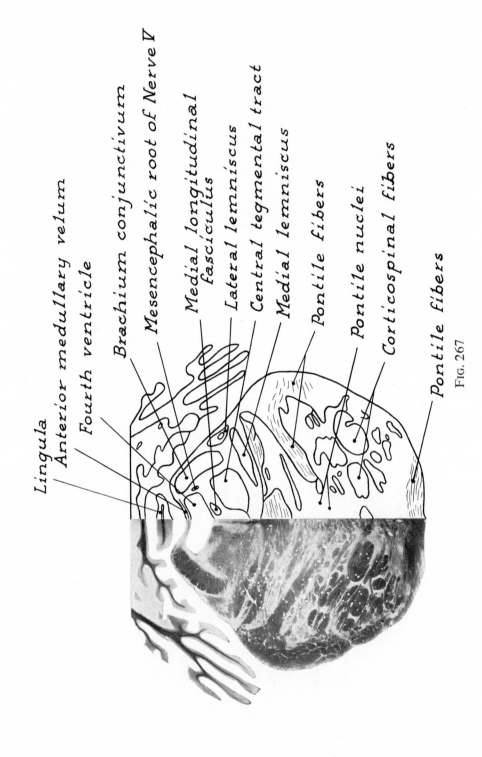

Lingula

Anterior medullary velum

Fourth ventricle

Brachium conjunctivum

Mesencephalic root of Nerve V

Medial longitudinal fasciculus

Lateral lemniscus

Central tegmental tract

Medial lemniscus

Pontile fibers

Pontile nuclei

Corticospinal fibers

Pontile fibers

Fig. 267

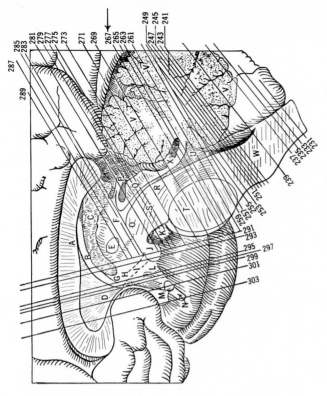

FIG. 267

FIG. 268

A, Corpus Callosum; *B*, Fornix; *C*, Choroid Plexus of Lateral Ventricle; *D*, Septum Pellucidum; *E*, Massa Intermedia; *F*, Thalamus; *G*, Interventricular Foramen; *H*, Anterior Commissure; *I*, Fornix buried in Thalamus and Hypothalamus; *J*, Mammillary Body; *K*, Basis Pedunculi; *L*, Tuber Cinereum; *M*, Optic Chiasm; *N*, Optic Nerve; *O*, Subthalamus; *P*, Pineal Body; *Q*, Superior Quadrigeminal Body; *R*, Cerebral Aqueduct; *S*, Tegmentum; *T*, Pons; *U*, Fourth Ventricle; *V*, Cerebellum; *W*, Anterior Medullary Velum.

Section through the rostral part of the pons. The lingula of the cerebellum, flanked by the adjacent areas of the cerebellar hemispheres, rests upon the anterior medullary velum which is seen stretching between the dorsal borders of the brachia conjunctiva to form the roof of the fourth ventricle. The mesencephalic root of the trigeminal nerve lies between the fourth ventricle and the brachium conjunctivum, on either side. The medial lemniscus is in the ventrolateral area of the tegmentum and the lateral lemniscus, with its nucleus, is in the angle between the outer end of the medial lemniscus and the lower border of the brachium conjunctivum. The medial longitudinal fasciculi, on either side of the median raphe, are immediately ventral to the floor of the fourth ventricle. A large part of the tegmentum is occupied by the central tegmental tract. The basis pontis contains pontile nuclei, corticospinal fibers, and pontile fibers. The last-named fibers are seen to collect laterally to form the anterior parts of the brachia pontis.

(365)

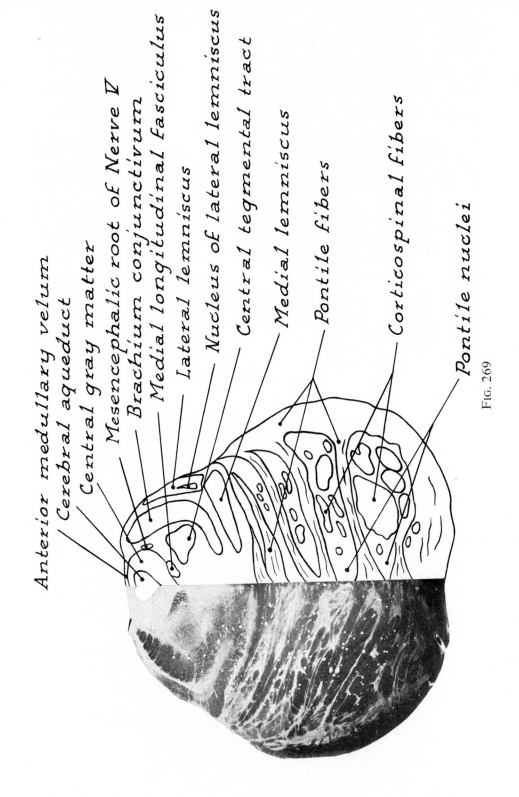

Anterior medullary velum
Cerebral aqueduct
Central gray matter
Mesencephalic root of Nerve V
Brachium conjunctivum
Medial longitudinal fasciculus
Lateral lemniscus
Nucleus of lateral lemniscus
Central tegmental tract
Medial lemniscus
Pontile fibers
Corticospinal fibers
Pontile nuclei

FIG. 269

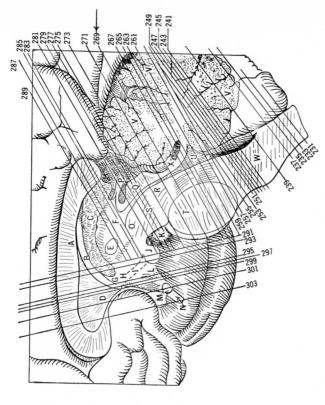

FIG. 269

Section through the pons showing the rostral limit of the fourth ventricle, surrounded by the central gray matter and covered dorsally by the anterior medullary velum. The mesencephalic root of the trigeminal nerve lies lateral to the central gray matter on either side and the medial longitudinal fasciculus is ventral to it. The central tegmental tract occupies a considerable area of the tegmentum and the brachium conjunctivum forms almost a right angle lateral to this tract. The medial extension of the lower end of the brachium conjunctivum is an indication of the beginning of the decussation of its fibers to the contralateral red nucleus and thalamus. The ventral and lateral areas of the tegmentum are occupied by the medial and lateral lemnisci. An area of gray matter within the lateral lemniscus is a portion of its nucleus; the nucleus of the lateral lemniscus is responsible for short relays in the auditory pathway. The basis pontis consists of pontile fibers, corticospinal fibers, some corticobulbar fibers, and pontile nuclei.

FIG. 270

A, Corpus Callosum; B, Fornix; C, Choroid Plexus of Lateral Ventricle; D, Septum Pellucidum; E, Massa Intermedia; F, Thalamus; G, Interventricular Foramen; H, Anterior Commissure; I, Fornix buried in Thalamus and Hypothalamus; J, Mammillary Body; K, Basis Pedunculi; L, Tuber Cinereum; M, Optic Chiasm; N, Optic Nerve; O, Subthalamus; P, Pineal Body; Q, Superior Quadrigeminal Body; R, Cerebral Aqueduct; S, Tegmentum; T, Pons; U, Fourth Ventricle; V, Cerebellum; W, Medulla; X, Anterior Medullary Velum.

(367)

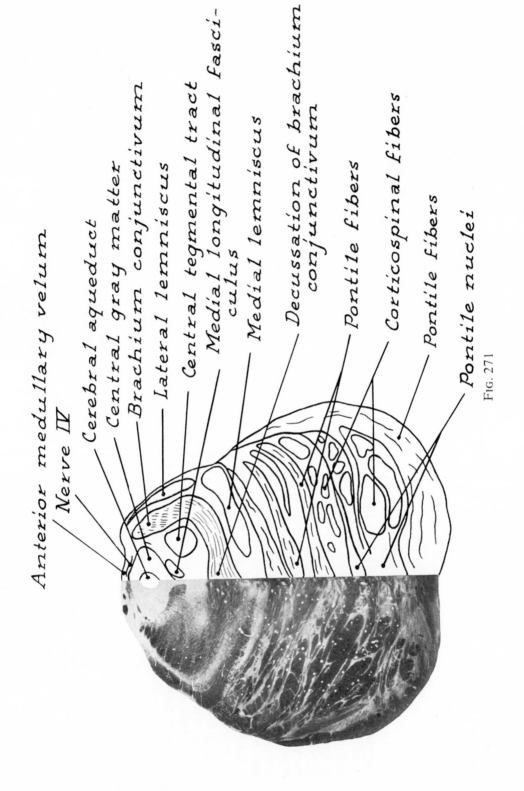

Anterior medullary velum

Nerve IV

Cerebral aqueduct

Central gray matter

Brachium conjunctivum

Lateral lemniscus

Central tegmental tract

Medial longitudinal fasciculus

Medial lemniscus

Decussation of brachium conjunctivum

Pontile fibers

Corticospinal fibers

Pontile fibers

Pontile nuclei

FIG. 271

(368)

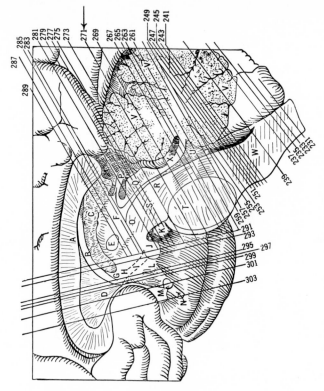

FIG. 271

Section through the rostral limit of the pons. The fourth ventricle, at this level, has narrowed down to the caliber of the cerebral aqueduct. The anterior medullary velum is seen dorsal to the central gray matter; at this level it contains the decussating fibers of the fourth nerves which, from this decussation, course laterally and ventrally around the lateral aspects of the brain stem to enter the cavernous sinuses. The brachia conjunctiva lie lateral to the central gray matter and fibers from their ventral areas are seen crossing the midline; these fibers constitute the caudal portion of the decussation of the brachia conjunctiva. The medial lemniscus lies in the ventrolateral area of the tegmentum on either side; dorsal to its lateral limit is the lateral lemniscus. Associated with the latter structure are the lateral spinothalamic fibers. The basis pontis contains transversely-coursing pontile fibers, longitudinally-coursing corticospinal fibers, and the pontile nuclei.

FIG. 272

A, Corpus Callosum; B, Fornix; C, Choroid Plexus of Lateral Ventricle; D, Septum Pellucidum; E, Massa Intermedia; F, Thalamus; G, Interventricular Foramen; H, Anterior Commissure; I, Fornix buried in Thalamus and Hypothalamus; J, Mammillary Body; K, Basis Pedunculi; L, Tuber Cinereum; M, Optic Chiasm; N, Optic Nerve; O, Subthalamus; P, Pineal Body; Q, Superior Quadrigeminal Body; R, Cerebral Aqueduct; S, Tegmentum; T, Pons; U, Fourth Ventricle; V, Cerebellum; W, Medulla; X, Anterior Medullary Velum.

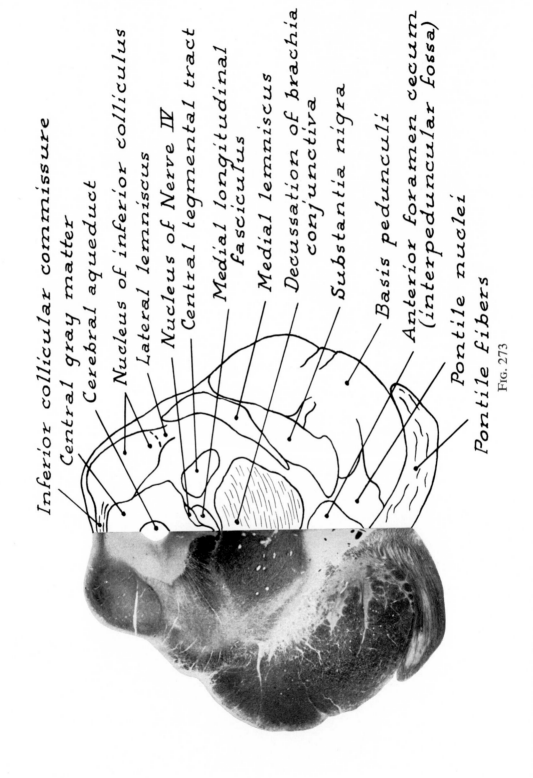

Inferior collicular commissure

Central gray matter

Cerebral aqueduct

Nucleus of inferior colliculus

Lateral lemniscus

Nucleus of Nerve IV

Central tegmental tract

Medial longitudinal fasciculus

Medial lemniscus

Decussation of brachia conjunctiva

Substantia nigra

Basis pedunculi

Anterior foramen cecum (interpeduncular fossa)

Pontile nuclei

Pontile fibers

Fig. 273

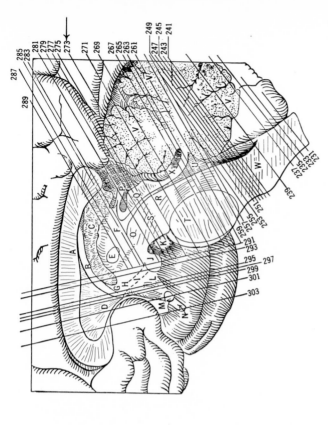

Fig. 273

Fig. 274

A, Corpus Callosum; B, Fornix; C, Choroid Plexus of Lateral Ventricle; D, Septum Pellucidum; E, Massa Intermedia; F, Thalamus; G, Interventricular Foramen; H, Anterior Commissure; I, Fornix buried in Thalamus and Hypothalamus; J, Mammillary Body; K, Basis Pedunculi; L, Tuber Cinereum; M, Optic Chiasm; N, Optic Nerve; O, Subthalamus; P, Pineal Body; Q, Superior Quadrigeminal Body; R, Cerebral Aqueduct; S, Tegmentum; T, Pons; U, Fourth Ventricle; V, Cerebellum; W, Medulla; X, Anterior Medullary Velum.

Section of the mesencephalon at the level of the inferior colliculi. The inferior collicular nuclei are seen as prominent almond-shaped structures on either side of the central gray matter. They are connected across the midline by the commissure of the inferior colliculi. The lateral lemniscus is seen terminating in the inferior collicular nucleus; the medial lemniscus lies ventral and, at its upper limit, lateral to the lateral lemniscus. The fibers of the lateral spinothalamic tract, at this level, are mingled with the terminal fibers of the lateral lemniscus. The nuclei of the fourth nerves lie in the ventral area of the central gray matter. Immediately ventral to the fourth nerve nuclei are the medial longitudinal fasciculi and ventral to them is the decussation of the brachia conjunctiva. The tegmental area is separated from the basis pedunculi, on either side, by the substantia nigra. The basis pedunculi, in its lateral one-fifth, is composed of temporopontile and parieto-pontile fibers; its medial one-fifth contains frontopontile fibers and its middle three-fifths is composed of corticospinal fibers. A lateral bundle of corticobulbar fibers is associated with the dorsal aspect of the middle three-fifths and a medial bundle lies in relationship to the medial one-fifth (*see* figure 119). The plane of the section is such that the anterior limit of the basis pontis is cut through; pontile nuclei and pontile fibers therefore are seen in relation to the medial and the ventral areas of the bases pedunculi. The plane of the section also results in the interpeduncular fossa's appearing as a foramen (anterior foramen cecum).

(371)

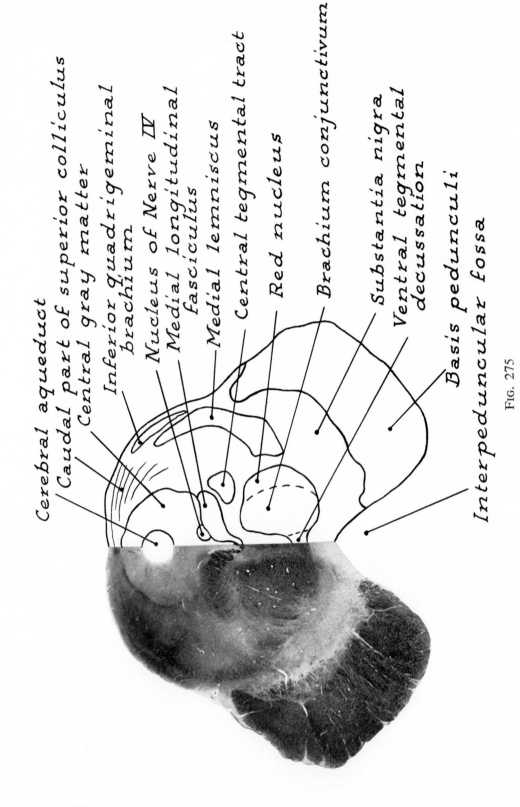

Cerebral aqueduct

Caudal part of superior colliculus

Central gray matter

Inferior quadrigeminal brachium

Nucleus of Nerve IV

Medial longitudinal fasciculus

Medial lemniscus

Central tegmental tract

Red nucleus

Brachium conjunctivum

Substantia nigra

Ventral tegmental decussation

Basis pedunculi

Interpeduncular fossa

Fig. 275

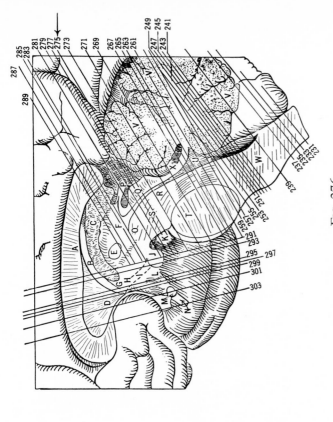

FIG. 275

Section through the mesencephalon at the junction of its superior and inferior collicular portions. The nucleus of the fourth (trochlear) nerve is in the central gray matter on either side of the midline and intimately related to the medial longitudinal fasciculus. The medial lemniscus occupies an arcuate area lateral and dorsal to the red nucleus; it is separated from the surface of the tegmentum by the inferior quadrigeminal brachium. The brachium conjunctivum, on either side, is seen entering the caudal end of the red nucleus. The lateral spinothalamic tract, although not indicated, lies in the angle between the dorsal end of the medial lemniscus and the inferior quadrigeminal brachium.

FIG. 276

A, Corpus Callosum; *B*, Fornix; *C*, Choroid Plexus of Lateral Ventricle; *D*, Septum Pellucidum; *E*, Massa Intermedia; *F*, Thalamus; *G*, Interventricular Foramen; *H*, Anterior Commissure; *I*, Fornix buried in Thalamus and Hypothalamus; *J*, Mammillary Body; *K*, Basis Pedunculi; *L*, Tuber Cinereum; *M*, Optic Chiasm; *N*, Optic Nerve; *O*, Subthalamus; *P*, Pineal Body; *Q*, Superior Quadrigeminal Body; *R*, Cerebral Aqueduct; *S*, Tegmentum; *T*, Pons; *U*, Fourth Ventricle; *V*, Cerebellum; *W*, Medulla; *X*, Anterior Medullary Velum.

(373)

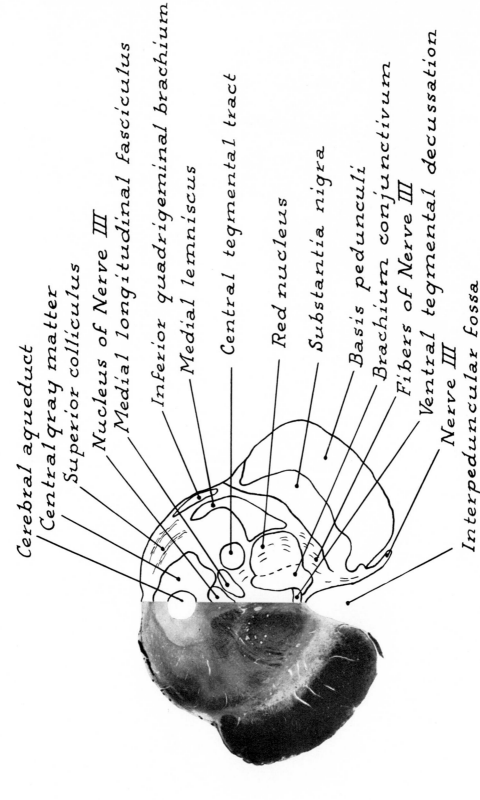

Cerebral aqueduct
Centralgray matter
Superior colliculus
Nucleus of Nerve III
Medial longitudinal fasciculus
Inferior quadrigeminal brachium
Medial lemniscus
Central tegmental tract
Red nucleus
Substantia nigra
Basis pedunculi
Brachium conjunctivum
Fibers of Nerve III
Ventral tegmental decussation
Nerve III
Interpeduncular fossa

FIG. 277

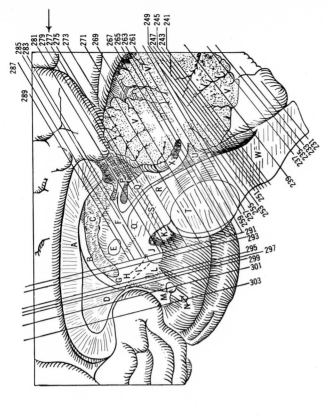

FIG. 277

Section through the mesencephalon near the junction of its superior and inferior collicular portions. On the right the stratification of the superior colliculus is somewhat in evidence. The substantia nigra separates the basis pedunculi from the tegmentum on either side; fibers of the third nerve are seen originating from their nuclei in the central gray matter, coursing through the tegmentum, and entering the interpeduncular fossa. The caudal areas of the red nuclei are apparent and fibers of the brachia conjunctiva are seen terminating in relation to them. Fibers of the rubrospinal tract, which arises in the red nucleus, are seen crossing the midline from either side to form the ventral tegmental decussation. The medial lemniscus lies lateral to the red nucleus and the inferior quadrigeminal brachium is lateral to the dorsal limit of the lemniscus.

FIG. 278

A, Corpus Callosum; B, Fornix; C, Choroid Plexus of Lateral Ventricle; D, Septum Pellucidum; E, Massa Intermedia; F, Thalamus; G, Interventricular Foramen; H, Anterior Commissure; I, Fornix buried in Thalamus and Hypothalamus; J, Mammillary Body; K, Basis Pedunculi; L, Tuber Cinereum; M, Optic Chiasm; N, Optic Nerve; O, Subthalamus; P, Pineal Body; Q, Superior Quadrigeminal Body; R, Cerebral Aqueduct; S, Tegmentum; T, Pons; U, Fourth Ventricle; V, Cerebellum; W, Medulla; X, Anterior Medullary Velum.

(375)

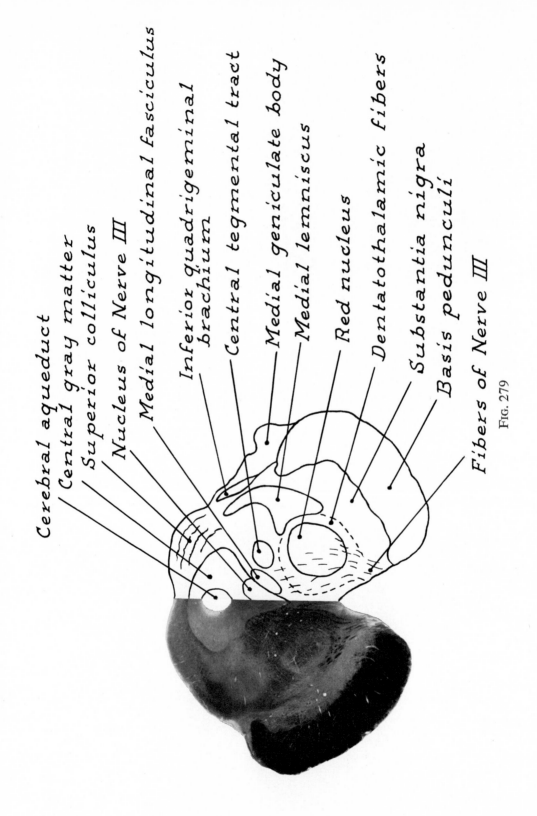

Cerebral aqueduct

Central gray matter

Superior colliculus

Nucleus of Nerve III

Medial longitudinal fasciculus

Inferior quadrigeminal brachium

Central tegmental tract

Medial geniculate body

Medial lemniscus

Red nucleus

Dentatothalamic fibers

Substantia nigra

Basis pedunculi

Fibers of Nerve III

FIG. 279

(376)

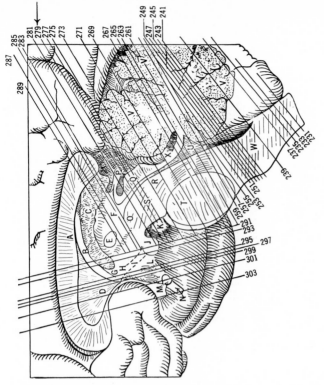

FIG. 279

Section through the mesencephalon which cuts through the more caudal areas of the superior colliculi. The right side which, because of slight asymmetry, is at a more rostral level than the left, shows the caudal end of the medial geniculate body. The tegmentum and basis pedunculi are widely separated from one another by the substantia nigra on either side. The red nuclei occupy the central areas of the tegmentum on both sides and the medial lemnisci are lateral to them. The inferior quadrigeminal brachia lie lateral to the medial lemnisci and, on the right, the brachium is in contact with the medial geniculate body within which it terminates. The oculomotor nuclei are located in the ventral area of the central gray matter on either side and the nerve fibers arising from them are seen coursing through the tegmentum to emerge on either side of the interpeduncular fossa.

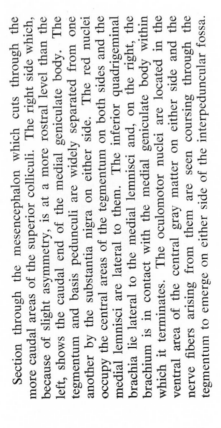

FIG. 280

A, Corpus Callosum; B, Fornix; C, Choroid Plexus of Lateral Ventricle; D, Septum Pellucidum; E, Massa Intermedia; F, Thalamus; G, Interventricular Foramen; H, Anterior Commissure; I, Fornix buried in Thalamus and Hypothalamus; J, Mammillary Body; K, Basis Pedunculi; L, Tuber Cinereum; M, Optic Chiasm; N, Optic Nerve; O, Subthalamus; P, Pineal Body; Q, Superior Quadrigeminal Body; R, Cerebral Aqueduct; S, Tegmentum; T, Pons; U, Fourth Ventricle; V, Cerebellum; W, Medulla; X, Anterior Medullary Velum.

(377)

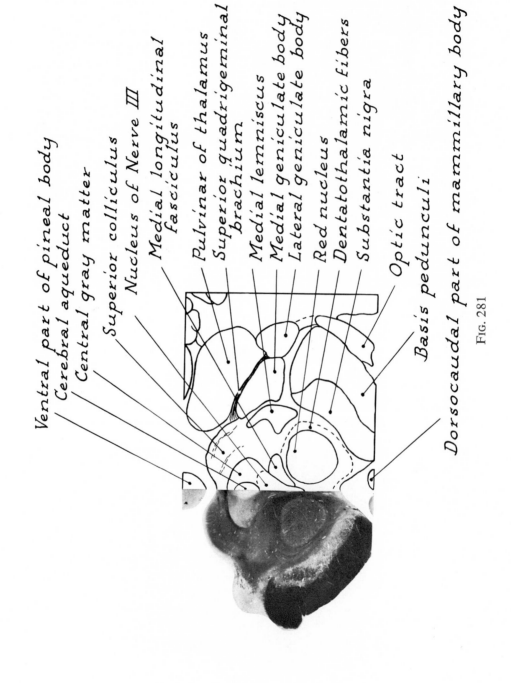

Ventral part of pineal body
Cerebral aqueduct
Central gray matter
Superior colliculus
Nucleus of Nerve III
Medial longitudinal fasciculus
Pulvinar of thalamus
Superior quadrigeminal brachium
Medial lemniscus
Medial geniculate body
Lateral geniculate body
Red nucleus
Dentatothalamic fibers
Substantia nigra
Optic tract
Basis pedunculi
Dorsocaudal part of mammillary body

Fig. 281

(378)

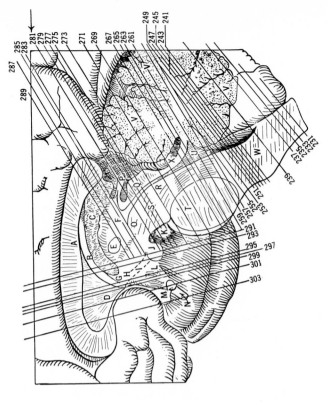

FIG. 281

Section through the superior collicular part of the mesencephalon. On the left the medial geniculate body is apparent; on the right, where the section is at a more rostral level, the pulvinar of the thalamus and the medial and lateral geniculate bodies are present. The optic tract on the right is seen entering its zone of termination in the lateral geniculate body. The superior quadrigeminal brachium on the right lies between the pulvinar of the thalamus and the medial geniculate body, as it courses from the lateral geniculate body toward the superior colliculus and pretectal region. The pineal body lies dorsal to and between the superior colliculi. Ventrally, in the rostral limit of the interpeduncular fossa, portions of the mammillary bodies are apparent. The red nucleus, on either side, occupies a large area of the tegmentum and the medial lemnisci are seen to have been forced into the lateral areas of the tegmenti by the red nuclei. The tegmental and basilar areas of the mesencephalon, on either side, are separated from one another by the substantia nigra. The stratification of the superior colliculi is evident but the various strata have not been specifically delimited and identified.

FIG. 282

A, Corpus Callosum; *B*, Fornix; *C*, Choroid Plexus of Lateral Ventricle; *D*, Septum Pellucidum; *E*, Massa Intermedia; *F*, Thalamus; *G*, Interventricular Foramen; *H*, Anterior Commissure; *I*, Fornix buried in Thalamus and Hypothalamus; *J*, Mammillary Body; *K*, Basis Pedunculi; *L*, Tuber Cinereum; *M*, Optic Chiasm; *N*, Optic Nerve; *O*, Subthalamus; *P*, Pineal Body; *Q*, Superior Quadrigeminal Body; *R*, Cerebral Aqueduct; *S*, Tegmentum; *T*, Pons; *U*, Fourth Ventricle; *V*, Cerebellum; *W*, Medulla; *X*, Anterior Medullary Velum.

(379)

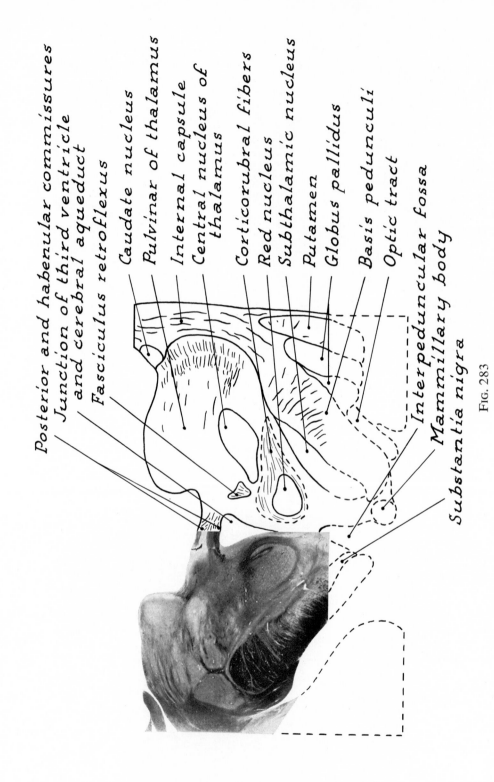

Posterior and habenular commissures
Junction of third ventricle and cerebral aqueduct
Fasciculus retroflexus
Caudate nucleus
Pulvinar of thalamus
Internal capsule
Central nucleus of thalamus
Corticorubral fibers
Red nucleus
Subthalamic nucleus
Putamen
Globus pallidus
Basis pedunculi
Optic tract
Interpeduncular fossa
Mammillary body
Substantia nigra

FIG. 283

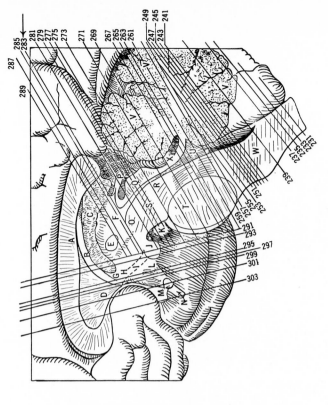

FIG. 283

Section through the brain stem at the level of transition between the diencephalon and the mesencephalon. The right half of the section is at a slightly more rostral level than the left half. On the right the pulvinar of the thalamus appears with the central nucleus of the thalamus lying in its ventral area. Corticorubral fibers are seen terminating in relation to the red nucleus on either side; the left red nucleus is larger than the right because it has been sectioned at a more caudal level. On the right the subthalamic nucleus lies between the basis pedunculi and the tegmental area. On the left the substantia nigra is still apparent. Also on the left the medial and lateral geniculate bodies appear immediately beneath the pulvinar of the thalamus (*see* preceding figure for identifications of these structures as they appear in the right half of the section). The ventral part of the figure has been schematically completed with broken lines to indicate that the mammillary body would have been cut through on the right side while the left half of the section is caudal to the level of the mammillary body. The posterior and habenular commissures are seen on the dorsal side of the junction of the third ventricle with the cerebral aqueduct. On the right the caudal areas of the putamen and globus pallidus of the lentiform nucleus appear for the first time.

FIG. 284

A, Corpus Callosum; *B*, Fornix; *C*, Choroid Plexus of Lateral Ventricle; *D*, Septum Pellucidum; *E*, Massa Intermedia; *F*, Thalamus; *G*, Interventricular Foramen; *H*, Anterior Commissure; *I*, Fornix buried in Thalamus and Hypothalamus; *J*, Mammillary Body; *K*, Basis Pedunculi; *L*, Tuber Cinereum; *M*, Optic Chiasm; *N*, Optic Nerve; *O*, Subthalamus; *P*, Pineal Body; *Q*, Superior Quadrigeminal Body; *R*, Cerebral Aqueduct; *S*, Tegmentum; *T*, Pons; *U*, Fourth Ventricle; *V*, Cerebellum; *W*, Medulla; *X*, Anterior Medullary Velum.

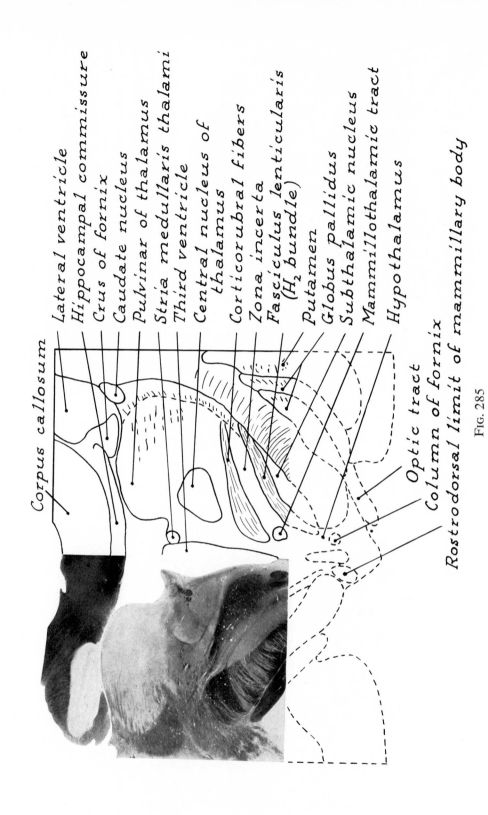

Corpus callosum

Lateral ventricle
Hippocampal commissure
Crus of fornix
Caudate nucleus
Pulvinar of thalamus
Stria medullaris thalami
Third ventricle
Central nucleus of thalamus
Corticorubral fibers
Zona incerta
Fasciculus lenticularis (H₂ bundle)
Putamen
Globus pallidus
Subthalamic nucleus
Mammillothalamic tract
Hypothalamus

Optic tract
Column of fornix
Rostrodorsal limit of mammillary body

FIG. 285

(382)

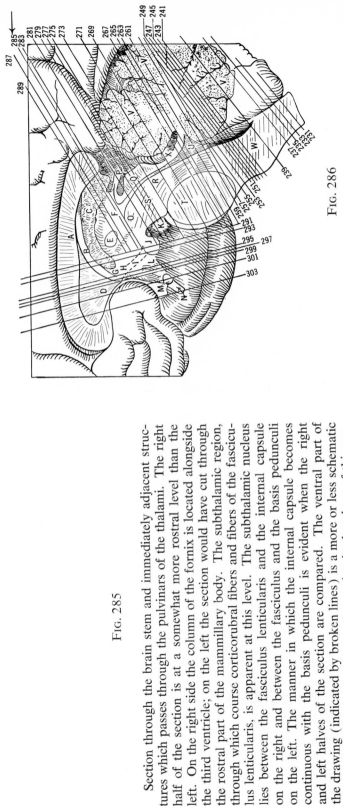

FIG. 285

Section through the brain stem and immediately adjacent structures which passes through the pulvinars of the thalami. The right half of the section is at a somewhat more rostral level than the left. On the right side the column of the fornix is located alongside the third ventricle; on the left the section would have cut through the rostral part of the mammillary body. The subthalamic region, through which course corticorubral fibers and fibers of the fasciculus lenticularis, is apparent at this level. The subthalamic nucleus lies between the fasciculus lenticularis and the internal capsule on the right and between the fasciculus and the basis pedunculi on the left. The manner in which the internal capsule becomes continuous with the basis pedunculi is evident when the right and left halves of the section are compared. The ventral part of the drawing (indicated by broken lines) is a more or less schematic completion of the ventral area of a section in the plane of this one.

FIG. 286

A, Corpus Callosum; B, Fornix; C, Choroid Plexus of Lateral Ventricle; D, Septum Pellucidum; E, Massa Intermedia; F, Thalamus; G, Interventricular Foramen; H, Anterior Commissure; I, Fornix buried in Thalamus and Hypothalamus; J, Mammillary Body; K, Basis Pedunculi; L, Tuber Cinereum; M, Optic Chiasm; N, Optic Nerve; O, Subthalamus; P, Pineal Body; Q, Superior Quadrigeminal Body; R, Cerebral Aqueduct; S, Tegmentum; T, Pons; U, Fourth Ventricle; V, Cerebellum; W, Medulla; X, Anterior Medullary Velum.

(383)

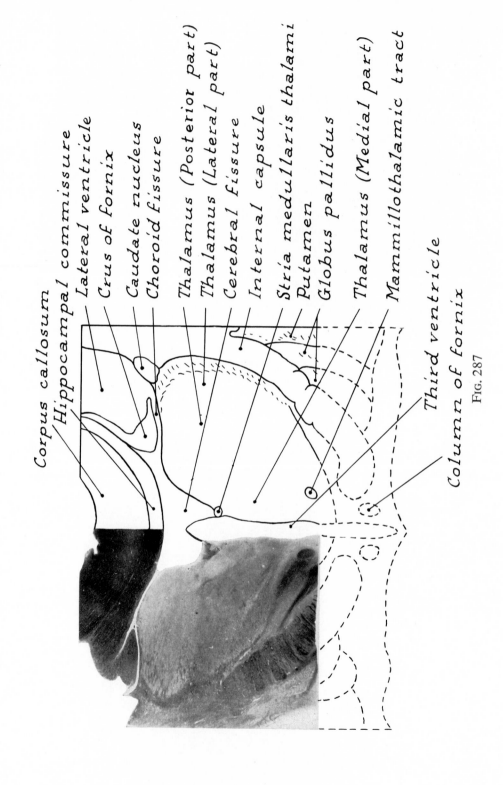

Corpus callosum
Hippocampal commissure
Lateral ventricle
Crus of Fornix
Caudate nucleus
Choroid Fissure
Thalamus (Posterior part)
Thalamus (Lateral part)
Cerebral Fissure
Internal capsule
Stria medullaris thalami
Putamen
Globus pallidus
Thalamus (Medial part)
Mammillothalamic tract
Third ventricle
Column of fornix

FIG. 287

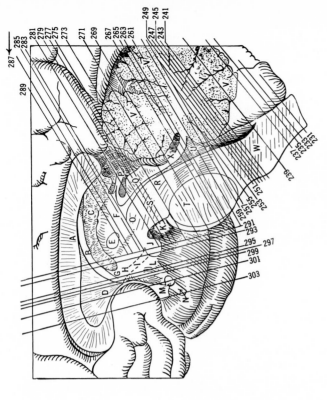

Fig. 287

Fig. 288

Section which is somewhat asymmetrical and therefore cuts through the left thalamus at a somewhat more caudal level than the right. The dorsal area of the left thalamus is characterized by the appearance of the rostral part of the expansion termed the 'pulvinar' of the thalamus. The ventral part of the figure has been completed diagrammatically in order to enable visualization of those structures of the brain stem which were included in the more rostral sections, cut in a different plane (*see* orientation diagram). The hippocampal commissure connecting the right and left hippocampi by way of the fimbria and crura of the fornix, is very well-developed at this level. The afferent and efferent tracts of the mammillary bodies are represented by the columns of the fornix and the mammillothalamic tracts on either side of the third ventricle.

A, Corpus Callosum; *B*, Fornix; *C*, Choroid Plexus of Lateral Ventricle; *D*, Septum Pellucidum; *E*, Massa Intermedia; *F*, Thalamus; *G*, Interventricular Foramen; *H*, Anterior Commissure; *I*, Fornix buried in Thalamus and Hypothalamus; *J*, Mammillary Body; *K*, Basis Pedunculi; *L*, Tuber Cinereum; *M*, Optic Chiasm; *N*, Optic Nerve; *O*, Subthalamus; *P*, Pineal Body; *Q*, Superior Quadrigeminal Body; *R*, Cerebral Aqueduct; *S*, Tegmentum; *T*, Pons; *U*, Fourth Ventricle; *V*, Cerebellum; *W*, Medulla; *X*, Anterior Medullary Velum.

(385)

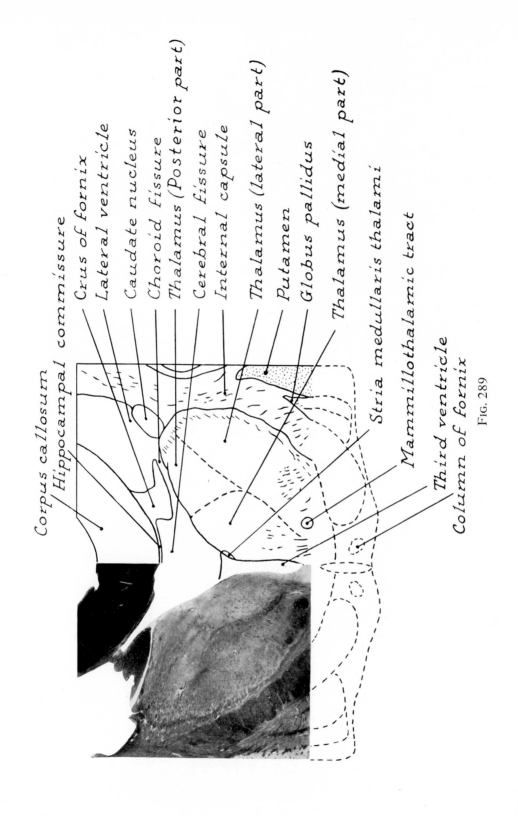

Corpus callosum
Hippocampal commissure
Crus of fornix
Lateral ventricle
Caudate nucleus
Choroid fissure
Thalamus (Posterior part)
Cerebral fissure
Internal capsule
Thalamus (lateral part)
Putamen
Globus pallidus
Thalamus (medial part)
Stria medullaris thalami
Mammillothalamic tract
Third ventricle
Column of fornix

Fig. 289

(386)

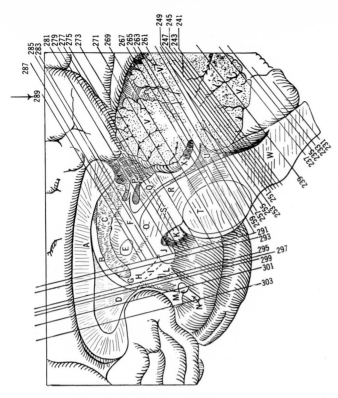

FIG. 289

FIG. 290

Section through the brain stem and adjacent structures in the plane indicated (*see* orientation diagram) which shows the medial, lateral and posterior nuclear groups of the thalami. The lamina, on the right, is indicated by dotted lines. The crura of the fornix are seen to be attached to the ventral surface of the corpus callosum and to be connected with one another by the hippocampal commissure. The ventral portion of the figure has been completed diagrammatically in order to show that portion which was included in more rostral sections cut in a different plane (*see* diagram). The third ventricle is divided into upper and lower portions in this section by the massa intermedia. The columns of the fornix are indicated in the ventral portion of the figure as they course caudally to end in the mammillary bodies. More dorsally the efferent fibers from the mammillary bodies to the anterior parts of the thalami—the mammillothalamic fasciculi—are seen dorsal to the medial ends of the internal capsules. The striae medullares are seen at the junctions of the dorsal and medial surfaces of the thalami. The tail of the caudate nucleus, on either side, is seen in the ventro-lateral wall of the lateral ventricle. The posterior limb of the internal capsule is interposed between the thalamus and the lentiform nucleus.

A, Corpus Callosum; *B*, Fornix; *C*, Choroid Plexus of Lateral Ventricle; *D*, Septum Pellucidum; *E*, Massa Intermedia; *F*, Thalamus; *G*, Interventricular Foramen; *H*, Anterior Commissure; *I*, Fornix buried in Thalamus and Hypothalamus; *J*, Mammillary Body; *K*, Basis Pedunculi; *L*, Tuber Cinereum; *M*, Optic Chiasm; *N*, Optic Nerve; *O*, Subthalamus; *P*, Pineal Body; *Q*, Superior Quadrigeminal Body; *R*, Cerebral Aqueduct; *S*, Tegmentum; *T*, Pons; *U*, Fourth Ventricle; *V*, Cerebellum; *W*, Medulla; *X*, Anterior Medullary Velum.

(387)

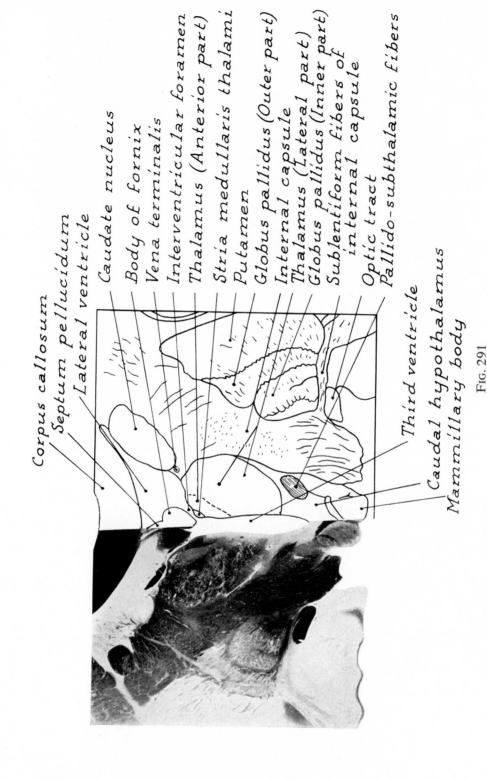

Corpus callosum
Septum pellucidum
Lateral ventricle
Caudate nucleus
Body of fornix
Vena terminalis
Interventricular foramen
Thalamus (Anterior part)
Stria medullaris thalami
Putamen
Globus pallidus (Outer part)
Internal capsule
Thalamus (Lateral part)
Globus pallidus (Inner part)
Sublentiform fibers of internal capsule
Optic tract
Pallido-subthalamic fibers
Third ventricle
Caudal hypothalamus
Mammillary body

Fig. 291

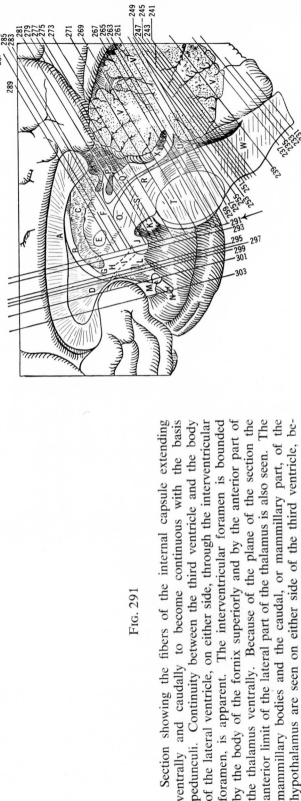

FIG. 291

Section showing the fibers of the internal capsule extending ventrally and caudally to become continuous with the basis pedunculi. Continuity between the third ventricle and the body of the lateral ventricle, on either side, through the interventricular foramen, is apparent. The interventricular foramen is bounded by the body of the fornix superiorly and by the anterior part of the thalamus ventrally. Because of the plane of the section the anterior limit of the lateral part of the thalamus is also seen. The mammillary bodies and the caudal, or mammillary part, of the hypothalamus are seen on either side of the third ventricle, between the mammillary bodies and the thalami.

FIG. 292

A, Corpus Callosum; B, Fornix; C, Choroid Plexus of Lateral Ventricle; D, Septum Pellucidum; E, Massa Intermedia; F, Thalamus; G, Interventricular Foramen; H, Anterior Commissure; I, Fornix buried in Thalamus and Hypothalamus; J, Mammillary Body; K, Basis Pedunculi; L, Tuber Cinereum; M, Optic Chiasm; N, Optic Nerve; O, Subthalamus; P, Pineal Body; Q, Superior Quadrigeminal Body; R, Cerebral Aqueduct; S, Tegmentum; T, Pons; U, Fourth Ventricle; V, Cerebellum; W, Medulla; X, Anterior Medullary Velum.

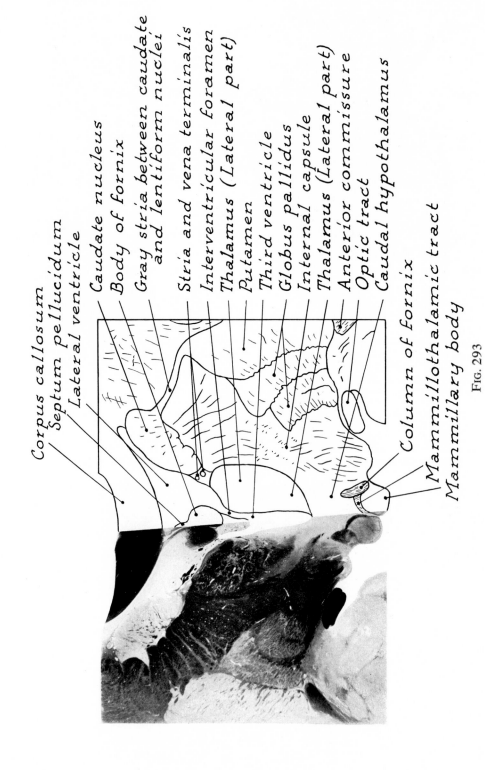

Corpus callosum
Septum pellucidum
Lateral ventricle
Caudate nucleus
Body of fornix
Gray stria between caudate
and lentiform nuclei
Stria and vena terminalis
Interventricular foramen
Thalamus (Lateral part)
Putamen
Third ventricle
Globus pallidus
Internal capsule
Thalamus (Lateral part)
Anterior commissure
Optic tract
Caudal hypothalamus
Column of fornix
Mammillothalamic tract
Mammillary body

Fig. 293

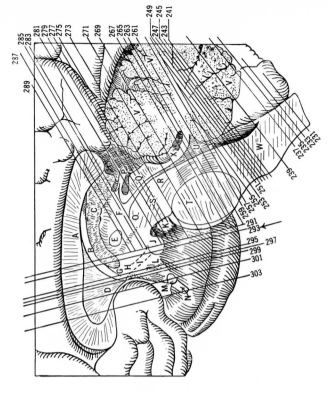

FIG. 293

Section in a plane such that it passes through the mammillary bodies, anterior part of the thalamus, and the interventricular foramina (of Monro). The bodies of the lateral ventricles are bounded superiorly by the corpus callosum, medially by the septum pellucidum and body of the fornix, and latero-inferiorly by the caudate nucleus and thalamus. The stria and vena terminalis are seen in the interval between the caudate nucleus and thalamus. The globus pallidus is divided into external and internal divisions by the internal medullary lamina. The internal capsule extends to the ventral surface of the brain stem on either side of the mammillary bodies. The columns of the fornix are seen as they terminate in, and the mammillothalamic tracts as they originate from, the mammillary bodies. The caudal hypothalamus lies in the interval between the thalami and the mammillary bodies.

FIG. 294

A, Corpus Callosum; B, Fornix; C, Choroid Plexus of Lateral Ventricle; D, Septum Pellucidum; E, Massa Intermedia; F, Thalamus; G, Interventricular Foramen; H, Anterior Commissure; I, Fornix buried in Thalamus and Hypothalamus; J, Mammillary Body; K, Basis Pedunculi; L, Tuber Cinereum; M, Optic Chiasm; N, Optic Nerve; O, Subthalamus; P, Pineal Body; Q, Superior Quadrigeminal Body; R, Cerebral Aqueduct; S, Tegmentum; T, Pons; U, Fourth Ventricle; V, Cerebellum; W, Medulla; X, Anterior Medullary Velum.

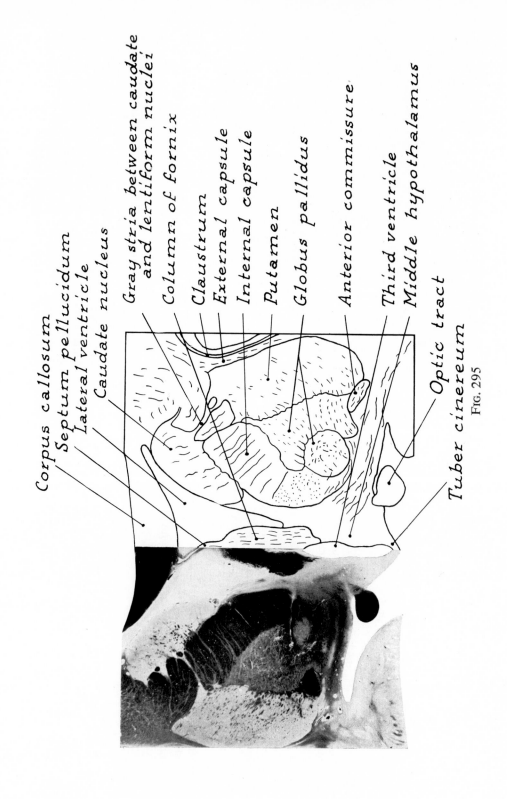

Corpus callosum
Septum pellucidum
Lateral ventricle
Caudate nucleus
Gray stria between caudate and lentiform nuclei
Column of fornix
Claustrum
External capsule
Internal capsule
Putamen
Globus pallidus
Anterior commissure
Third ventricle
Middle hypothalamus
Optic tract
Tuber cinereum

Fig. 295

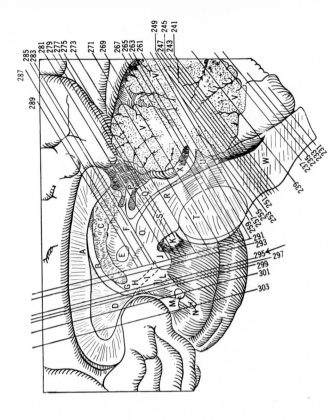

FIG. 295

Section showing the anterior horns of the lateral ventricles, bodies of the caudate nuclei, outer ends of the anterior commissure, columns of the fornix, lentiform nuclei, and optic tracts. The globus pallidus of the lentiform nucleus, at this level, is rather indistinctly subdivided into internal and external portions.

FIG. 296

A, Corpus Callosum; *B*, Fornix; *C*, Choroid Plexus of Lateral Ventricle; *D*, Septum Pellucidum; *E*, Massa Intermedia; *F*, Thalamus; *G*, Interventricular Foramen; *H*, Anterior Commissure; *I*, Fornix buried in Thalamus and Hypothalamus; *J*, Mammillary Body; *K*, Basis Pedunculi; *L*, Tuber Cinereum; *M*, Optic Chiasm; *N*, Optic Nerve; *O*, Subthalamus; *P*, Pineal Body; *Q*, Superior Quadrigeminal Body; *R*, Cerebral Aqueduct; *S*, Tegmentum; *T*, Pons; *U*, Fourth Ventricle; *V*, Cerebellum; *W*, Medulla; *X*, Anterior Medullary Velum.

(393)

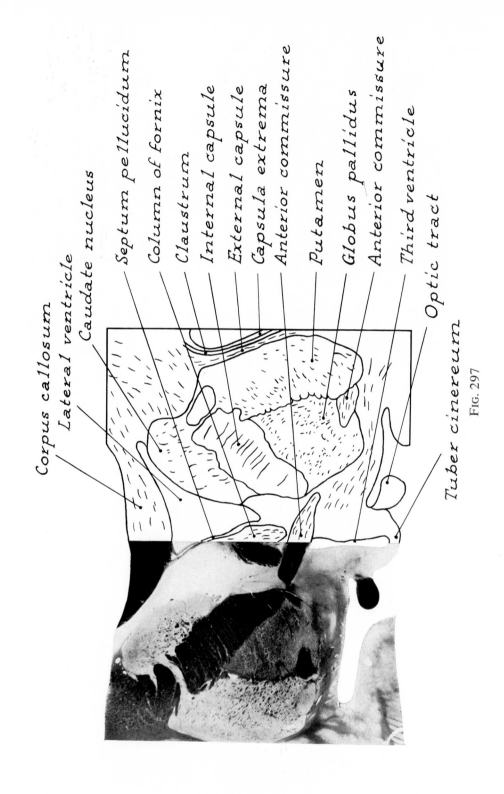

Corpus callosum

Lateral ventricle

Caudate nucleus

Septum pellucidum

Column of fornix

Claustrum

Internal capsule

External capsule

Capsula extrema

Anterior commissure

Putamen

Globus pallidus

Anterior commissure

Third ventricle

Optic tract

Tuber cinereum

Fig. 297

FIG. 297

Section through the central area of the brain showing the middle and outer portions of the anterior commissure and the columns of the fornix in relation to its middle portion. The right and left optic tracts lie in relation to the tuber cinereum. The lentiform nucleus is seen to be divided into inner and outer portions—the globus pallidus and putamen.

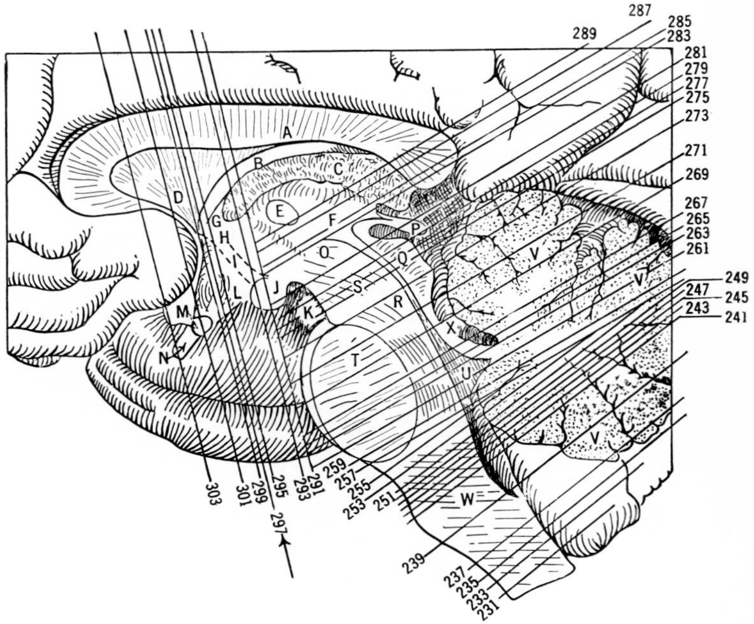

FIG. 298

A, Corpus Callosum; *B*, Fornix; *C*, Choroid Plexus of Lateral Ventricle; *D*, Septum Pellucidum; *E*, Massa Intermedia; *F*, Thalamus; *G*, Interventricular Foramen; *H*, Anterior Commissure; *I*, Fornix buried in Thalamus and Hypothalamus; *J*, Mammillary Body; *K*, Basis Pedunculi; *L*, Tuber Cinereum; *M*, Optic Chiasm; *N*, Optic Nerve; *O*, Subthalamus; *P*, Pineal Body; *Q*, Superior Quadrigeminal Body; *R*, Cerebral Aqueduct; *S*, Tegmentum; *T*, Pons; *U*, Fourth Ventricle; *V*, Cerebellum; *W*, Medulla; *X*, Anterior Medullary Velum.

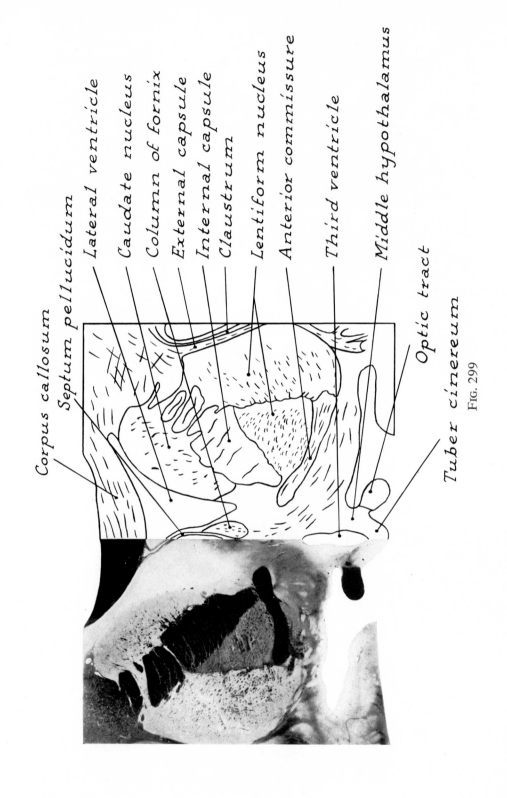

Corpus callosum

Septum pellucidum

Lateral ventricle

Caudate nucleus

Column of fornix

External capsule

Internal capsule

Claustrum

Lentiform nucleus

Anterior commissure

Third ventricle

Middle hypothalamus

Optic tract

Tuber cinereum

Fig. 299

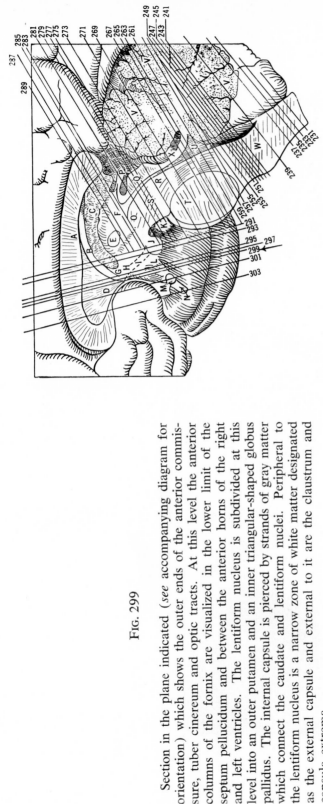

FIG. 299

Section in the plane indicated (*see* accompanying diagram for orientation) which shows the outer ends of the anterior commissure, tuber cinereum and optic tracts. At this level the anterior columns of the fornix are visualized in the lower limit of the septum pellucidum and between the anterior horns of the right and left ventricles. The lentiform nucleus is subdivided at this level into an outer putamen and an inner triangular-shaped globus pallidus. The internal capsule is pierced by strands of gray matter which connect the caudate and lentiform nuclei. Peripheral to the lentiform nucleus is a narrow zone of white matter designated as the external capsule and external to it are the claustrum and capsula extrema.

FIG. 300

A, Corpus Callosum; *B*, Fornix; *C*, Choroid Plexus of Lateral Ventricle; *D*, Septum Pellucidum; *E*, Massa Intermedia; *F*, Thalamus; *G*, Interventricular Foramen; *H*, Anterior Commissure; *I*, Fornix buried in Thalamus and Hypothalamus; *J*, Mammillary Body; *K*, Basis Pedunculi; *L*, Tuber Cinereum; *M*, Optic Chiasm; *N*, Optic Nerve; *O*, Subthalamus; *P*, Pineal Body; *Q*, Superior Quadrigeminal Body; *R*, Cerebral Aqueduct; *S*, Tegmentum; *T*, Pons; *U*, Fourth Ventricle; *V*, Cerebellum; *W*, Medulla; *X*, Anterior Medullary Velum.

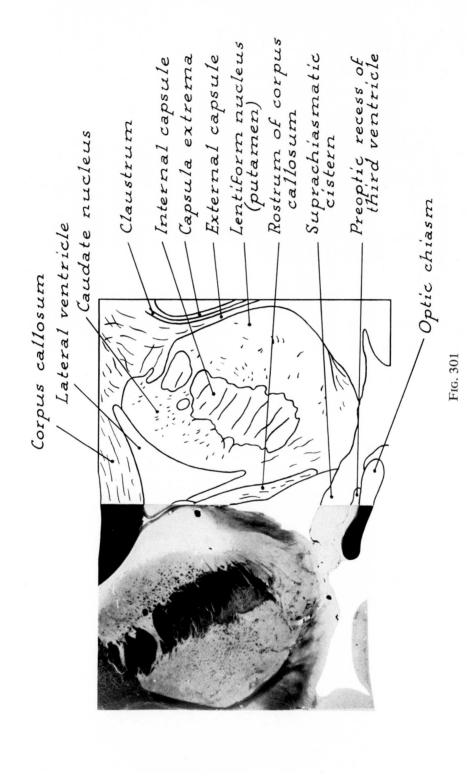

Corpus callosum

Lateral ventricle

Caudate nucleus

Claustrum

Internal capsule

Capsula extrema

External capsule

Lentiform nucleus (putamen)

Rostrum of corpus callosum

Suprachiasmatic cistern

Preoptic recess of third ventricle

Optic chiasm

FIG. 301

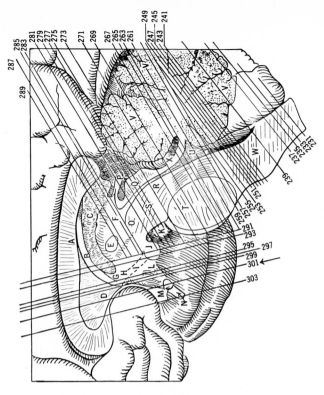

Fig. 301

Fig. 302

Section through the brain stem, corpus callosum, internal capsule and basal ganglia at the level of the optic chiasm. The most caudal fibers of the corpus callosum are seen to be attached to the inferior margin of the septum pellucidum. The anterior horns of the lateral ventricles are bounded by the corpus callosum, septum pellucidum, caudate nuclei, and rostrum of corpus callosum. The anterior limb of the internal capsule, on either side, lies between the caudate nucleus and the lentiform nucleus, except ventrally, where the two nuclei are continuous. The strands of gray matter which penetrate the internal capsule and connect the caudate nucleus with the lentiform nucleus are responsible for the term "corpus striatum" which is applied to caudate nucleus, lentiform nucleus, and lenticulocaudate portion of the internal capsule. The plane of the section is such that the preoptic recess of the third ventricle appears on the upper aspect of the optic chiasm, and above this the suprachiasmatic cistern of the subarachnoid space is clearly outlined.

A, Corpus Callosum; *B*, Fornix; *C*, Choroid Plexus of Lateral Ventricle; *D*, Septum Pellucidum; *E*, Massa Intermedia; *F*, Thalamus; *G*, Interventricular Foramen; *H*, Anterior Commissure; *I*, Fornix buried in Thalamus and Hypothalamus; *J*, Mammillary Body; *K*, Basis Pedunculi; *L*, Tuber Cinereum; *M*, Optic Chiasm; *N*, Optic Nerve; *O*, Subthalamus; *P*, Pineal Body; *Q*, Superior Quadrigeminal Body; *R*, Cerebral Aqueduct; *S*, Tegmentum; *T*, Pons; *U*, Fourth Ventricle; *V*, Cerebellum; *W*, Medulla; *X*, Anterior Medullary Velum.

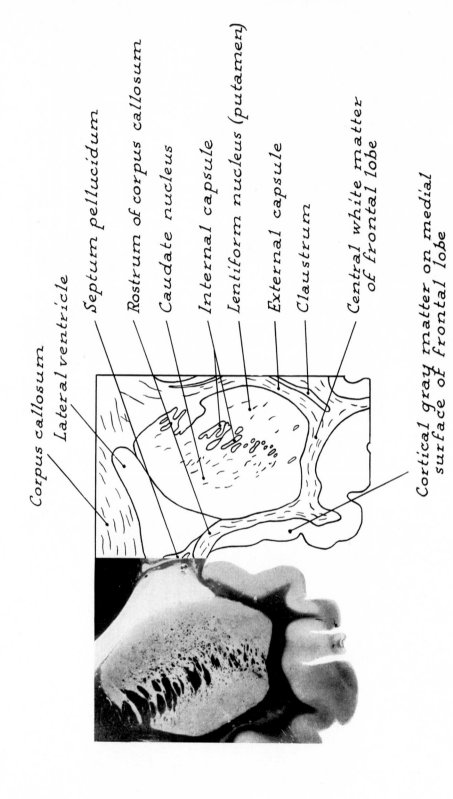

Corpus callosum

Lateral ventricle

Septum pellucidum

Rostrum of corpus callosum

Caudate nucleus

Internal capsule

Lentiform nucleus (putamen)

External capsule

Claustrum

Central white matter
of frontal lobe

Cortical gray matter on medial
surface of frontal lobe

FIG. 303

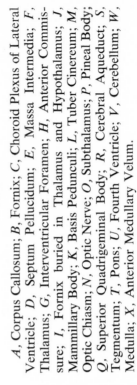

FIG. 303

Section through anterior horns of lateral ventricles, rostral limits of anterior limbs of internal capsules and body and rostrum of corpus callosum. The rostrum of the corpus callosum is seen to be continuous with the central white matter of the frontal lobes. Ventrally, the head of the caudate nucleus and the putamen of the lentiform nucleus are continuous around the inferior limit of the internal capsule on either side.

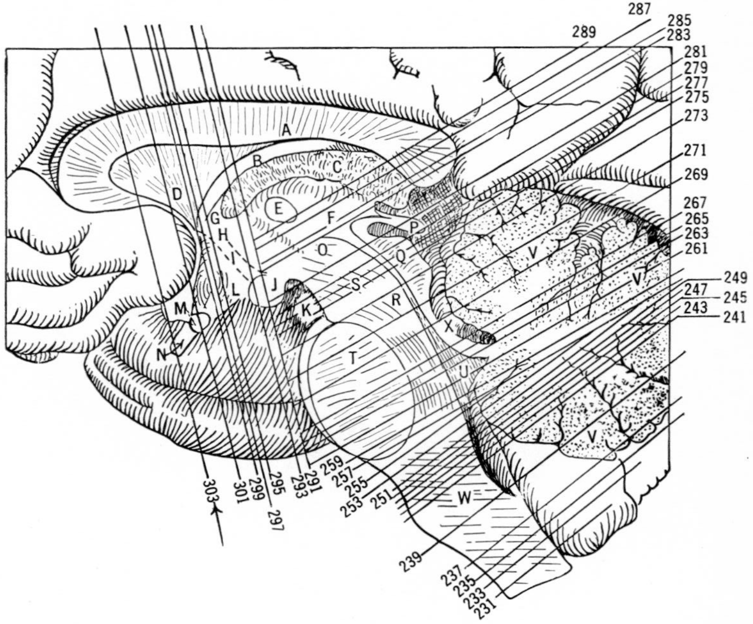

FIG. 304

A, Corpus Callosum; B, Fornix; C, Choroid Plexus of Lateral Ventricle; D, Septum Pellucidum; E, Massa Intermedia; F, Thalamus; G, Interventricular Foramen; H, Anterior Commissure; I, Fornix buried in Thalamus and Hypothalamus; J, Mammillary Body; K, Basis Pedunculi; L, Tuber Cinereum; M, Optic Chiasm; N, Optic Nerve; O, Subthalamus; P, Pineal Body; Q, Superior Quadrigeminal Body; R, Cerebral Aqueduct; S, Tegmentum; T, Pons; U, Fourth Ventricle; V, Cerebellum; W, Medulla; X, Anterior Medullary Velum.

Atlas Index

for Figures 231 to 304 (by pages)

Index

Bold face numbers indicate principal references.

A